The
Noble
Bastard

The Noble Bastard

The Story of
Robert Dudley

ANGELA McLEOD

Matador
9 Priory Business Park,
Wistow Road, Kibworth Beauchamp,
Leicestershire. LE8 0RX
Tel: 0116 279 2299
Email: books@troubador.co.uk
Web: www.troubador.co.uk/matador
Twitter: @matadorbooks

ISBN 978 1789018 943

British Library Cataloguing in Publication Data.
A catalogue record for this book is available from the British Library.

Printed and bound in the UK by T J International, Padstow, Cornwall
Typeset in 11pt Aldine401 BT by Troubador Publishing Ltd, Leicester, UK

Matador is an imprint of Troubador Publishing Ltd

To Christopher Hanson Smith,
the kindest of critics and best of friends.

ACKNOWLEDGEMENTS

This book has developed, through stages, from an idea into print, but it could not have been done without the generous help of many people. I am very grateful to all of them.

Heartfelt thanks go to Desmond Maxwell, who has done both proof-reading and editing, not only for the hours of work he has spent on it, but for the research and the many discoveries he has made on the book's behalf, both written and pictorial; also, for his thoroughness and the excellent English he has brought to the reading of the text.

Many thanks, also, go to Pamela Baker, for her assistance with the construction, at all stages, of the book and her watchful eye on the content; not least, for her encouragement, support and considerable talent in dealing with recalcitrant computers.

I am also most grateful to Sarah Campbell for her detailed help during the final stages when everything began to look confused.

As always, I could not have managed without Paul, of Matrix in Oban, for preventing mechanical failure and thereby avoiding panic.

Last, and far from least, I thank my husband, David, for his Job-like patience in putting up with interruptions and calls for help on a daily basis, and my far flung children whose keen enthusiasm has never lagged.
Angela McLeod

CONTENTS

INTRODUCTION

While writing *"The Brilliant Stage: The Story of Frances Walsingham"* I became aware of the presence, on that stage, of a personality who could not be ignored. That of Sir Robert Dudley, the Earl of Leicester's only surviving, but supposedly bastard son. He refused to retire into the background but recurred; an arresting personality whose achievements proved every bit as great, if not greater, than those of his famous father. His life and activities appeared so irresistible that I deliberately put him aside "for later".

He died in what is now the Villa Castello, near Florence, having drunk deeper of the cup of life than most and having married three wives, one bigamously, and produced around twenty children.

In 1594, at the age of twenty, he led an expedition to the New World and he accompanied the Earl of Essex on the Cadiz raid in 1596. They appear to have been very much birds of a feather; the father of one was the step-father of the other and they must have been constantly in each other's company, although Robert was the younger by seven years.

He left to posterity six beautiful volumes containing detailed charts and maps of the entire oceanic world, "Dell'Arcano Del Mare", "The Secrets of the Sea", written and produced in Italian. He drained the marshes around Leghorn, built a thriving port there and undertook other building projects in Tuscany on behalf of the Medici Grand Dukes. Having converted to the Roman Church, he served three successive Grand Duchesses of Tuscany as Great Chamberlain. His uncle's and also his grandfather's titles were restored to him by the Emperor, Ferdinand II, endorsed by the Pope and he died in that Tuscan villa the Duke of Northumberland and the Earl of Warwick, the stain of bastardy finally eradicated, though not in his native country until 1644. The earldom of Leicester passed to the Sidney family of Penshurst.

He was a naval and military Commander, an explorer and navigator, an expert cartographer, a civil and military engineer, a shipbuilder and architect and a successful chemist. There appears to be little he could not and did not do.

What drove this gifted man? Was it the need to heal the slight of bastardy, such a condemnation in his time, through exhaustive achievement, or was it a determination to equal his renowned father? Perhaps it was neither but that he was born with a character which demanded that he lead rather than follow; ambition was second nature to the Dudleys. When thwarted by the circumstances of his birth, he turned to unexplored fields for goals recognised by his world as great. He remained, however, convinced that he was Leicester's legitimate son and his whole life was a quest for proof and recognition.

His known portraits show a tall, very well built man who obviously took pride in his appearance without undue extravagance. There is a slightly guarded look in the round eyes inherited from his mother. They in no way resemble Leicester's. His brain, however, he clearly owed to the Dudleys together with their formidable drive and arrogance.

He was brought up from the age of five as Leicester's son, acknowledged and loved, but not as his legitimate heir. At what point did he discover this, suffer, and chart his own course?

His beautiful mother, Lady Douglas Sheffield, born a Howard and a sister of the Queen's Lord High Admiral, Howard of Effingham, claimed that Leicester had, indeed, married her "in wintertime" in 1573. She contradicted this story somewhat when persuaded to marry Sir Edward Stafford as Leicester's interest shifted to Lettice, Countess of Essex. Had she really married Leicester, she would have tacitly admitted bigamy.

Lady Douglas appears to have been somewhat hen-witted and indecisive, a striking contrast to her rival, Lettice Knollys, who knew exactly what she wanted and how to get it. Lady Douglas was outgunned and Leicester married Lettice, apparently unworried by any supposed former marriage. Bigamy was an ecclesiastical crime to the Elizabethans, but not a legal one. There was a son of this marriage, Robert, Lord Denbigh, who died as a child, thereby throwing the question of the Leicester inheritance wide open.

The whole of Robert Dudley's life as it began to unfold for me was a search for excellence which involved huge leaps of faith from one diverse project to another. He seems quite undaunted by the scale of these or the possible consequences of failure.

The one devastating exception, the rejection and suppression of his legitimacy case brought before the Lords of Star Chamber in 1605, had the effect of changing the course of his life. It was the most bitter of blows and it resulted in his departure from England, to which he never returned, and his eventual adoption of Italy, in particular Tuscany, as his permanent home.

He turned his back on his family, his native land, and the considerable property he had inherited on Leicester's death, which included Kenilworth Castle. He virtually began life again at the age of thirty-one; for his time, almost middle age. But he did not go alone. His beautiful cousin, Elizabeth Southwell, accompanied him, disguised as his page. They were subsequently married in Lyons, despite his current wife and five children in England. The couple wisely and promptly converted to Catholicism and obtained Papal dispensation for their union on the grounds that the Protestant marriage was performed by heretics and therefore invalid. This seems flimsy to say the least and one cannot doubt Robert's powers of persuasion. There was also the small matter of consanguinity. He and Elizabeth were first cousins, once removed, but this also seems to have been successfully swept under the Papal carpet.

Robert Dudley's faith in himself must have been enormous, a gift so infectious that it inspired those around him with confidence.

A sense of humour he certainly had. His first ships were named "The Bear", "The Bear's Whelp", "The Earwig" and "The Frisking"; the first two a parody of the Dudley arms, the "Bear and Ragged Staff". He had little trouble, young as he was, in obtaining the Queen's permission for him to command these small ships and sail across the Atlantic to explore the Orinoco River and its delta. This included claiming Trinidad for the English crown and a certain amount of piracy.

He accompanied his stepbrother, the Earl of Essex, on the expedition to attack Cadiz in 1596 and, later, he outfitted and sent an expedition to China from which only one survivor returned. Still later, he managed to persuade the Grand Duke of Tuscany to entrust him with huge sums for the project at Livorno; an illegitimate Englishman, son of the man reputed to have been the English Queen's lover, and a very recent convert to Catholicism. Not only was the harbour to be constructed by him, but ships, palaces and villas also. He was a master draughtsman and possessed the drive to get his plans realised.

In 1620, the Pope endorsed the Tuscan Grand Duchess Maria Madalena's request to her brother the Hapsburg Emperor, that Dudley's

English titles be restored to him. He must have charmed these Italian birds out of their cypress trees and he appears to have been on excellent terms with the Vatican which turned such a blind eye on both his questionable legitimacy and his bigamous and inter-related marriage.

He was so busy exploring, inventing, planning and building that he has not left very much of himself except for his monumental work, "Dell' Arcano del Mare" and the journals of his voyages. What follows is the story of his life written, sometimes, with the hair rising on my head. Any ship of his would have been well-named "Dauntless", as was one of my own father's. The story is as factual as I have been able to make it and, for this, I owe a great deal to John Temple Leader and his book "Life of Sir Robert Dudley, Earl of Warwick and Duke of Northumberland" of 1891. To quote from Leader, "My hope is that it may give as much pleasure to the reader as it has given me in the writing of it."

THE DUDLEY-SIDNEY-HERBERT FAMILIES (abridged)

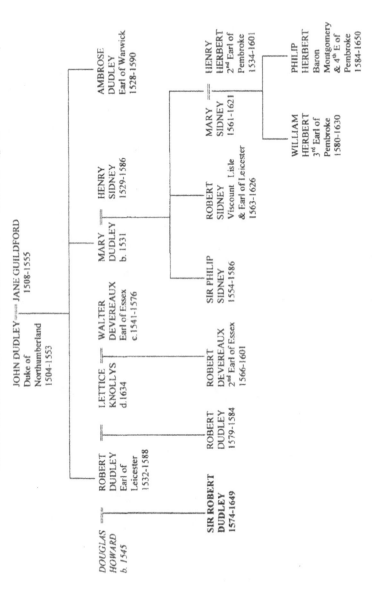

THE HOWARD FAMILY (abridged)

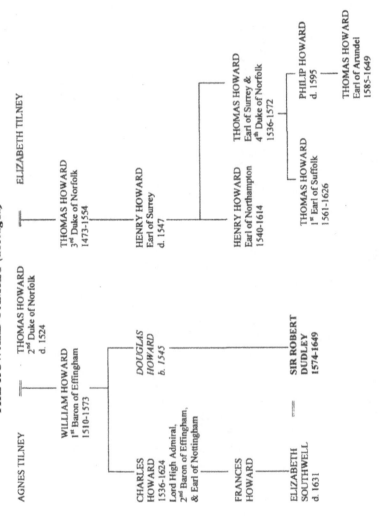

AGNES TILNEY ═ **THOMAS HOWARD**
2nd Duke of Norfolk
d. 1524

ELIZABETH TILNEY

WILLIAM HOWARD
1st Baron of Effingham
1510–1573

THOMAS HOWARD
3rd Duke of Norfolk
1473–1554

DOUGLAS HOWARD
b. 1545

HENRY HOWARD
Earl of Surrey
d. 1547

CHARLES HOWARD
1536–1624
Lord High Admiral,
2nd Baron of Effingham,
& Earl of Nottingham

HENRY HOWARD
Earl of Northampton
1540–1614

THOMAS HOWARD
Earl of Surrey &
4th Duke of Norfolk
1536–1572

FRANCES HOWARD

SIR ROBERT DUDLEY
1574–1649

THOMAS HOWARD
1st Earl of Suffolk
1561–1626

PHILIP HOWARD
d. 1595

ELIZABETH SOUTHWELL
d. 1631

THOMAS HOWARD
Earl of Arundel
1585–1649

The Marriage of the Earl of Leicester and Lady Douglas Sheffield

In order to understand the nature of Robert Dudley the forces which formed and drove him must be explored. The circumstances of his birth and the marital gyrations of his parents are so important to his story that all aspects of their association which had a part in forming his character should be considered. It is a much stranger and more convoluted story than fiction and it does not have a conclusive ending; far more frustrating for Dudley, himself, than for any historian. The doubts, when they came, must have been devastating to a child who had been brought up to believe he was a privileged being with a powerful father and an ever-present and devoted mother.

The marriage between the Earl of Leicester and Lady Douglas Sheffield is one of those grey areas which neither time nor the efforts of many historians have been able to illuminate with certainty. It was, however, of paramount importance to one person: their son, Robert Dudley. The question of his birth influenced his whole life and the dark cloud of bastardy was ever present until dispelled towards its end. He, himself, had no doubts.

Another grey area in Elizabeth's England was the status and purpose of betrothal and marriage ceremonies. They were all too alike. They did not have to take place in a church and they could be conducted by a member of the clergy in front of a required number of witnesses. The exchange of rings and the pledging of troths was included in both. In fact, any kind of mutual promise given before witnesses which was followed by co-habitation, was regarded in law as a valid marriage. Given these circumstances, there was certainly room for manoeuvre.

Leicester met the young and beautiful Lady Sheffield at Belvoir Castle during the summer of 1571. She was the sister of Lord Howard of Effingham, later the Lord High Admiral of Armada fame. She was also a first cousin, once removed, of the Queen. Her Majesty had gone

1

north that year on her Summer Progress, with the Earl of Leicester in attendance, and Lord and Lady Sheffield were also guests of the Earl of Rutland at Belvoir Castle. According to one Gervase Holles, a connection of the Sheffields: "Thither the principal persons of Lincolnshire repaired to see their Queen and do their duty. And among others, the Lord Sheffield and the fair young lady of his who shone like a star in the court, both in respect of her beauty and the richness of her apparel. Leicester, seeing her and being much taken with her perfection, paid court to her and used all the art (in which he was master enough) to debauch her." Bluntly put but probably true.

The first open notice of the affair came in a letter from the indefatigable gossip, Gilbert Talbot, to his father the Earl of Shrewsbury which states: "My Lord of Leicester is very much with Her Majesty and she shows the same affection to him that she was wont; of late he hath endeavoured to please her more than heretofore. There are two sisters now in the Court that are very far in love with him, as they have been long; my Lady Sheffield and Frances Howard; they of like striving who shall love him are at great war together, and the Queen thinketh not well of them and not the better of him; by this means there are spies over him."

In other words, the sisters were fighting over him like cats and had been for some time. Sheffield had, all too conveniently, died in 1572; whether the affair began before or after his departure is not certain, but very likely before.

Douglas triumphed and, in May 1573, Leicester agreed to marry her and the purported wedding took place in Leicester's house in Esher "in wintertime" that year, witnessed by Sir Edward Horsey, the Captain of the Isle of Wight and an old friend of Leicester, a kinsman, Robert Sheffield, a Doctor Giulio Borgherini, Leicester's Italian doctor, and members of the household. Douglas was pregnant at the time and Robert was born on 7th August 1574 at Sheen House in Surrey and, prophetically, in a room known as "The Duke's Chamber." The news of his birth was carried to Leicester by a member of Lady Douglas's household, William Clewer. The Earl was attending the "Queen's Progress" in the West and Clewer found him at Gloucester and gave him the news. Clewer then returned to stand as proxy godfather in place of Sir Henry Lee, the Queen's Champion, at Robert's christening. Also standing as sponsors were Leicester's brother,

Ambrose, Earl of Warwick, Lady Dacre and a Mrs. Erisa. Lady Dacre was represented by Leicester's Italian doctor, the somewhat doubtful character, Giulio Borgherini.

Though acknowledging Robert, at the time, as his legitimate son, Leicester insisted that his marriage remain secret, not an easy task, and that it should certainly not be brought to the attention of the Queen on the grounds that it would compromise his position as her favourite. Perspicacious as she was, Her Majesty probably knew very well that Douglas was his mistress.

However, when Leicester became enthralled by Lettice, then Countess of Essex, around 1575 (he had already done more than look her way ten years earlier), he tired of Douglas and since Lettice, becoming pregnant, stood out for nothing less than marriage, he was faced with a familiar dilemma. They were both already committed; Lettice to Essex, and with a quiverful of children, and Leicester to Douglas with the longed-for son, Robert. Looking at the situation without fear or favour, they would be obliged to get rid of both the Earl of Essex and of Douglas which would mean denying Robert his birthright. It would also mean taking a chance on Lettice's capability to produce further heirs; she was then well into her thirties and she had already given Essex two sons and two daughters.

The dilemma was nothing new to Leicester. He had pursued the Queen in his youth with definite intent and little less than kingship in mind, and with no regard to the miserable existence of Amy Robsart, his Norfolk-bred wife to whom he had been married at the age of nineteen. She remained on the sidelines of his life and out of the Queen's sight, although she had been at Court in the early days of their marriage. The saga of her questionable death, whether a convenient demise, suicide, or murder, was never brought to any conclusion.

Leicester's monumental mistake was a belief that it left the field clear for his conquest of the Queen. Never, in this world, would she have married him under such a cloud; a cloud which would not only have implicated her but ruined her reputation and alienated her subjects. Her head ruled and he was set at a distance, at the expense of her heart. Much later, even the nineteen days' wonder of the Royal visit to Kenilworth, with its continuous and staggering entertainment, could not sway her. The fact that he had a supposed wife, a year old son and a mistress in the wings at the time, does not appear to have fazed him in the least. To have invested the Elizabethan equivalent of millions in the visit, strongly suggests that he still believed, after all those years, that he had a chance of marrying the Queen. He was a past master of entertainment, the more extravagant the better, and the days at Kenilworth that hot July had never been equalled, nor were they for centuries. Fireworks, pageants, jousting, masques, sylvan plays on rafts drifting around the lakes and appearing from nowhere, the roars of artillery to greet the Queen every time she emerged and perfectly endless feasting, music and dancing. A young boy named William Shakespeare certainly witnessed some of the goings on and his memories emerged in a play called "A Midsummer Night's Dream". The scenes behind the scenes can only be imagined. It was high summer, the heat was intense, there were 1,000 sweating men at arms and their sweating horses in place to guard the Queen, not to mention the phalanxes of cooks, bottle-washers and servants, both general and personal. The wonder was that at the end of such excess, the guests were still able to stand and had survived the mountainous meals and rivers of strong drink.

What was certain was that the Earl of Essex, then Earl Marshal of Ireland, returning home earlier in the year, had been met with rumours of an affair between Leicester and his wife. Stories spread that she had borne two children during his absence in Dublin. There ensued a considerable confrontation which probably resulted in Essex giving guardianship of his children to his relatives, the Earl and Countess of Huntingdon. It was unthinkable, under the current code of conduct, that a peer of the realm should seduce the wife of another during absence on his country's service. Feelings ran high. Leicester, caught in the crossfire between his supposed wife, Douglas, his mistress, Lettice, and her infuriated husband, Essex, must have felt somewhat besieged. Last, and most important, were his obligations to his Queen. All in all, it was not a pretty story.

Douglas, the mother of his son, was there at Kenilworth that blistering July of 1575, and far from happy. It is possible that Lettice, who was never backward in coming forward, had the gall to attend also, keeping her toe in the door and protecting her place in this fantastic love quartet. Her husband, Essex, was, by that time, safely back in Ireland from where he would never return. It is very much to Leicester's credit that he managed to keep all these balls in the air at once. A furious encounter with Essex, a lachrymose Douglas to send on her way, Lettice to keep on a string and the monumental organisation needed for the pageant at Kenilworth; all were more than enough to stretch him to the limit. It must have taken powerful ambition to attempt such achievements and all for the purpose of persuading the Queen, at this late stage, into a doubtful marriage. He really deserved to succeed although England's future might have been very different if he had. Such was the Dudley character inherited by his son, Robert.

Confronting the situation, Leicester trod much the same path as he had before. According to Douglas, he offered her money to deny their marriage and, when she furiously refused, threatened her. Much later, in 1605, in the Court of Star Chamber, she averred that she had given way because she feared she was being poisoned. Knowing Leicester's reputation and claiming that her hair was falling out and her nails beginning to blacken, she had agreed to deny her marriage and her son's legitimacy. It seems strange that Douglas, at this point, did not call upon her own powerful family, the Howards, to support her and put pressure on Leicester; her brother, Lord Charles Howard of Effingham, was Lord Chamberlain at the time. She did not appear to do so and, magnanimously, Leicester produced another husband for her in the person of Sir Edward Stafford of Grafton, so giving weight to the argument that if they both re-married, it would prove that their own marriage had never taken place. It had been a mere betrothal. Some of the letters he wrote to Douglas before and at this time were tender, loving and considerate. But, between the lines, he had tired of her and his sights were fixed on a very different kind of Countess.

So, were the Earl of Leicester and Lady Douglas Sheffield ever really married? Was she frightened into denying it, and was the Earl of Essex poisoned, violently and horribly, in Dublin Castle in September 1576, his death, at the time, being blithely put down to dysentery or "the Irish flux"? Was it a repeat of the wretched Amy Robsart's fate? Essex, in his death throes, had gasped out that "there was evil in his drink". Given that Leicester had befriended, and employed as his own physician, Giulio Borgherini, known as Dr.Julio, a skilled pharmacist of sorts, rumours arose that this man had been responsible for the removal of Essex and others standing in Leicester's way (possibly including Douglas's husband, Sheffield). He was also, reputedly, a witness to the marriage between Leicester and Lady Sheffield. Sir Henry Sidney, the Lord Deputy of Ireland and in Dublin at that time, immediately called for a post mortem on the Earl of Essex's body and nothing untoward was found at all. Two others serving in the castle had died in similar circumstances, all put down to dysentery, so the Earl was not alone. It was, however, the stuff of melodrama: the cuckolded and unwanted husband, the unfaithful wife and her noble lover and, like a rabbit out of a hat, the handy Italian poisoner, Dr.Julio. The story was too good not to spread, and with embellishment, until it all spilled out in "Leycester's Commonwealth", a horrible little pamphlet pinning most crimes known to man on the Earl of Leicester.

Douglas, having been persuaded to marry Sir Edward Stafford, went with him to Paris and proved a very successful Ambassadress, but she remained out of Robert's life until he was fifteen. Leicester had claimed him completely, refusing to allow him to go to Paris.

Perhaps the truth concerning the marriage of Leicester and Douglas Sheffield will never be known. Whatever ceremony took place that winter evening in Esher, she, counting it as marriage since they had co-habited for some time, was content and clearly considered herself Leicester's wife. He, meanwhile, thinking of the rainy day when he might want to change the situation, particularly if the Queen should ever soften towards him and re-consider his suit, preferred to think of it as a betrothal only. Lady Douglas certainly considered herself a Countess, but was addressed as such only "in her chamber". There were letters from Leicester to her signed "Your Loving Husband...RL," although the tone of irritation and boredom could be seen in these as time went on.

Lettice achieved marriage with Leicester on 28th September 1578 at Wanstead, surrounded by a phalanx of her close relatives to ensure the validity of the union. She was pregnant at the time and was clearly taking no chances. This baby did not survive but was followed by the birth of a son, though the triumph was short-lived. She, and the ghost of small Lord Denbigh, continued as the elephants in the corner of Robert's existence. From that time on, Robert Dudley was deemed illegitimate.

Had Leicester decided to change his will at the end of his life, in view of the fact that he had no legitimate heir, and to acknowledge Robert as his lawful son, both he and Douglas would have admitted bigamy; Lettice would then have had to admit, in turn, that she had never been legally married to Leicester either. The moment at which Leicester must have been most tempted to do this was at the death of the small Lord Denbigh but there was no possibility that Lettice would allow it.

What a tangled web they had woven and one from which Robert, alone, could extricate himself. The lengths to which Leicester went to cover his tracks and ensure Douglas's silence, including large bribes and threats, strongly suggest that their marriage was legal, if unorthodox. Also, the fact that he acknowledged Robert as his legitimate son until he was five years old, corroborated by many, adds weight to her insistence that it was a marriage and not a betrothal. The other very convincing piece of evidence is that he left Kenilworth and its lands to Robert and a large part of what remained of his fortune. This was in the face of Lettice's opposition and she made a strong attempt to claim the castle after Leicester's death. Had Robert really been a bastard, he could have palmed him off graciously with some land and a minor title.

Not content with these machinations, Leicester continued to intrigue. Staying with his old friend, Bess of Hardwick, the wife of the Earl of Shrewsbury, in 1577, he made an agreement with her to marry the four year old Robert to her granddaughter, Arbella Stuart. They were the same age. Arbella was in direct line to both the Scottish and the English thrones, a cousin of the Queen and a niece of Mary Queen of Scots, and Leicester, perhaps, had visions of his son as consort to a Queen, his own blood flowing in the next royal heir, and himself the power behind the throne; in fact, much the same performance as his father had attempted with Lady Jane Grey. Bess of Hardwick, a lady with a hard head and an equally hard will, would never have accepted a bastard for her precious granddaughter's hand while there was the possibility of a legitimate son of Leicester. The treasured Lord Denbigh was promptly exchanged with Robert and betrothed to Arbella. This idea never got any further though the children were sent portraits of each other. It was, at best, a risky scheme. Had the Queen of England been aware of it, Leicester would have been in serious trouble. Arbella, herself, had ideas of her own which, later, ended sadly in imprisonment and death. Since his father's death in 1588, no other candidates for his marriage had been suggested and Robert was free to choose his own bride.

Having pieced the story of his origins together, Robert Dudley was never in any doubt that he, and he alone, was Leicester's legitimate heir and his life and actions were based on that belief and a determination to prove it.

CHAPTER ONE

Childhood to Tilbury – 1579-1588

The old man reclining in a captain's chair breathed deeply and closed his eyes. A telescope of his own invention lay ready on a table beside him together with a compass and a glass of rich local wine. The wind drifted through the maritime pines behind him, whispering sweet-scented nothings in the late afternoon; jasmine, lavender and rosemary mixing with thyme and resin. He was reflecting on his fortunes over the years.

Life had favoured him, but not without a great deal of his own effort and a fair amount of luck. He was not given to introspection; there had never been time for it, so he did not dwell upon his own personality or how it had contributed to his achievements. His faith in himself was absolute, he had never considered it, though he used it unconsciously on those within his orbit.

He had outlived all three of his wives and several of his numerous children. He smiled gently as he reflected that his renowned father, the Queen of England's best beloved, famous throughout Europe for good or bad, had at best, produced only two children and achieved no more than an Earldom. The Duke of Northumberland smiled more broadly as he reflected on his own titles and his nineteen or twenty children; he could not recall exactly how many. His native country and his King had pronounced him illegitimate, heir to his father's property, but not to his titles. Yet here he was, both Duke and Earl of Warwick, acknowledged by the Hapsburg Emperor and the Pope. No matter that England had turned a cold shoulder for over forty years.

Scenes flitted through his mind behind the closed eyes; scenes that had shaped his life and still burned in the memory.

A small boy, muddying his knees on the stableyard cobbles absorbed in the charms of a newly acquired puppy. It was an enormous Kuvasz puppy, a rare breed used as guard and hunting dogs by the Hungarian nobility for centuries. King Mathias I, 1458-1490, was never without one and was said to rely more on the dogs than his human guards. Woolly and bright-eyed and almost as big as he was, it had already knocked him flat. Two much bigger boys, riding into the yard and dismounting from their horses, wandered across to watch, swaggering slightly in the uncertain way of youth set on making an impression.

Whose puppy, they demanded, was that and what made him think he could play with it? He was only a midget and the dog was too big and too good for him. He rose warily and replied that my Lord of Leicester, his father, had given it to him. They roared with laughter, saying the dog was certainly far too good for a bastard. He did not know what a bastard was but their tone made it clear this was no compliment. The small fists came up, the round eyes narrowed and he flew at the red-haired boy who had spoken the word, kicking furiously at his shins, butting with his head and hitting hard with his knuckles. He gave such a good account of himself that the other boy, laughing, hauled him off, held him at arm's length and dusted him down. His tormentor, hopping on one foot and rubbing his battered shin, thought better of thrashing him and coming down to eye level, suddenly grinned at him and ruffled his hair. He would, he said, value such a warrior in battle – but on his own side. Still laughing, they strolled away.

The dog pushed up beside him, its nose under his elbow. The two stood, solemn and united, daring further outrage. He was five years old.

Robert Dudley had been at Kenilworth only a few days. It was his father's principal country seat, an immense castle, daunting, unknown and with a host of people living and moving around within it. Its core had been built in the 12th Century and generations had added to it down the ages. He had ridden in stages from his mother's home in Blackfriars after a departure awash with tears and lamentation. Her marriage to Sir Edward Stafford in November 1579 was followed by their imminent departure for France where Stafford was to take up the Ambassadorship in Paris. It had given the Earl of Leicester every reason to claim Robert completely and to insist that he now be in sole charge of his upbringing. This, naturally, entailed a struggle, his mother being most unwilling to give him up, and knowing that she was unlikely ever to get him back. From an early age he had been in the care of John Dudley, a relative of Leicester's and Roger, Second Baron North of Newington, though with his mother whenever she wanted. The exact circumstances of his birth would remain in doubt although, at this time, it was generally accepted that his parents had never married despite their prolonged liaison. They had both re-married and thereby would hang a long and bitter tale. Meanwhile, the child was now fully acknowledged as Leicester's son, though not his heir.

Robert's position in his father's household was not clearly defined and several awkward situations had arisen. Where should he sit at table if he joined his elders; should he bear or wear the Dudley arms; how many servants should wait on him and what stable-room should be allotted to his small entourage? The Earl had made it very clear that the boy was to be treated with respect and as his son but minor points of precedence had yet to be resolved.

There was also the Earl's recently married and formidable wife Lettice to consider. Having cornered Leicester in marriage at the age of thirty six amid a welter of unpleasant rumour regarding the convenient death of her husband, Walter Earl of Essex, she did not take kindly to the idea of her rival's bastard son joining her household. She had paid a high price for her marriage too. The like of the Queen's rage and anguish had rarely been seen. Lettice was her cousin, very similar in looks, temperament and determination and she had stolen the only man Her Majesty had ever loved. When Lettice appeared at Court immediately after the marriage, dressed to kill as a Countess, and with many attendants, the Queen swept down upon her, boxing her ears and shouting: "As but one sun lights the East, so I shall have but one Queen in England." Lettice had been banished from Court and would remain so for many years. It had taken all the Earl's powerful charm and tact, besides a spell of feigned sickness, to avoid a visit to the Tower of London. He was well acquainted with it and had almost lost his head there during his father's bid to put Lady Jane Grey on the throne.

The majority of statesmen and courtiers, wilting at the task of breaking the news of the marriage to Her Majesty, had left it to Simier, the delightful but oily marriage broker for the Duc d'Anjou. His only axe to grind was a chance that the Queen's outrage would result in her throwing herself into the arms of his master. He was happy to oblige and the Court reverberated for days.

Leicester was pleased with his son. He was well grown for his age, self-possessed and good looking. He had inherited some of his mother's beauty and a great deal of his father's confidence and presence. Not to put too fine a point on it, he had also inherited his arrogance, though this would emerge only as he grew older. Leicester had made it clear to his mother that he did not relish his son's departing to Paris with her. The massacre of St.Bartholomew's Eve was only seven years ago, the atrocities well-remembered, and France had always been volatile. He would not risk his son in such an environment. Sir Francis Walsingham, Ambassador in Paris at that time, had never fully recovered. His pregnant wife and small daughter had also been cooped up for days in a city that resembled an abattoir. Leicester's own nephew and heir, Philip Sidney, had been with them and given him a full report. He was unequivocally against Robert being reared in France.

The stableyard encounter, however, needed further explanation, and quickly. The boy sought out Lord North in whose company he had travelled to Kenilworth. North was a kindly man in his forties, a close friend of Leicester and himself a former Ambassador to France. He had also served in the Netherlands and taken part in the famous charges at Zutphen. At this time, though one of a large family, he was unmarried. He was fair but firm and a good understanding with young Robert Dudley had been achieved after one or two notable skirmishes. His mother, the lovely Lady Douglas Sheffield, had spoilt him to death and he had seldom felt the rod, although the children of her first marriage had kicked him around from time to time.

Having found his preceptor, after a prolonged search through the huge establishment, he stood squarely before him and demanded to know what a bastard was and why he had been called one. Lord North sat down and asked for a description of the culprit. Robert was unlikely to know or recognise anyone at this stage; he could only say the boy was tall, had red hair and laughed a lot. Also that he had ridden a dun coloured horse with a black mane and tail. It was, in fact, a recognizable and pithy description of the young Earl of Essex, the eldest son of Lettice, Countess of Leicester. It was unlucky that the son and the stepson of the Earl, with few drops of related blood between them, should have confronted each other so soon and so undiplomatically. The other boy had most probably been Richard de Burgh, son of the Irish Earl of Clanricarde.

Lord North sighed and pulled Robert towards him. He had known this day would come and had prepared a direct and truthful reply but he had not reckoned with the difficulty of delivering it, or the widening

11

of the boy's grey eyes as the truth went home. He stood quite still for a moment then asked whether, if his parents were now to have further children, would they also be bastards? This was equally difficult and, when he was given the unpalatable answer, he turned abruptly, seeking no comfort, and ran out of the room and down the long corridor beyond. North could hear the frantic little feet receding into the distance. The world had disintegrated.

The old man in the comfortable chair sat up and reached for the telescope. He was very proud of it and the other instruments he had designed and made, both civilian and nautical. Many of his inventions had been influenced by the works of Galileo for whom he had a deep respect despite the trouble into which some of his theories had landed this genius of a man. He peered through the telescope, adjusting it carefully and focusing on one of the many hills around him. Like most, it had a *"podere"* perched on the top, the winding track to it lined with tall, thin cypresses pointing dark fingers at a cloudless sky. It was the house and its garden he sought. At this time of day, when the sun had left the terrace, he might well get a glimpse of the handsome lady who lived there. Her day's work done, she would sidle out to get the air. He loved women deeply and there was little he did not know about them or how their wayward minds and bodies worked. This one reminded him of his second wife; dark and generously constructed. She did not look as strictly pious as the virtuous Alice, but had a roguish, inviting air about her, almost as if she knew he had her in his sights. Perhaps she did; perhaps the sun had flashed from the telescope's lens and given him away. There she was. The telescope was so successful he could pick out a geranium tucked behind her ear, the fringe of her shawl and the deep cleavage revealed as she leant forward, can in hand, to water her plants. The Duke sighed happily. The good things of life did not change. The wine he was drinking came from his own vineyards; still young, it was delicious and would mature very nicely. His hands behind his head, he leant back again in his chair, letting mind and memory rove at will.

The first major excitement of his life, sharply outlined from the past and a prelude to early maturity, had been the threatened Spanish invasion of 1588 and the defeat of King Philip's great Armada. He was up at Oxford, surrounded by excited intellectual young hotheads like himself, when it became clear that the Spaniards were, at last, on the move. Even at the age of fourteen, he had felt the rising fear in the country and the grim-faced determination to give the Spaniards more than they bargained for. England had not, like other European countries, faced the horrors of foreign subjugation for decades although King Henry VlII had not been slow, for a variety of reasons, to foist his Church of England on to a previously Catholic population, and with brutal force. But the new faith was home grown, in the English language and for the English people. Spanish Catholicism with its Inquisition, its mass *"autos da fe"* and its intolerance of heretics, would be a very different kettle of fish. Memories of Queen Mary's reign, too, lived on; the fires of Smithfield, so often spattering the horn windows with human fat when the wind blew, were not easily forgotten.

Now, this summer of 1588, Robert was in a fever of excitement; watching and waiting for word from his father requiring his presence. A letter from Leicester had asked him to hold himself in readiness. The Earl, now in command of the land forces of England, had returned from the campaign against the Spaniards in the Netherlands a year ago in June 1587. This he had also commanded without, so far, any notable success. The initial and grateful welcome from the Dutch had deteriorated into fractious bickering and the only victories had been the taking of Axel and Doesburg and the small but gallant effort to prevent supplies reaching the besieged town of Zutphen. During this outnumbered and brilliant action, his nephew, Sir Philip Sidney, was fatally wounded. Leicester, whose heir he was at the time, was devastated and England mourned a hero; Sidney had been greatly loved. Leicester, in contrast, returned home depressed and ill, to a domineering wife, no legitimate heir and an ungrateful Queen who appeared blinded to everything but her latest favourite, his delightful stepson, Robert Devereux, Earl of Essex. There was nothing triumphal in this return, only prolonged carping about the money spent on the campaign and the number of knighthoods scattered like confetti on many who had barely unsheathed their swords.

Robert had implored his father to take him to the Low Countries in any capacity; groom, squire, cupbearer, anything to serve him, travel and see some action. This had been firmly refused. He was too young and must attend to his books.

He felt painfully his separation from Leicester. His father's marriage to Lettice, Countess of Essex in 1578, had resulted in the birth of a son in May 1581, yet another Robert, but triumphantly legitimate and with the title of Baron Denbigh. The rejoicing had been intense, adoration poured on "the noble imp", and Lettice's position as the mother of the heir greatly enhanced. This had been a bad blow for the seven year old Robert Dudley, till now, his father's only child. He sensed exclusion in every way, and was, as a result, resentful and bitterly jealous. Lettice lost few opportunities to make him feel inferior and unwanted and would no longer allow him in the household. He was sent to live with his uncle and godfather, Ambrose Earl of Warwick, from where he attended school at Offington, near Worthing in Sussex. Ambrose, with no children of his own, became fond of him, took him as his page on visits and oversaw his schooling. His own house, Dudley House in Worthing, became Robert's base. Other exciting breaks in the routine of his childhood came in the shape of visits to Sir Henry Lee, his godfather, at Ditchley. Sir Henry was the current Queen's Champion; he oversaw and organised most of the jousting, so much a part of Court life. He was an ex-military man with a gallant record and one of the leading horsemen of his day. He taught Robert a great deal, both on all matters equine and the history, procedure and correct conduct of the joust and those taking part in it. From him came Robert's love of the sport and his future excellence. The boy put heart and soul into this; Leicester had made sure he was well taught and he had fallen off his first pony by the age of three. He also absorbed all the theatre of the joust and some of the organisation that went into it.

Denbigh, the "noble imp", however, was not long for this world. He died suddenly at Leicester's house at Wanstead in July 1584, only three years old, leaving his father heartbroken and without a legal heir. Fond though he was of his "base" son, he tended to refer to him jokingly as the "badge of my sin". Lettice's chances of another child were now remote and her dislike of ten year old Robert Dudley, not surprisingly, deepened to loathing though Leicester, despite his many duties, remained in close touch with his son until his own departure to the Low Countries in 1585.

In 1587, Robert was entered for Christ Church, Oxford with the status "filius comitis", "Earl's Son", where a Thomas Chaloner became his main tutor and mentor. Chaloner was to remain a close and lifelong friend who shared many interests with his pupil. He was, himself, an illegitimate son, and had a fellow-feeling for Robert. Both were natural mathematicians, marine engineering being Chaloner's particular passion. It was a partnership that would give Robert a broad base of knowledge and was to lead him down undreamed of paths of virtuosity and, among other things, would establish him as the leading cartographer of his age.

For the present, he was kicking up his heels among kindred spirits who acknowledged him as a leader besides being the son of England's leading nobleman; balm to the spirit after having to fight his corner as a bastard during childhood. There had been many hurtful episodes despite his father's protection and he had learnt the hard way what to avenge and what to ignore. He had also developed, beyond his years, a ready tongue and ready fists, both of which had brought early mental and physical maturity. He looked like a boy of seventeen.

Robert's turbulent impatience was rewarded at the end of June. Into Oxford's crowded streets and headed for Christ Church clattered a well-mounted group clad in the Leicester colours and leading a spare horse. Spotting them, Robert, who had packed a bag with his best clothes days before, grabbed his cloak and raced headlong down the spiral stone staircase from his rooms, yelling for his body servant. He erupted into the quadrangle as the horsemen turned through the entrance. Heads appeared in every window, some hanging out in blatant curiosity. The Dean of Christ Church, stately and silver-haired, called Robert to stand by him and receive the visitors, muttering under his breath about "raucous and unseemly behaviour".

An hour later the column rode out, headed for London, Robert on a powerful grey horse of his father's choosing. He was an instinctive horseman and had never lacked good mounts. The Officer with them gave him what information he could. They were going to Tilbury to join the main English defence force encamped in and around the old Roman fort, with nearby Gravesend also fortified. Leicester had made this his headquarters and, if intelligence and look-out reports were correct, the Spaniards were expected off the coast of Cornwall within days. Sir Francis Walsingham's agents had given information indicating an attack on Kent or London, via the Thames, rather than a south coast landing, though this, together with the Isle of Wight, was being closely watched. It was believed that, after achieving its first objective, the defeat of the English fleet, the Armada would head for a rendezvous with the Duke of Parma's force of armed men and flat-bottomed barges gathering in and around Flushing, Brill and Ostend. The nearest objectives from there would logically be Dover, London, or both, escorted by King Philip's ships.

Lord Howard of Effingham, Robert's uncle (his mother was born a Howard) had been put in command of the English fleet, a highly responsible and unenviable task since it entailed controlling the antics of such legendary tars as Drake, Hawkins, Raleigh and Frobisher whose free-booting tendencies made it difficult to weld them into a disciplined fighting force. They were all too fond of tangents of their own making and to their own advantage. They would obey orders but could seldom resist any opportunity for a profitable diversion. Leicester, in command of the land forces, had behind him Walsingham and Burghley, united in preparing England for battle on land as well as at sea. After some persuasion, the Queen had acknowledged that it would be extremely dangerous to leave the defence of England to her seamen. Any Spanish landing would have been met only by patriotic but bucolic farmers wielding scythes and hay forks. Leicester's voice had been among the loudest in deprecating her resistance to keeping her army mobilised and her ships and sailors fully commissioned and she had, eventually, listened. The cost of the unsuccessful war in the Low Countries had been huge and the national coffers were at a low ebb. No one knew better than the Queen how to "hold household"; insolvency was her worst nightmare and the cost of defence was going to be high. Nevertheless, eleven new ships had been built and, in April, twelve more were refurbished. Even now, after the Armada had reportedly left Spanish waters, the Queen was still frantically negotiating with Parma and King Philip for peace. Both these crafty gentlemen had given her to believe that they were open to discussion in order, successfully, to delay her own defence plans. Most of the Netherlands contingent had already been rushed home in Leicester's wake and a concentrated effort made to integrate them, together with levies of men and arms from all over the country, into an effective military force. A line of beacons stretching the length of the South coast, long in disuse, had been re-furbished and made serviceable. The main body of the English fleet at Plymouth was on battle stations. Tension was mounting.

As Robert and his small escort rode towards London and Tilbury, they heard, in almost every town and village they passed through, town criers bawling out requests or orders for supplies of every kind; food, drink, ropes, timber and horses to be sent to muster points for victualling and supplying the troops being marshalled for the defence of England. They passed marching men, wagons, carts, sheep and cattle and flocks of geese being driven to the capital. This slowed their progress somewhat but the mood of these throngs was one of fierce good humour and rising anger.

Robert, exchanging news and banter with the troops and the suppliers, felt their outrage and their belligerence. England, since the fall of Calais an isolated fog-bound island off the coast of Europe, was on the move. The excitement of being in the thick of it, and shortly to be at the hub, thrilled him to the core. He mentally ran through what he carried in the way of arms – two daggers and a rapier. He fenced well for his age but a cavalry charge would need more than that.

They skirted London and arrived at Tilbury two days later to find perfect chaos. The road became more and more jammed with men and horses, carts and wagons; tempers were getting frayed and the escort resorted to much yelling and whacking. On arrival, they picked their way through the pandemonium of the camp and arrived at Leicester's tent, his banner flying over it and a guard mounted at its entrance.

Robert was startled by his father's appearance; he had not seen him for several months. His hair was thinner and completely grey, his face had a high colour and his girth had increased. He did not look well; the intermittent malaria that plagued him was taking its toll. Added to this was the daily stress of his huge responsibilities, the constant travelling between Council Room, camp and coast and the knowledge that the largest fleet ever assembled, "so great that the oceans groaned under it", was bearing down on England. It was now known to have sailed on 30th May.

He was plainly delighted to see his son, however, and looked him up and down. He liked what he saw and noted that the boy was mature for his age with big shoulders and dark shadows on chin and upper lip. The merry eyes looked him back directly and Robert thanked him for the horse he had sent. They ate together, Leicester explaining the present state of affairs, why they were at Tilbury and what defences were already in position. It was as chaotic as it looked.

The Earl had thoughtfully brought Robert's dog in his train. Now nine years old, he was huge and almost white, with a dense, silky coat and vast paws. Like everyone else, he was prepared for war and sported a formidable spiked collar. Boy and hound fell upon each other and thereafter he accompanied Robert everywhere, glued to his heels and taking up most of the tent allotted to him.

Many of the troops due to foregather at Tilbury were late. Four thousand had arrived from Essex, but there was not enough food to feed them and Leicester had, as yet, no authority to force victuallers to comply with the appeals for food and drink. The boom constructed to close the Thames in case of attack had broken, and the temporary bridge to allow the passage of soldiers across the river was not yet complete.

While they ate, trumpets blared and there was a swirl of activity on the western side of the camp, accompanied by cheers and the sounds of large numbers of horses. Leaping to his feet, Robert caught a glimpse of vivid orange and white banners and trappings advancing towards them and knew at once that they heralded the arrival of the Earl of Essex. The Devereux colours were hard to mistake and there were a great many of them to be seen.

Not one to do anything by halves, Essex had arrived with two hundred light cavalry and sixty harquebusiers, a repetition of his efforts before joining Leicester as his Commander of Horse in the Netherlands. He had again scraped the barrel of his estates in Staffordshire and Wales and added to the huge cost by decking his men out in the startling colours of his house. With him was young Richard de Burgh, with a string of spare horses from his own estates in Ireland.

Leicester staggered to his feet to greet them while Robert launched himself from the tent to take their horses heads and pelt them with questions. He had spent much time during his childhood in the company of Essex who, with the generosity of spirit that characterized him, treated him as a younger brother, and with Richard de Burgh who behaved as an equal though two years his senior. Both he and Richard were the sons of earls but Richard had been taken from Galway into the Essex household at the age of six as surety for loyalty to the Crown by his father the Earl of Clanricarde. Bog Irish, barefoot and furious, with a brogue that rendered him unintelligible, he too had been treated to jibes and sneers as a child and known misery and isolation. He had recognised the same fury in Robert, but the careless affection and protection of Essex had been a saving grace to them both. The years between them shrank as they grew older and this was a happy reunion.

The camp began to fill as the levies poured in, together with supplies, and gradually a military structure emerged with some kind of discipline and order. Second in command to Leicester was Sir John Norris who had served under him in the Netherlands. He was the most experienced of the Queen's generals, had fought through almost every campaign and had little time for Leicester. They had fallen out seriously before and after Zutphen, but it was his doing that the camp was now being rapidly transformed and the troops properly fed.

Robert was fascinated by everything he saw and took part in. The horse lines, the blacksmiths and leather-workers, the armourers, the rapidly erected field kitchens, even the digging of latrines. He had a practical nature and a vast interest in how things could be made to work successfully. He took to accompanying Norris on his inspections and several of his suggestions, hesitantly made, bore fruit. He took it for granted that they would be and, with deep enjoyment, made himself useful wherever possible. He rapidly absorbed all this military procedure and organisation, the questions pouring out of his mouth as they entered his head. Norris, who liked him and put up with such an enthusiastic shadow, explained that what applied to a camp applied also to a ship and that nothing could succeed without discipline, direct orders instantly obeyed, and a thorough knowledge of the subject. Fighting men, on land or sea, must be properly equipped, housed and fed or they would not fight.

A week later, with still no sign of the Spanish fleet, the race against time accelerated. The troops at Tilbury and Gravesend, now given quarters and food, were beginning to hold military exercises outside the camp in which Robert was allowed to take part. Riding in formation with Essex's cavalry, he quickly learnt the sounds and signals of command and began to master the art of dealing with a horse, a sword or lance, a dagger in his belt and an axe strapped to his saddle. He had been issued with basic armour but had privately decided to cut this down to the bare minimum; it was cumbersome and hot and he felt he would perform far better without it. Much of what he had learnt while with Sir Henry Lee was now employed.

Listening to after dinner tales of battles, skirmishes, triumphs and near misses was stirring stuff; meat and drink to a boy of his ilk and his nightly prayers were mainly for a Spanish landing and the chance to take part in a charge.

Even more fascinating for him were the guns and firing pieces currently used by foot soldiers. Not everyone was lucky enough to own one. An income of £100 per annum was necessary to possess a gun at all, and an average soldier's pay was £10 a year. Robert quickly found armourers willing to let him examine and, eventually, dismantle various pieces in use; mostly these were matchlocks, but one or two of the richer and rarer flintlock guns now becoming popular were owned by officers. He practised loading and firing until he could do it nearly as quickly as the proud possessors. Big guns and their manoeuvrability were of particular interest to him.

The sense of urgency pervading the camp made him doubly anxious to acquire as much knowledge of arms, armoury and anything resembling a fighting device while he had this golden chance. He was like a child in an overstocked toy shop; the days were simply not long enough.

Lying back in the Tuscan sun, the Duke of Northumberland's mouth curved in a smile as he recalled how this knowledge had widened and applied to the ships he had later built and commanded. There was nothing like a cannonade of big guns delivering a broadside at precisely the right moment. His mind moved swiftly on to exploration, sea battles, Cadiz blazing in the night and the walls of Famagusta with its guns thundering in defence. His life had never been uneventful.

CHAPTER TWO

The Armada – 1588

The tops of the Spanish masts were sighted off the Lizard on 19th July 1588, having made heavy weather of the journey. The Bay of Biscay had not been kind. The huge crescent of towering galleons and men-'o'-war presented a terrifying sight to those tracking it as the fleet proceeded majestically up the Channel. The Commander, the Duke of Medina Sidonia, no sailor and horribly seasick, was weighed down with minute, detailed instructions from King Philip. On board every ship, to be distributed among her people in due course, were thousands of copies of a papal Bull declaring the Queen of England's excommunication, calling upon her subjects to rise and depose her, and blessing the enterprise.

The chain of beacons flared along the south coast, chosen men galloping flat out from one to the other. The country held its breath while the English fleet, like hunting dogs "low and snug in the water", put out from Plymouth under cover of darkness on the night of 19th July. Closing in behind the Spanish ships, they proceeded to stalk them up the Channel, within sight but out of range. Unlike King Philip, the Queen had authorised the Lord High Admiral to "conduct all engagements according to his own judgements". Well she knew that Drake and his fellow Commanders were at his elbow. Now that the moment had come, she was calm and composed, her own prayer of intercession for her realm being read in every church.

There was a brief engagement two days later off Eddystone, not far from Plymouth. On 23rd July a much sharper attack took place near Portland during which several of the Spanish galleons were damaged, two more being wrecked off the Isle of Wight on 25th. The English fleet, now flying the green and white colours of the Tudors, continued to prowl behind the Spaniards, keeping out of range until the Armada anchored off Calais on 27th July where the Duke of Parma waited with sixteen thousand troops. The Dutch fleet was also patrolling nearby in support.

Hearing that the Queen fearlessly proposed riding in person to lead her southern levies, Leicester, horrified, suggested that she should visit Tilbury to "comfort" her army gathered there instead. No one yet knew precisely what was going on in the Channel, though alarming rumour was hurtling round the country. Not one of those close to the Queen knew better than Leicester how to conduct ceremonial and create an impressive occasion; he had been doing it for her since her coronation.

Robert was then privileged to see his father, despite failing health, race back to Tilbury and stage manage a perfectly timed piece of theatre at what might have been a crucial moment during the threatened invasion. The date for the Queen's visit was to be 8th August. Events were to prove how lucky this was.

On 28th July, at midnight, orders were given by the English Commanders who had followed the Armada to Calais to loose five "hellburners", fireships stacked with pitch and wood, among the Spanish galleons gathered there. With a rising wind behind them, they did a huge amount of damage creating an inferno with all the attendant chaos and panic. It was a horrible scene, men and masts burning like torches, and it left the Spaniards unable to reform properly. The following day, off Gravelines, with the English fleet now on more even terms, the final battle was fought. Medina Sidonia did his best, with some success, but the wind was not on his side. He lost a further eleven ships and two thousand men; the English just fifty men. Both sides ran out of ammunition, but the wind now changed again, accompanied by savage storms, which drove the Spaniards northwards, scattered and off course. Despite the lack of ammunition, Effingham, with lighter ships and formidable seamanship, pursued them as far as the Firth of Forth, but they were in a terrible state of disarray and he decided to leave them to the storms and the jagged Scottish rocks. "Many of them will never see Spain again" remarked one English sailor trenchantly. He was right: of the hundred and thirty ships that sailed under Medina Sidonia, only forty four returned to Spain; two thirds of their men were missing. The English had lost a hundred men but not one ship. Not for the last time the "Protestant wind" had come to their aid.

There remained, however, the threat of Parma's army of men and barges sitting at Calais, with the watchful Dutch navy in attendance. With a good wind they would still be able to make the crossing but the returning

English fleet, equally watchful, could re-stock with ammunition and bombard them as soon as they showed their noses out of Calais. Without the protection of the Spanish ships the prospects did not look good for an invasion. "The Duke of Parma is as a bear robbed of his whelps", wrote Drake gleefully from Gravelines on 10th August.

When news of the devastating defeat reached King Philip, he retired to the Escorial Palace in a cloud of incense, holy regret and determination to return to the fray. Parma was given orders to "Stand down".

Ignorant as yet of events, the camp at Tilbury was flung into a maelstrom of preparation. The army practised drill and manoeuvres while every other living soul was flung into a frenzy of cleaning, clearing, polishing, painting and scrubbing. Leicester's talent for display was applied to every detail. Down from London came the trappings of panoply while anything remotely sordid was relegated to the background.

Robert Dudley, wildly excited by the prospect of the Queen's visit, served as Leicester's "runner". His feet hardly touching the ground, he raced from one commander to another from dawn to dusk, carrying orders, plans and instructions, very often offering his own practical advice and help. He became a familiar sight in every corner of the camp, with his great dog pounding along behind him. It was here at Tilbury that he learned the business of organising State occasions, what was entailed and how it was conducted. The foundations were laid here for another, much later, chapter of his life.

Not forgotten and foremost in all these preparations was the fact that, so far as anyone knew, England was still under threat, and while receiving and entertaining their Queen, this army at Tilbury would also be responsible for her protection and expected to lay down their lives in her defence. If the worst happened, the last battle would be fought here and would be theirs. It kept her away from vulnerable London and the heart of her army was undoubtedly the safest place for her.

Robert made sure that he drilled with the army every day, both as a foot soldier and a cavalryman, in addition to his duties to his father. This was usually very early in the morning, soon after dawn, and before the heat of the day. He was rapidly becoming skilled in both defence and attack, despite some spectacular falls and bruises, and the men he rode and marched with showed him respect and camaraderie. He took his tone from Essex, a cavalry commander who always led from the front, was very easy with his men, and whose courage and reputation as a soldier was well established. The Earl was twenty two years old, the apple of their Queen's eye and they would follow him as no other.

The night before the Queen's arrival, exhausted as he was, Leicester called Robert to his tent and commissioned him as a Colonel of foot, though under the supervision of a senior officer. It was his son's fifteenth birthday, he was proud of him and he recognised in him his own ambition and driving determination and wished to reward the support ungrudgingly given him during these weeks at Tilbury. Was this a hint of another kind of recognition; an acknowledgement of something deeper that had been allowed to remain buried for fifteen years, an injustice done to a child because he himself had not admitted the truth? Or was it merely pride and affection? Perhaps he sensed that he was not far from facing judgement himself, on a much higher level, and wished to make as much reparation to his son as time allowed. None of this crossed Robert's young mind; he was speechless and delighted. For him, life could not have been better. For Leicester, the sands were running out and he had one final great effort to make.

The Queen duly arrived at Tilbury by state barge from St. James's Palace on 8th August. She, too, had done some preparation. She was clothed in white velvet, "attired like an angel bright", with a burnished silver cuirass over the bosom and, on disembarking, she immediately mounted a great grey gelding led by Leicester himself. Before her went a page carrying her silver helmet on a white cushion, and the Earl of Ormonde bearing the sword of state. Pennants and flags dipped then fluttered in the breeze and the pipes and drums struck up. The Queen proceeded to inspect the miraculously tidy squadrons of infantry and cavalry drawn up before her. Essex was well to the fore, caparisoned in violent white and orange, while Robert, scrubbed and immaculate in a new colonel's uniform, stood before his men and went down on his knee shouting "Lord preserve our Queen" with the rest. "God Bless you all," she responded as Leicester led her through the ranks, ensigns, lances and swords being lowered as she passed. A moving service of intercession was then held in which all took part, after which Her Majesty retired to a manor house at Saffron Garden where she was to spend the night. Chosen for her by Leicester, it belonged to a Mr.Edward Ritchie and was described to her as: "a proper, sweet, cleanly house, the camp a little mile of it, and your person as sure as at St. James's."

On her return to the camp the following morning, there was a huge burst of spontaneous applause so loud that: "the earth and air did sound like thunder." This was a pivotal moment in Elizabeth's career and she rose magnificently to the occasion. Her speech, resounding down the ages, bore a strong resemblance to that delivered by a famous statesman and war leader four hundred years later when England was again threatened by an overwhelming force and faced a very dark hour. She would fight, she would die among them and she would never surrender:

"My loving people," she began...........""Let tyrants fear. I have always so behaved myself that, under God, I have placed my chiefest strength and safeguard in the loyal hearts and goodwill of my subjects, and therefore I am come amongst you, as you see, at this time, not for my recreation and disport, but being resolved in the midst and heat of battle to live and die amongst you all, to lay down for my God and my kingdom, and for my people, my honour and my blood, even in the dust. I know I have the body of a weak and feeble woman, but I have the heart and stomach of a king, and of a king of England too, and think it foul scorn that Parma or Spain, or any prince in Europe, should dare invade the borders of my realm; to which, rather than any dishonour should grow by me, I myself will take up arms, I myself will be your general, judge and rewarder of any one of your virtues.............."

The deafening roar that followed this oration was more than any general could have hoped for. The speech was copied and widely distributed. Woe betide any Spaniard landing on English soil.

Robert was lucky to be close enough to both see and hear the Queen. It was a moment never to be forgotten nor had the memory faded. He could see her now, her white robes and silver armour gleaming and carrying in her hand a small gold truncheon. His father stood by her side, bareheaded, with his hand on her horse's bridle. Her final words had been: "In the meantime, my Lieutenant General shall be in my stead, than whom never a prince commanded a more noble or worthy subject, not doubting that by your obedience to my General, by your concord in the camp and your valour in the field, we shall shortly have a famous victory over these enemies of God, of my kingdom, and of my people."

She had publicly honoured him, she had thanked him and she had shown him affection, all of which he had justly earned. Robert felt a surge of pride that he was this man's son; would that he had been hers as well.

25

She was right. News of the "famous victory" was not long in coming. At noon that day, when a rumour arrived that Parma and his troops were about to sail for England, the Queen refused to leave Tilbury. After such a public declaration it would have been unthinkable. By nightfall, however, came more news that confirmed the defeat of the enemy at sea and Parma's decision to withdraw. Jubilation and triumph swept through the camp and unbridled rejoicing lasted until morning.

Robert had been presented to Her Majesty that night, while she dined with his father. Despite the doubt and tension before the news of victory finally arrived, she had been composed and gracious, smiling upon him as she would on any personable young man, but with a gleam of recognition and interest and a few arch words. He was overwhelmed and enslaved and, much later, fell asleep to the roars of camp-fire singing and the firing of muskets. There were a great many thick heads in the morning.

The camp at Tilbury was disbanded on 17th August and Leicester returned to London in the Queen's wake, tired as never before but content in the knowledge that no stone had been left unturned in the defence of the country and Elizabeth's person. Their long and close relationship fully restored, the failure in the Netherlands forgiven and forgotten, there was little she was not prepared to do for him; in her gratitude, she even drew up Letters Patent to give him the title Governor General of England. This was too much for Burghley and Walsingham, however, and they promptly vetoed such a concentration of power in one individual, particularly Leicester. Even Essex, her brilliant boy, took a back seat, fuming and disappointed that, despite his mustered men, he had been denied the chance to fight. He was bored, restive and power-hungry.

Leicester took Robert with him, wanting him to witness this hour of triumph, both his own and the Queen's. He also felt loth to part with the boy. He was now fifteen and well able to take his place at Court, although he would first have to return to Oxford to complete his studies. In this time of celebration, however, the Earl wanted his son beside him. They rode knee to knee, relaxed and companionable, discussing, re-living and laughing in relief over the events of the last days. Glancing sharply sideways at his father, Robert noticed a change in his face. The high colour had gone, replaced by a bluer, mottled look and his hands on the reins, despite the heat of the day, were purple. Their ways would diverge when London was reached. Lettice would be waiting at Leicester House, the Queen at

Whitehall; the two women in Leicester's life would once more claim him. Robert, himself, would be with the Earl of Pembroke and his sons.

Back in London, the pace did not slacken. Many national celebrations were being planned and the city was in uproar; they could hardly push their way through the euphoric crowds to Leicester House on the Strand. Robert, riding just behind his father was almost pulled off his horse, flowers were flung at him, girls reached to kiss him, wine by the gallon was handed up to him. He particularly appreciated the girls. Essex had done his duty as a brother at Tilbury and introduced him to the delights to be found among selected camp followers; there was little he could not tell Robert in that direction and he had an apt and appreciative pupil who could not wait to put into practice what he had so far learnt. It was the beginning of a life time's devotion to women.

On 20th August Robert attended the service at St.Paul's Church in thanksgiving for the victory and on 26th, far more exciting, a military review at Whitehall which included jousting and mock fighting. Essex was matched against the Earl of Cumberland and acquitted himself brilliantly. Robert, dressed in his best and green with envy, cheered his stepbrother at the top of his lungs. He was sitting in the tiered seats below the "Queen's window" and swore to himself that the next time he came to the tiltyard, it would be beside Essex, carrying his shield or pennant. Leicester sat with the Queen; these two, whose lives had been so closely bound almost from childhood and were now in the autumn of their days, quietly rejoiced in each other's company.

That evening, Leicester sent for Robert in his own chamber in Leicester House. He was leaving in the morning, first to take the healing waters at Buxton, then on by stages to Kenilworth. He needed rest and could not play his part in any further celebrations; Lettice was accompanying him and Robert was to return to Oxford that day also. The adventure was over. Father and son embraced with mutual affection and respect and went their ways.

Leicester never reached Kenilworth. He was taken ill on 3rd September while at Cornbury House, his hunting lodge near Woodstock, and died on the morning of 4th with few but Lettice beside him. Despite a chequered and, at times, questionable career and a great deal of unpopularity, he had remained the Queen's beloved, giving, at the end, every ounce of his remaining strength to ensure her safety.

Robert had reached Oxford on the crest of a wave and very full of himself. Admittedly, he had seen no action except drilling and cavalry manoeuvres but he was now a Colonel and he had no finer feelings when it came to bragging about what he had done and how he had run around the corridors of power. Modesty was not one of Robert's virtues; he was barely fifteen and could be brash and bumptious but he did not have long to bask in any reflected glory. The stately Master of his college, who could not abide either Leicester or his son, called him to his rooms and, without inviting him to sit, coldly informed him in precise and finicking tones, that his father had died at Cornbury. He had leave to attend his funeral but, when he returned, he was to cease flaunting his rank and his adventures and apply himself solely to his books. He could not resist rubbing in the fact that Robert was not his father's heir. He would remain plain Robert Dudley. He got a venomous look for his pains and the suggestion of a slammed door as the boy abruptly left the room. He would not forget.

But for his uncle, Ambrose, Earl of Warwick, he was very much alone and must now shape his own future.

CHAPTER THREE

Prelude to Trinidad – 1591-1593

Hampton Court in May 1591 was a joy to behold. Spring had come early with summer not far behind it. The leaves still had the fragile yellow green of youth, trees were laden with flower, the cherry blossom hanging almost to the ground, and the fruit trees in the walled gardens were bursting with bud. It had been a foul winter, freezing mud making many roads impassable, stock dying even in the byres, not to mention the toll of human life which had been high. Nature, having ruthlessly weeded out the oldest, poorest and weakest, was making up for its shortcomings and beginning to smile. The sap was rising in abundance.

In the Queen's presence chamber a mission from France was being received by Her Majesty. It consisted of the Duke of Turenne, Henry IV's representative from France and his delegation, and concerned the sending of a possible force from England to support that ebullient Protestant monarch in his efforts to prevent the formation of a Spanish corridor along the north coast of France. Spain had landed troops in Brittany in order to join the Catholic League in France and Spanish forces from the Netherlands, thereby providing a base for further attacks upon England. King Philip had by no means thrown in the sacred sponge since the Armada. The English royal heels were dragging, however, the Queen deploring any further expensive foreign wars. The exchequer had seldom been in a worse state.

Robert Dudley stood, supposedly attentive, with his back to a window, his hands behind him and his gaze shifting from the face of his Monarch to that of a very pretty girl to his left and slightly in front of him. Small, round and softly fair, she reminded him of a pouter pigeon which had just settled its feathers. She could not have appeared in greater contrast to the Queen whose aquiline features and heavily painted face fought to hold back the years, while this girl, with little artifice, was longing to add to them.

He knew her quite well. She was the sister of Thomas Cavendish, the explorer, circumnavigator and sometime privateer and she was a Maid of Honour to the Queen. She had smiled shyly and invitingly at him on the occasions when they met though she was not aware that he stood behind her now, and not by chance either. He moved as if slowly easing his limbs, not taking his eyes from the Queen, and stealthily arrived just behind her. From there, it was easy to slip an arm round her, and whisper in her ear not to squeak or turn her head. Her colour rose, but she did not move, only leaning back against him. A few minutes of this was too much for him and he gently bent his head and kissed her.

There was a roar of outrage from the Queen's dais. "Master Dudley" was ordered to leave the presence chamber at once and await her pleasure. He bowed deeply in her direction and went briskly from the room, his head held high.

The interview that followed with his Sovereign was not something he wished to remember. She did not spare him, tore his character to shreds and let it be known she would not tolerate any such public exhibition of lust, nor flirtation with any of her ladies in her presence. How dared he behave so in public and, worse, before foreign emissaries? He stood unmoving before her, his eyes boldly fixed on hers, as if their roles were reversed. There was no hint of shame or apology, though his lips formed a few appropriate words. She had seen that look before; he was very much his father's son and she was hard put to it not to smile. She ordered him to leave Court for two months and would have turned on her heel except that he stepped forward and begged a further word.

He wished her to understand that he intended to marry Mistress Cavendish and, therefore, that he wanted no blame to fall on her. He had yet to obtain her brother's consent.

Also, he had further plans for outfitting ships at this time; ships to cross the Atlantic to the New World for exploration of the coast of South America and, possibly, much further. He had studied routes, consulted cartographers and explorers such as Cavendish himself. He would claim territory in his Queen's name and bring home whatever New World treasure he could find for her.

His eyes never left her face; there was a formidable will behind the request, almost a command. He would do what he proposed to do and he was quite undaunted by putting his demand hard on the heels of a disgraced and public dismissal. Her Majesty's lips twitched and, instead of bawling him out, she replied that she would give the matter thought and, on his return from banishment, he was to lay a detailed proposition before her. As for his marriage to Mistress Cavendish, they were both young, but, if Cavendish gave his consent, she would consider that matter also. The remembered smile was her reward; more of a delighted boyish grin in this case, which lit his face and creased his eyes. She made a shooing motion with her hand and left the room before she relented further.

This was not the first fit of gallantry she had witnessed. Last year he had compromised Frances Vavasour, another of her Maids of Honour and been contracted to marry her. The Queen had refused permission on the grounds of Robert's youth. Mistress Vavasour, a very dashing lady, older than he was, had abandoned him and married Sir Thomas Shirley, a seasoned soldier and reprobate. The Queen, privately in sympathy with Robert, had banished the pair from Court; thereby would hang a far-reaching and complicated tale. At seventeen, his reputation was growing. What had she done to be plagued with such a boy, when she had Essex ranting at her daily for permission to lead a contingent to France? She needed all her own considerable will to control their antics.

She was aware, also, of Robert's previous schemes and dreams since her permission was needed before the start of any maritime exploration. This expedition would not be the first. Last year, he and Cavendish had their heads together plotting a Far Eastern voyage. Robert had offered to equip vessels to send to the Philippines under Thomas's command and preparations were almost complete. Financially, he was now well able to do this. Manila was the trading point at which goods from all over Asia – silks, spices and precious metals were bought and sold. Spain sent two enormous vessels each year, the "Manila Galleons" to trade and bring back its bounty. Robert had put their plans before the Queen and begged to be allowed to sail with them. Having served an apprenticeship in seamanship, he was afire to prove himself and his skill. The Queen refused point blank to let him go. He was then still a mere seventeen, all that was left of Leicester and too precious to risk in the far corners of the earth. Her reaction was predictable; her favourites always had to battle for their freedom and ambitions.

Robert Dudley was now eighteen and a man of substance. Leicester's sudden death had been a severe blow and there were many battles to fight and demons to face down, both personal and fiscal. The Earl died leaving colossal debts, mainly to the Crown, and these were not yet fully honoured. The Queen's grief was intense and doubly hard to bear since she was still surrounded by celebration and rejoicing among the rest of the population, many of whom felt that Leicester's death was no great loss. William Camden, the historian, commented that the universal joy was "no whit abated" and that "All men, so far as they durst, rejoiced no less outwardly at his death than for the victory lately obtained against the Spaniard." She shut herself in her room for days and a letter, from Cornbury House, was found in her chamber after her own death, inscribed "His last letter."

Despite her genuine and deep sorrow, however, she lost no time in dunning his widow, Lettice, for everything possible. She wanted her detested cousin and rival to reap no unnecessary reward from what, she considered, had been her predatory and, possibly, bigamous marriage. This required the sale of much property including personal effects and land. The Queen noticeably concentrated her efforts on property left to the Countess rather than that left to Robert Dudley. Of the £60,000 owed, the Countess would be required to pay £20,000. She had been left the Staffordshire estates, Wanstead in Essex and Leicester house on the Strand. This last she promptly sold to her son, the Earl of Essex and his new wife Frances Sidney, Walsingham's daughter and the widow of Philip Sidney.

Robert had been left the castle and estate at Kenilworth and the lordships of Denbigh and Chirk, but without much money for their upkeep; nonetheless, a very generous legacy. These were to be held in trust for him by his uncle and godfather, Ambrose, Earl of Warwick. The pill to swallow was that Leicester had clearly stated in his will that these properties were left to his "base" son, a phrase repeated several times, and that had hurt beyond measure. Might this have been changed had Leicester been given more time to consider? Not if Lettice had anything to say in the matter; it was probable that the reiteration of the word "base" in the document had been her doing. Neither Robert, nor anyone else, would ever know the answer to this though many considered that such a legacy tacitly indicated that Leicester had, indeed, married Douglas Sheffield, as she later claimed, and that Robert was his legitimate son and always had been. Had Leicester acknowledged him, his marriage to Lettice would have been null and void, and well she knew it.

This boiling pot had not yet fully erupted, however, and the still beautiful Lady Douglas had returned from Paris, strangely, on the day of Leicester's death, and was given an appointment at Court as a Lady of the Bedchamber, one of the highest positions among the Queen's ladies. The Queen had always taken her part in the vicious triangle of events between Lettice, Leicester and Douglas, and it was, possibly, a gesture to show her support for mother and son. The appointment made it easy for Douglas to obtain a Court permission for Robert which would keep him under her Majesty's eye. She had proved a most successful ambassador's wife being, surprisingly, favoured by the French Queen Mother, Catherine de Medici. This sinister mother of Kings (though no founder of dynasties) became very attached to her and had sought her advice on several homely aspects of the re-building in the Palace of the Louvre. Douglas had borne Stafford two sons during her sojourn in Paris, but both had died in babyhood.

Robert's inheritance was to be administered by Ambrose, Earl of Warwick, since he himself was barely fifteen at the time of Leicester's death and considered too "young and casual" to have charge of his own affairs. Young he was, but casual he certainly was not.

Ambrose had died childless a mere eighteen months later, in February 1590 and Robert then inherited a great deal of his uncle's land and possessions, in addition to those left him by his father. He now lacked for little and was quite a marital prospect. Leicester may not have been popular, but his aura remained and his son was not only eye-catching, but financially well endowed. A contemporary described Robert Dudley at eighteen as "of exquisite stature, with a fair beard and noble appearance"; also as "a handsome youth, learned in mathematics and an admirable horseman".

Lettice had lost no time either and married again, within months, a tall dark soldier, nearer her son's age than her own. Christopher Blount had been Leicester's Commander of Horse in the Netherlands campaign where he had lost half an arm. He was also a former agent of Walsingham's, involved in the downfall of the Queen of Scots, and a close friend of Essex. This over-prompt re-marriage had given rise to some pretty pungent speculation on the circumstances surrounding Leicester's death, none of them lost on Robert who loathed Lettice and felt fully justified in doing so. Several brutal scenes during his childhood had been her doing; beatings and incarcerations in dark rooms.

Rumours on the subject of her new marriage included the use of poison, administered by the same agent, the ubiquitous Dr.Julio, reputed to have murdered her first husband the Earl of Essex. Also, a long-standing extra marital affair with Blount, concealed pregnancies and anything else the fertile popular mind could dredge up. Many of these scurrilous stories originated from the publication "Leycester's Commonwealth" printed in 1584, accusing him of the murder of his first wife, Amy Robsart, and those of the husbands of his mistress, Douglas, his second wife, Lettice, and a great many others besides. This vitriolic pamphlet, though verbally denounced by the Queen and, in writing, by Sir Philip Sidney, had thoroughly damaged Leicester's reputation.

Lettice remained quite impervious to all the scandals and proceeded to please herself as she always had done. She continued to travel between Leicester House (re-named Essex House after its sale), her estates at Wanstead in Essex and those in Staffordshire. She refused to give up some of the property inherited by Robert after Leicester's death and made a spirited attempt to retain Kenilworth itself, assuming "squatter's rights" until, though Blount led the defence, she was eventually evicted. As a result, a mountain of mistrust and abhorrence was building up between herself and her stepson. She was made of stern stuff, however, and let very little stand in her way, although she remained firmly barred from Court.

Six weeks after his fall from grace, Robert was back in London. The grass had not grown under his feet either. His banishment had given him time for two important missions.

Margaret Cavendish's brother, Thomas, had given his consent to a marriage with his sister. No difficulty there; the Earl of Leicester's son was a good match, particularly as he was now the possessor of Kenilworth Castle and much of his uncle Warwick's property. Thomas knew that money had also been left by Ambrose and was delighted that Robert had invested so lavishly in his own expedition, poised now to sail again to the Far East. This current voyage would follow Cavendish's previous sensational westbound circumnavigation, completed just after the defeat of the Armada, and was intended to open up trade with Japan and China. It did not, however, exclude whatever chances of piracy presented themselves.

Robert now ensured, during their meeting, that this expedition and the one he was planning to lead himself, would not duplicate each other in any way. He also obtained a great deal of valuable information and advice from Thomas Cavendish and the promise that two ships, at present outfitting in Portsmouth, were to be part of Margaret's dowry. Robert had great admiration for his future brother-in-law, an outstanding seaman and adventurer who had included the Cape Horn passage, the west coast of South America, the vast uncharted heart of the Pacific and the mysterious islands of Japan in his circumnavigation. His accounts of what he had encountered, which included, among many adventures, a bruising and successful engagement with a 600 ton Manila Galleon, the "Santa Anna", transporting to Spain the precious proceeds of a year's trading in Asia. A great deal of this he had appropriated and brought back with him. Also, the killing and salting, for food, of two barrels full of penguins at Punta Arenas in Chile.

For Robert another world was opening up which made the shores of England and Europe seem small. He had always loved the sea; by his own admission: "Having, since I could conceive anything, been delighted with discoveries of navigation, I fostered in myself that disposition until I was of more years and better able to understand such a matter." Perhaps gazing at the grey Channel waters from his schoolroom in Worthing, instead of at his books, had something to do with it. His two Howard uncles and his grandfather had all been very distinguished seamen and his association with Thomas Chaloner at Oxford had urged him down this path of discovery and maritime expertise, though neither occupation was considered wholly suitable for a young aristocrat. All very well for the Drakes, Raleighs, Hawkins and Frobishers; despite being government and crown sponsored pirates and knights of the realm for their achievements and their prowess, they were not the sons of earls.

Nevertheless, Robert would have given anything to be going with Cavendish. They had a rollicking farewell dinner together with Richard Hakluyt, a great recorder of sea voyages and married to Margaret's sister, decided they were all as good as brothers and toasted the success of the coming voyage to the last dregs.

Robert's friendship with Chaloner was deep and would last for life; the older man had read the character of the younger and realised that he was not destined to spend his life bowing and scraping around some royal court or taking his place among the also-rans of the aristocracy who happened to be born out of wedlock, but that he was, primarily, an instigator and not one to accept any form of second place. He was fiercely aware of his birthright, had been raised in the traditions of chivalry, honour and feudal responsibility which had seen such a resurgence during Elizabeth's reign, and he was beginning to question closely the circumstances of his own legitimacy. Robert Dudley did not conform to sixteenth century notions of social pigeon-holing; he went his way regardless of his birth and all accepted standards. In fact, his personality was something no one but he had any part in shaping. Circumstance might influence it, but, in many ways, he had cast his own mould and had no doubts about his place in society. He would not, in fact, have given such matters one thought.

Thomas Chaloner was a rare soul and a man of great ability. He was to travel in Italy, Tuscany in particular, where he advised the Medici Dukes of Florence on naval and technical matters, and his career was, later, to include tutoring the sons of King James the First of England.

He introduced Robert to Abraham Kendal, a great bear of a man and a master mariner who was to teach him, first hand, the art of managing ships, the intricacies of sail, wind, weather and tide, and who roused in him a fascination with cartography. This had been fuelled by Thomas Cavendish's detailed drawings brought back from his epic voyage. Few had greater knowledge of navigation than Kendal and his further interest lay in naval architecture, or shipbuilding. Robert served an apprenticeship with him after leaving Oxford and learnt, apparently, "enough navigation for an Admiral." He had earned Kendal's respect, young as he was, and a promise to sail with him as the Master of his flagship on his first voyage.

His next objective was marriage and for this he needed his mother's blessing. Lady Douglas was well acquainted with Margaret Cavendish. Ladies of the bedchamber, though senior, were in constant contact with Maids of Honour and kept a strict eye on them. Douglas had no fault to find with Margaret or her lineage and approved both her prettiness and her dowry although she considered her son too young as yet to be tied down by marriage and a family. Why, she asked, was he in such a rush? He could surely wait until this uncalled for voyage was over. She had the most natural doubts and fears about what she considered dangerous adventuring; not at all the usual occupation for a young man of his standing. Privately, she hoped the Queen would, again, forbid him to go. However, she was no match for the iron in Robert's nature and she quickly capitulated. The Cavendishes came from Suffolk and were large landowners related to Charles Brandon Duke of Suffolk, the Earls of Shrewsbury and several other prominent families.

What Douglas did not know, and Robert had omitted to tell her, was that his decision to marry so young was well-founded and based on two conscious ambitions. Firstly, it was stated in Leicester's will that if his son did not survive to the age of twenty and had no heir, his inheritance would pass either to the Earl of Essex or to Robert Sidney, the younger brother of the dead Philip. This meant that the sooner Robert could produce such an heir the better. He hoped, before long, to embark on a voyage to the other side of the world during which anything could happen to him; so much safer, in the event of his death before twenty, to ensure there was a son to succeed him. The race was on, therefore, and time was short; all of which fully justified an early marriage. He wished to found the dynasty his father had failed to do. Leicester had made a shambolic disaster of his married life and had died, as his brother had done, with no legitimate heir. In his youth, he had been blatantly determined to marry the Queen although his wife was alive and well, albeit mainly apart from him. Amy Robsart's unexplained death at the foot of the stairs at Cumnor Hall was as dubious as his supposed marriage to Douglas and his subsequent union with Lettice. His honour and, therefore, the honour of his heir were in jeopardy and this had to be overcome. There was no time like the present. There was, also, a part of Robert which demanded that he be the patriarch of a large family. His sons would be outstanding and his daughters beautiful and, come hell or high water, his family would be one of the greatest in the land. That was not something to be acquired; it was his by right. There were also the memories of a lonely and shifting childhood to be erased. He would seek an audience with the Queen as soon as possible and lay before her his plans for his marriage and his voyage.

It had not occurred to him that Margaret would do anything but accept him and nor she did. When he found her alone, he stole up behind her, put his hands over her eyes and kissed the back of her neck. She turned, took one look at his laughing face and returned the kiss with abandoned sensuality. She was a delightful armful, no deep thinker perhaps, but charming to look at and anxious to please. She was plainly prepared for a proposal and melted happily and gratefully into his arms. After all, he was quite a catch and extremely good-looking. In due course, perhaps, she would be My Lady Dudley or something even better. She was fifteen years old and the prospect of marriage to the Earl of Leicester's son was exciting and would provoke much envy among the ranks of the Maids of Honour.

The next rung on his very ambitious ladder was the Queen's permission for his own expedition. In view of her refusal to allow him a passage with Thomas Cavendish to Asia, the most he could hope for was a voyage to South America with a chance to harry Spanish shipping on the way and relieve them of their cargoes. He had maps and plans from Cavendish, a charted route of his own and nothing would be left to chance if he could help it.

When the interview was granted, he dressed in sober but sumptuous steel grey brocade with a small white lace ruff and a large winking emerald (a Dudley heirloom) on one finger, gathered his neatly rolled plans and planted Margaret outside the door to wait until he should summon her. Taking a deep breath, he marched in and bowed with every ounce of the grace he possessed. As he looked up at the woman seated before him, so girt about with magnificence and dripping with a King's ransom of jewelry, he wondered what she had been to his father in their youth. His eyes, grey as the sea, looked directly into hers, a merry twinkle in their depth. In turn, she took in the sombre grandeur of his dress and the blazing emerald, there to remind her of Leicester. He was learning. She knew that he was lawless and ruthless but, she believed, any recklessness would be carefully calculated.

By the time he had laid out his plans (even the ships were shown in minute detail down to the crew's quarters) and had answered every question she could fire at him, including such subjects as provisions, guns, communications and ammunition, she had a sense of his extensive knowledge. This was a change from the exuberant, broad brush plans of Essex which could carry him, and others, along on the crest of a wave that had a habit of breaking under them. They were alike in many ways; their fearlessness and enthusiasm matched, but this boy would count one man lost too many and a disgrace to himself.

She gave her permission for him to sail to Trinidad and Guiana and to explore the Orinoco river, but not to attempt the perilous Cape Horn passage. The Atlantic route to the Caribbean was well travelled and documented and he could cut his teeth on that. It was apparent to her that, despite his youth, he was not hungry for personal wealth from this voyage, but for achievement; be it in battle or discovery, it was success that mattered. He had chosen exploration because it combined those things that most interested him. So far, not one penny had been asked of her Treasury to help finance the venture. His pockets were deep, but he would have to dig far into them for ships, crews and supplies. It was common knowledge that Sir Walter Raleigh was also planning a journey to the Caribbean and Robert was anxious to be ahead of him.

For many years, now, there had been traveller's tales of the legendary "El Dorado", lying deep in the jungles of Guiana; a city built of gold, supplied by vast mines and its inhabitants dressed in not much more than gold dust. Its discovery would augment the English exchequer, so far behind that of Spain, whose sources of wealth from the New World had kept it rich. Robert was very enthusiastic about making that discovery. The Queen agreed but made it clear that while he might send men into the jungle he was not to go himself.

Robert then approached the subject of his marriage, not quite in the same breath, but hard on its heels. When he had stated his case, he backed to the door, seized Margaret by the hand and whisked her into the room. Together they advanced, made obeisance and waited, Margaret with lowered eyes, her hands folded demurely in front of her, and Robert fixing his guileless gaze squarely upon the Queen. Her Majesty found herself amused, but with a sense that she was being both gently bludgeoned and manoeuvred. She granted them permission to marry, but not until Christmas. She could not spare Margaret from her duties immediately and they were both young. Robert would be tied to England until his fleet was ready and that would take well over a year.

Events had been made to move, nonetheless, and Robert was exuberant. Having bowed himself and his future bride out of the Queen's presence, he rushed her down the long passage outside and beyond to the scented rose gardens. Here they fell into each other's arms with relief and abandon. Hampton Court was not a private place, but the roses, now in full bloom, were extremely vigorous that year.

They married in early January 1592 on a snowy evening at the Cavendish family home at Trimley St.Martin in Suffolk. Grimston Hall lay close to the point where the broad estuaries of the River Stour and the River Orwell met and flowed into the sea. This appealed to Robert who could keep one eye on the wind, tide and the restless grey North Sea. The cry of seabirds was never far away and he felt at home.

Margaret was attended by her sisters, including Anne, the wife of Richard Haklyut, who was also present. Though considerably older, Haklyut had become a firm friend of Robert's and stood as a witness together with George Clifford, 3rd Earl of Cumberland, a fellow explorer and jouster and the present "Queen's Champion". William Cavendish was, by this time, tossing about somewhere between St.Helena and South America, having sailed with his fleet in August the previous year, but the Cavendish clan was large and much in evidence.

With fat flakes of snow drifting past the tall windows against a sky that was already dark purple, Margaret looked, in the candlelit chapel, demure and enchantingly pretty, her fair hair hanging loose almost to her waist, and her blue eyes shining at her bridegroom. She had no doubts about the pleasures of this marriage or her ability to produce an heir in quick time. With such a husband and lover it would be no trial at all and she could not wait for the moment when the bed curtains were drawn around them. There was the usual feast to come, with much wine flowing, bawdy jokes, ritual disrobing and putting to bed, all amid gales of laughter. Having been obliged to wait for six months, there was not very much in store that could surprise her. Robert was not noted for his patience and their wedding night lived up to all expectation.

During that six months interim, Robert had been constantly on the move between London, Southampton, where his ships were being built or overhauled, and Kenilworth to ensure his stewards were ready and able to repel any further encroachment from Lettice (still calling herself Countess of Leicester) and her new husband. Cristopher Blount, Leicester's former Gentleman of Horse, was a close friend of her son, Robert Devereux, Earl of Essex. Surprisingly, and in spite of his hatred of Lettice, Robert's own relationship with Essex had remained unchanged, brotherly and warm. In many ways, they were two of a kind, mirror images, despite the years between them, and with much the same blasting energy and magnetism. Essex had learnt to calculate the effect this had on others, particularly in his dealings with the Queen and, indeed, with many other women with whom he had no business to be dealing at all. Robert, partly through circumstance, had emerged from boyhood abruptly and precociously and was already a force to be reckoned with. Essex recognised and respected that force; the young brother was rapidly becoming, as had he himself, a "caged tiger" afire to command men in battle on land or in a fleet of ships.

Mere jousting, however accomplished, was a poor substitute and the pair of them were longing for freedom from the stifling observances of Court and Queen.

Nevertheless, Robert's ambitions concerning the joust had been fully realised; it was an outlet for some of the pent up energy that drove him and he was carrying Essex's banner by the time he was sixteen. Already an exceptional horseman, his short time at Tilbury had been packed with cavalry action and had taught him much about the bearing of arms. At seventeen, he was big and burly and had run his first course successfully. Sir Henry Lee, Robert's godfather, had taught him and Essex had given him the chance to perform. He had improved upon their teaching and made a name for himself. Sir Henry, the Queen's Champion for so many years, had relinquished his position to George, Earl of Cumberland, who had also contributed greatly to Robert's natural skill. Though arrogant and occasionally boastful, Robert knew when he faced real excellence and had the grace to listen and learn. Cumberland, although older, had earned his respect and become a good friend. He was also a noted seaman, had commanded a ship under Drake during the Armada engagement, and had led an expedition to the New World.

Jousting had become something of a "tour de force" by the later part of Elizabeth's reign. It was sport for the Court and the upper echelons of society, although open to view by the populace if they could manage to squeeze themselves into the crowded Tiltyard. It had evolved into something of a production and it was necessary to do a great deal more than fight. There had to be a theme and an element of theatre to a contest. The contenders would dress elaborately, riding into the yard accompanied by standard bearers and often buglers. They would approach the Queen's "window" and pour out impassioned verse, carrying on their shields an *"Impresse"* or symbol and motto, to illustrate their sympathies or their stories. This was drama which took time and imagination to devise and, inevitably, a great deal of money to produce. It was no longer enough to polish the armour, sharpen the lance and charge.

Essex had eventually got his way and sailed, with his younger brother Walter, to France, in August 1591. Robert had been sorely tempted to accompany them, but the organisation of his expedition could not be left to others. The campaign to bolster King Henry IV of France against the Spanish invasion and to reclaim Rouen, had started with a bang and ended with less than a whimper. Walter had been shot, fatally, in the face outside its walls and Rouen had not fallen. Insidious disease and desertion eventually put paid to the campaign. Bearing his brother's body, Essex had recently returned, chastened and the worse for wear, but he had the generosity to further Robert's voyage in every way he could. He had learned a lot from this campaign, his first overseas command, but had he learned enough to justify the Queen ever giving him another?

Margaret returned briefly to Court after the marriage, while Robert was overseeing, and participating in, the building of two ships for the forthcoming voyage. They were to be constructed in Southampton; the first, his flagship, and the other a similar but smaller version. With this, he had a great deal of technical help from both Thomas Chaloner and Abraham Kendal, and, in the process, laid a sound foundation for a future career in naval architecture. He proceeded at breakneck speed, soaking up knowledge by the day and piling on the pressure to hasten the building process. Any imperfection was instantly pounced upon and the work redone. Robert was precise and demanding and his preceptors even more so.

Once both ships were beginning to take shape, he and Margaret visited Kenilworth together and agreed that the pomp and grandeur of the castle was not something she could live in or manage on her own at this stage. She was overcome by the daunting vastness and magnificence of it all. Kenilworth could, and had, housed Kings, Queens and squads of aristocracy since before the Plantagenets and John of Gaunt. It had been the childhood home of Henry V. Every crack and cranny reeked with history, but it was not ideal for a couple not yet out of their teens and but newly married. It would be for their future. In the meantime, they made the Cavendish Manor at Trimley St.Martin, their home.

By May 1592, Margaret was expecting their first child and hopes were running high. She had fallen deeply in love with her husband and would do anything to please him and keep him by her side. He was all she had ever dreamed of; tall, unconsciously autocratic, a pleasure to behold and extremely generous. His reputation as a jouster and horseman was outstanding for one so young and she revelled in the envious looks that came her way from other ladies at Court. He made much of her, making her laugh through the miseries of early pregnancy, teasing her out of tears and, when he was not head-down over detailed plans and drawings, making her feel she was the centre of his world. She was shrewd enough to know that she was not, but when he was called away by Thomas Chaloner, Abraham Kendal or the host of others involved in his plans or properties, he put her aside gently, always promising an early return.

Her brother, Sir Thomas Cavendish, had sailed in August 1591, hoping for another triumph in the Pacific and a chance to further direct trade with China and Japan. He was certainly not shy of having another confrontation with the Manila Galleons if he happened on them. The last expedition had been highly successful and made him a very rich man. His attempt this time to navigate the Magellan Straits, however, was disastrous. The seas were monumental, biting cold drove ice to form on spars, sails and masts and he was forced back into the South Atlantic to be met by further atrocious weather. He and his fleet then sailed up the South American coast to Brazil and encountered a Portuguese fleet off Vitoria. The battle that ensued lost him most of his crews and, with the remains of his fleet badly damaged, he retired in the direction of St.Helena. He died, of causes unknown, off Ascension Island in May 1592. His expedition, led now by his second-in-command, John Davis, set off again undaunted, from St.Helena, and discovered the Falkland Islands.

The news of Cavendish's death did not reach England until the following year. Two of his ships that limped back via Ireland, the "Leicester" and the "Roebuck" were later delivered to Robert, a part of Margaret's dowry. Cavendish had been one of England's greatest navigators, circling the globe in less time than it had taken Drake and arriving back in England just after the defeat of the Armada, to universal acclaim.

Margaret lost her first child after a punishing ride from Suffolk to London. She would not wait for the weather to allow her to travel by coach, so anxious was she to see Robert. Her horse slipped and came down with her, and, although she was no more than bruised, the baby did not survive the accident. It was a bleak and miserable time for them both. Margaret, not yet seventeen, remained fragile for some time after, beset by feelings of guilt and staying within the family circle in Suffolk. Robert's disappointment was hard to conceal, but he, at least, could lose himself in his project and the construction of the new ships.

CHAPTER FOUR

The Deep Blue Yonder – 1594-1595

On a broad reach, the deck of "The Beare" shuddered and heaved, though not with any great rhythm. Between the long pulls of a big swell, short, steep seas were breaking over her bow and tossing her about. She was a good ship, around two hundred tons, and carrying thirty guns. She was well built, and had already proved her sea-worthiness, speed and manoeuvrability. Robert having both overseen and taken part in her construction himself was extremely proud of his flagship. Carved into her mizzen mast was the emblem of his house, the Bear and Ragged Staff. She was his castle, his kingdom and his creation; a live thing moving under his braced feet at his direction and under his control. She would go where he took her and his faith in her was absolute.

The effort of the last two years was fulfilled and with each plunge of the deck beneath him, the greater grew the sense of release. All the grinding work and the many frustrations were sliding behind with each sea mile.

It had been a bitter wrench to leave Margaret, again pregnant and in floods of tears, though safely in the bosom of her family in Suffolk. This had become their base and Robert had grown to love its gentle, rich country and the broad drawl of its people. He could not even guess when he would return. He hoped, within a year, and to find his wife with a son in her arms.

Putting this moving picture aside, he saw reality in the person of Abraham Kendal standing at the wheel, his huge hairy paws hardly moving as he leant to the ship's movement, almost a part of her, anticipating, correcting and cajoling every ounce of speed from the taut, creaking sails. She was creaming along through a very blue sea covered in white crests whose spray kept coming at them, drying their lips and making sure the rest of them was damp. Robert did not generally consider his own feelings, there was never time, but at this moment he felt completely at ease and content. They were on their way from the Canary Islands, via Capo Blanco on the West African coast, to Trinidad.

His little fleet had mustered at Southampton last November but not before Robert had taken time and trouble in the selection of his officers and crews. After much dashing around the seaports, he had managed to assemble some excellent soldiers and seamen, including two hundred and seventy veterans. To them he was an unknown quantity; an aristocratic halfling whose only recommendations were his famous father and uncles, and it needed persuasion and the approval of Kendal to convince them they would be neither drowned nor unpaid. There was also the procuring of essentials for the ships: flags, sails, ensigns, ropes, anchors, merchandise for trading with the indigenous people he might encounter, and, of course, provisions and victuals of every kind. Then there were muskets, ammunition, shot, money to pay crews and their transport to Southampton. The list was endless and the times for delivery had to be meticulously arranged. It was a huge task and one that needed careful delegation.

"The "Beare", his flagship, was commanded by himself as "Admiral", or "General". The Queen had recently commissioned him herself as "General" of the expedition while Captain Thomas Jobson was to sail as "Lieutenant General". Jobson, though older, was related to Robert in that his mother had been a half-sister to Robert's grandfather, the Duke of Northumberland. He had previously sailed with Drake and was well acquainted with the West Indies. He had also acted as a witness to Robert's first effort at matrimony; his so-called "contract" with the flighty Frances Vavasour.

Captain Benjamin Wood was another very experienced officer who had been in Virginia in 1584. Recruited at Falmouth was the large red-haired veteran, Captain Peter Michell, from Calenick in Cornwall, who had served directly under Drake as his Gunnery Officer in the "Golden Hind"; a person of some authority, his father being Mayor of Truro.

In charge of his fighting forces was Captain Wyatt, once described as "the old and discreet soldier", who later recorded the voyage in detail. He had been in the Netherlands campaign, under Leicester at Bergen-Op-Zoom, but this was his first voyage across the Atlantic and he loudly sang the praises of both Robert and his "Beare." He reported that the ship was "fast and singular in her sailings". He also sang the praises of Abraham

Kendal and described him as: "excelling all others in his profession as a rare scholar – a most seldom thing in a mariner". Kendal had wide experience of disease and sickness at sea which was to prove extremely useful. He was a big, uncompromising man with arms like a baboon and the face of a bad-tempered gargoyle.

Robert was not without personal attendants. He was waited on by a gentleman known as "Ancient" Barrow and a page named William Bradshaw. "Ancient" Barrow was an old retainer and sometime poacher at Kenilworth from whom Robert had learnt the arts of tickling trout, ferreting, and how to croon pheasants out of trees. He could doctor animals with supernatural skill and looked like something between a bog and a bird's nest. He treated Robert with no respect whatever but would have cheerfully marched into Hell for him. He had been scrubbed up and polished for this venture but showed signs of reverting. William Bradshaw was his nephew and a much tidier individual. He kept Robert's gear in good order, saw that he was properly fed and waited at table. "Ancient" did the cleaning, including boots, and mended anything that broke. He also carved, from unwanted bits of wood, delightful and sometimes rude little images of anything that took his eye. Though feigning deafness, he played the fiddle like an angel and was reputed to hear the clink of coinage through a castle wall. He had never been beyond Kenilworth until now and was enjoying himself immensely. Robert's personal staff included a distinctive cat named McElvey, supposedly of Scottish island origin, whose talents as a ratter exceeded any terrier. There was plenty of scope for his activities; even a new ship was never free of rats. Huge and densely grey with pink-rimmed eyes that missed nothing, he kept Robert's quarters free of rodents, his main vice being to eat them with relish as close to Robert's feet as he could arrange, spitting out bits of fur and bone the while.

The "Beare's Whelpe", around 100 tons, was commanded by Captain Muncke, the "Vice Admiral". With them were the much smaller pinnaces, "Frisking" and "Earwig".

They set out from Southampton on 6th of November 1594, with all crews having taken Communion and dined, "in one body". Because of head winds and bad weather, they arrived in Plymouth only on the 19th to take on stores, food and drink. It was not, perhaps, the best time of year to sally forth across the Atlantic. No sooner had they left their native shores, heading for Spanish waters on 21st November, when a storm blew up, separating the flagship and the "Earwig" from the "Beare's Whelpe" and the "Frisking", forcing them back to separate ports; Robert's two ships to Plymouth and Muncke's to Falmouth. Robert sent immediate word to his Vice Admiral, to join him in the Canary Islands or in Capo Blanco, later named Casa Blanca, on the African coast as soon as he was able. This wonderfully casual directive revealed both extreme optimism and extreme youth. In fact, their ways had parted for good and very much to Muncke's advantage. He subsequently pursued, and overcame, two "great and rich galleons" and returned independently to England towing his trophies. He had the grace to share the proceeds of these with Robert later.

The "Beare" and the "Earwig" sailed again on 1st December, bound first for the West African coast and then for the Canaries. Their hope was to challenge and raid Spanish shipping on the way, but most vessels they encountered were from friendly nations. Robert, disgusted, wrote in his journal:

"Having parted company with my Vice-Admiral, I went alone wandering on my voyage, sailing along the coast of Spain, within sight of Cape Finisterre and Cape St.Vincent, the north and south capes of Spain. In which space having many chases, I could meet with none but my countrymen, or country's friends, I directed my course, the 14th December, towards the Isles of the Canaries. Here I lingered twelve days for two reasons: the one, in hope to meet my Vice-Admiral: the other, to get some vessel to remove my pestered men into, who being 140 almost in a ship of 200 tunnes, there grew many sick".

He had clearly been longing to put the "Beare" through her paces, to see how she performed as a fighting unit, and to test his own skills as a commander in a sea battle. His reference to "many chases" spoke for itself. He was after every sail he saw and became very frustrated that none of them were Spanish. He did, in fact, manage to have the best of six with some truculent French ships off the coast of Africa, which relieved his feelings. He had mistaken them for Spaniards and that, somewhat naturally, they resented.

Off Finisterre, soon after their departure, the "Earwig" sank in big seas and her rescued crew swelled the numbers aboard the "Beare", so reducing the supply of fresh water and food on board and the consequent overcrowding causing sickness among the men. Abraham Kendal's wide knowledge of disease at sea and its prevention was put to good use. On his advice Robert, also worried, frequently inspected conditions below deck and insisted on the strictest of sanitary rules. Although he had to take a deep breath before descending to the crew's quarters, he personally ensured that they were kept as clean as possible, that everything was scrubbed daily, and that rations were evenly divided. Even so, the stench reflected the overcrowded conditions and some of the men were breaking out in boils and disgusting sores, usually a sign of some infection. Most of those in a fit state preferred to remain above deck which meant that they were cold and constantly wet. There was nothing romantic about a seaman's life aboard a privateer ship; probably even less than when it was famously described a few centuries later as: "nothing but rum, sodomy and the lash".

So it was not surprising that Robert gave orders to sail to the Canaries, hoping that Captain Muncke, with the "Beare's Whelpe", would have already arrived to join him, and that he might be able to grab one or two more ships in which to disperse his men. On arrival, there was neither hair nor hide of the missing Muncke. Kendal, however, gave immediate orders that all those suffering should eat as much of the local fruit and vegetables, particularly citrus produce and bananas, as could be gathered ashore. He had been left with a crew full of scurvy here before and had got them all safely home.

With better luck, however, they happened upon two Spanish "caravels", small ocean-going craft, at Tenerife and, having driven them ashore, Robert sent Captain Wood and Captain Michell to capture them. He then manned them with his own sailors and put Wood in charge of them. The Spanish crews were treated with respect and goodwill and retired from the fray with gratitude. Robert's first, and most necessary, action had been a success and he re-named the caravels "Intent" and "Regard".

They celebrated Christmas at Tenerife, swimming between the three vessels and feasting one another in each. Robert, who loved a party and had acquired some excellent Gascon wine while in Plymouth from a ship returning from France, reflected that the presence of women, of any kind, would have made it even better. The crews danced, sang and celebrated nonetheless.

His log recorded: "I took two very fine caravels under the calms of Tenerif and Palma, which both refreshed and amended my company, and made me a fleet of 3 sails. In one caravel, called "Intent," I made Benjamin Wood Captain: in the other one Captain Wentworth. Thus cheered as a desolate traveller, with the company of my small and new erected Fleet, I continued my purpose for the West Indies". Not, however, before he had returned to the bleak wastes of Capo Blanco to look for Muncke, where he left a message in a wooden box provided for the purpose. It was all somewhat haphazard and very like leaving a message in a bottle at sea. Muncke never found it. He and Robert appeared to be passing like the proverbial "ships in the night", since the "Beare's Whelpe" also found her way to the Canaries later.

From there, it took Robert's little fleet twenty-two days to reach Trinidad and they sailed into Cedros Bay in the Gulf of Paria on 31st January 1595. To do this they had to pass through what was known as "The Serpent's Mouth", a narrow, turbulent bit of tidal race between the island and the Orinoco delta. This culminated in a huge jagged rock, "El Diablo", set in swirling brown water with fearsome currents creating whirlpools and crashing waves; a hazard for any but the experienced. On arrival, Robert's journal was full of wonder.

"On lst February we came to anker under a point thereof, called Curiapan, in a bay which is very full of pelicans and I called it Pelican Bay. About 3 leagues to the eastward of this place we found a mine of Mercazites (marcasites) which glister like golde, but all is not golde that glistereth, for so we found the same nothing worth, though the Indians did assure us it was CalTori, which signifieth gold with them. These Indians are a fine shaped and gentle people, all naked and painted red, their commanders wearing crowns of feathers. These people did often resort unto my ship, and brought us hennes, hogs, plantans, potatos, pinos, tobacco and many other pretie commodities, which they exchanged with us for hatchets, knives, hooks, belles and glass buttons.

The country is fertile, and full of fruits, strange beasts, and fouls, whereof munkeis, babions (howler monkeys) and parats were in great abundance.

Right against the most northern part of Trinidad, the maine was called the high land of Paria, the rest is very low land. Morucca I learned to be full of a green stone called Tacarao, which is good for the stone. Caribes I learned to be man-eaters or cannibals, and great enemies to the Islanders of Trinidad.

In the high land of Paria I was informed by divers of these Indians, that there was some Perota, which with them is silver, and great store of most excellent cane-tobacco".

It seemed the promised land after the hardships of their voyage, flowing with good food, tobacco, and cheerful red-painted Indians, not to mention the possibility of precious stones and metals. The marcasites were clearly a disappointment, but what about the "perota" and the promise of El Dorado, lurking somewhere beyond the Orinoco delta? Robert knew all about this and had pursued every known source of information before his departure. Stories had circulated for many years of the vast golden city, "the Lost City of Manoa". The suspected location had shifted dramatically over time, from furthest Peru, through northern South America to Guiana, and Robert's restless mind had followed it; his interest not so much in the city, but in the mines which fuelled it. The least he could do, while in the vicinity, was to search for it. His crews would not swing peacefully in their hammocks for long.

The Indians of this area of Trinidad were of the Arawak tribe and Robert took time and trouble to learn some of the Arawak words and phrases. He also gave orders that they were to be treated with respect by his seamen and neither their women nor their houses were to be in any way molested. Their goodwill was important to him and this chivalrous attitude was to pay dividends in the way they cooperated with him. Those of them who had escorted the hopeful English on the march to the marcasite mines, however, may have been through this routine before with a variety of explorers and probably knew what they were worth. Columbus had been the first to discover the island as long ago as 1496 and named it after The Holy Trinity. The other natural source of value, revealed by the tribesmen, was a large lake of pitch, not far from their anchorage. This the crews made full use of in caulking the hulls of their vessels, as many had before them.

Robert had, in fact, discussed the matter of El Dorado with Sir Walter Raleigh of whom he was, with good reason, extremely wary, even suggesting that they should rendezvous in Trinidad and make a joint sortie up the Orinoco river. Raleigh was not at all fond of Robert Dudley, a much younger and equally gifted version of himself with many of his own virtues. But where Raleigh, with his ridiculed West Country burr, had worked hard and successfully at the social climbing required to obtain the Queen's favour, Dudley had been born into the inner circles of the Court with an aristocrat's upbringing and the inbuilt qualifications to secure Royal favour. He was also the stepbrother of the Earl of Essex whom Raleigh loathed with a deep and jealous loathing. He would make use of young Dudley but was not likely to do him any favours.

After being confined for so long within the restricted space of his ship, Robert was now bristling with ideas that had occurred to him on the voyage and could not wait to put them into action. The exploration of any kind of mine was uppermost in his thoughts. Captain Peter Michell, well acquainted with the tin mines of Cornwall, was knowledgeable on the subject of mining generally and knew one metal from another. He had been quick to recognise that marcasite was neither silver nor gold.

Firstly, though, Robert had given consideration to the claiming of Trinidad for the English Crown. He did not want to waste time fighting the resident Spaniards and their Governor, ensconced at San Jose de Oruna, just east of what was later Port of Spain, and risk losing the few men he had in a battle he was not likely to win or an occupation he could not sustain. He, therefore, contented himself with a few rude messages to the Governor, whose gifts he had returned, giving him to understand that there would be no fraternisation on the grounds that their countries were at war and that the Spanish King had, through various agents, several times attempted to murder his Queen.

He felt, nonetheless, that he should go through the motions of colonial expansion before tackling the search for gold up the Orinoco. After the disappointing outcome of the hard march to the marcasite mine, which he had shared with his men to their great appreciation, there might well be other, valuable mineral resources on the island which would make it worth appropriating for the English Crown. The Indians had certainly mentioned "perota", or silver. Ancient Barrow, who never let Robert out of his sight if he could avoid it, had shared the march to the mine and had no opinion at all of wading up to his armpits through swamps and rivers; he was a small man and could not swim. He did, nonetheless, stand guard over Robert during the night spent on the journey, having first draped his own colours over him in a rather funereal manner.

With a view to claiming Trinidad for the Queen, therefore, Robert first ordered the building of a small, ramshackle "fort" from which he flew the Queen's colours. He followed this up by marching his few troops, under Wyatt, halfway across the island, yet again, to a position near the purported mine and through some very thick forest. Here they found a tall, solitary tree and, while displaying the Queen's colours (alongside Robert's own), Wyatt nailed to the tree a lead plate bearing the Queen's arms together with an appropriate Latin inscription, all to the accompaniment of much beating of the drums they had hoisted along with them. Jobson was sent to "claim" nearby Paracoa or Port Peregrine in much the same way.

The Governor of San Jose de Oruna, having heard of these antics, smiled in his beard. Not for long, however, because Raleigh, on his arrival with a much larger force, sacked the town in March and took him prisoner. Robert, feeling he had now done his duty to the Crown, turned his attention to the Orinoco and "El Dorado".

He decided that he could not sit in his ship while others ventured upriver despite the strictures by the Queen that he was not to do so. It was too tempting and he would cross that bridge when he came to it. He then commandeered a Spanish-speaking Indian named Balthasar, who had taken up residence in the ship and seemed to have a good knowledge of the river, to undertake the task of escorting him, with a select party, to a supposed mine at Orocoa at the head of the Orinoco delta. Again, it was reputed to contain gold. Having investigated this, they would then proceed upriver in search of anything resembling "El Dorado". He proposed that he, with Jobson and twelve picked men would go, together with their guides, in one boat. The delta was enormous and they would need all the help their Indian guides could give to find the right way up the river.

Trouble, and on a grand scale, immediately arose. Jobson and Kendal protested with horror at the thought of Robert so risking himself and all crews promptly mutinied at the thought of being left in the charge of Kendal. They, apparently, "feared the villainy of Abraham Kendal, who would by no means go". Grinding his teeth with frustration and disappointment, Robert was obliged to stand down, so near and yet so far from one of the main objectives of his voyage. It was exactly the sort of adventure he was looking for and an excellent opportunity to steal a march on the imminently approaching Raleigh. It was clearly not to be. An appointed time and place were therefore arranged to meet the explorers on their return and Jobson, with his small party, then set off amid cheers and hopes of a golden return. They braved "El Diablo", the looming rock, in the small boat and arrived among the mangroves on the mainland. The "Beare", not far away, although well within the vast Orinoco delta, stood further out and in deeper water.

Robert could not imagine what had induced his crew to threaten mutiny, but the truth was that he had earned their respect and rough devotion by the way he had treated and cared for them, not to mention the Spanish crews of the "Intent" and "Regard", when he had seized their caravels in the Canaries. They knew Kendal for a hard man despite his formidable seamanship. They had also observed Robert's navigation and realised that he was anything but reliant on Kendal, and he had marched as one of them on the gruelling journey to the mines. They were not going anywhere without their young Admiral and General.

Having regretfully watched Jobson and his small party dwindling to a dot against the shoreline, Robert proceeded to explore as much of the Orinoco Delta as the "Beare" could safely navigate. Thanks to his charts and Kendal's sounding skills, they covered a large area, weaving their way among the countless islands. The Orinoco delta covered two hundred and seventy miles of coastline and was rich in animal and bird-life. They saw long-nosed alligators up to twenty feet long, the strange pale pink dolphins local to the delta, the capybaras, like enormous aquatic guinea pigs, and the big, blunt-nosed otters, all going about their business in the murky waters. To them the birds were startling and fantastic; multi-coloured parrots and parakeets, hundreds of frigate birds and "herons of white, crimson and carnation".

Travelling north of the delta, they came across a beautiful, unmarked and wooded island some way north west of the Orinoco. Here, where the muddied waters had cleared, the sands were brilliant white, and, as the shore met the sea, the colour of the water was a dazzling aquamarine, turning abruptly to deep cobalt. As they drew nearer, it could be seen that this was because the land dropped very steeply into the ocean allowing the ship easy access. It was a magically beautiful place, more so than Trinidad, and they lowered their boats and went ashore. There was no sign of habitation and the macaws and parrots let them approach with no sign of fear. A few caimans yawned lazily on the sand with turtles floundering around them. Fresh water was running in a little gully from between the trees and they filled every vessel they had with it. It was cold and delicious and must have come from a deep spring nearby. One gaunt seaman expressed the belief that he had died and gone to heaven.

Robert took a few men with him and entered the trees, expecting to find that they became dense and jungle-like. There was none of the impenetrable mangrove found around the delta. Palms seemed to grow only on the shoreline and the towering trees, tall with bare trunks, were spaced out as they went inland, occasionally thinning to grassy clearings. Further on, they gave way to reveal rocky hills and sweeping pasture: small deer were grazing peacefully, merely raising their heads and glancing in their direction. Despite the heat, they walked for miles, enchanted by what they saw. When they got back to the shore, they found that the rest of their party had caught big crayfish and were toasting them over a fire. In the warm, silky twilight, the sky so full of stars there was no need for lanterns, they rowed back to the ship.

Robert summoned Ancient Barrow immediately and told him to carve a sign claiming the island for his Queen. It would be called "Dudleiana" and it was to remain the yardstick for any future island he might visit throughout his life.

He then sailed back to Port Peregrine to await the return of Jobson and his party. They waited and waited, frequently going back to the appointed meeting place but there was no sign of the little boat and its crew.

During this time, Robert managed to "persuade" seven or eight of the Indian chiefs of Trinidad to: "yield their duties and allegiance to Her Majestie". This piece of diplomacy, he felt, would enhance his efforts to claim the island for the Crown. The chiefs also had information of a village where "calcurie" or gold was being melted out of ore, but this, sadly, proved to be yet one more red herring.

Already ensconced in Port Peregrine they found another explorer from England who was also awaiting the arrival of Raleigh. He had made the journey in a pinnace from Plymouth, dropping anchor during their absence. Captain George Popham was no stranger to the Caribbean and his family were enterprising settlers who, later, founded the first English colony in New England. Robert had met him while victualling the expedition in Plymouth and was delighted to see him. He was stout, kindly and very interested in Robert's adventures, his ships and his future plans. He reported that Raleigh could not be far behind him and also that he had heard tell of a Spanish "Silver Fleet" expected to sail before long from Havana, in the direction of Bermuda, and which might be worth a raid. Robert, in fact, had been told of this fleet by the Queen herself, with instructions, before his departure, to attack any likely stragglers, should he come across them. They decided that they would wait for the return of Jobson and his crew before making any decisions about departure. Whatever the result of a possible confrontation with Raleigh, Robert was not going to abandon without a search, the faithful Jobson whom he had grown to like and respect. The expedition had now been gone over a fortnight.

Eventually, when Robert was beginning to feel seriously anxious about the safety of his missing men, they awoke one morning to the firing of a musket as a little boat entered Port Peregrine bay. The expedition had returned.

They rushed to man the "Beare's" guns and fired a thundering salute of welcome and relief.

Jobson and his crew, reduced to twelve, were ragged, sunburnt and desperate for food and water. They had found no "Beare" at the meeting place and had been obliged to row for a further two days, exhausted and despairing. Jobson, bone loyal, was not having any criticism of his Admiral. He had made it plain to his men that Robert would never abandon them and that he had faith enough in him to proceed to Port Peregrine where he would be found.

The story of their adventuring was long in the telling. They had arrived at Orocao, the village at the mouth of a branch of the Orinoco, to discover that, yet again, stories of a gold mine were unfounded. There were traces of gold made into small artefacts to be seen, but they were merely alluvial fragments, swept down by the river and smelted. It was no El Dorado and there was no mine.

Their subsequent journey, under the directions of Balthasar and his accompanying guide, though fascinating in what they had seen, was a disaster. Led from the main stream into a meandering series of tree-strewn tributaries, it was soon plain that they were completely astray. Balthasar melted away into the night and it was not until they had beaten the other guide to pulp that they managed to get themselves moving in the right direction. Not surprisingly, he also disappeared with alacrity leaving them to struggle back about a hundred and thirty miles with dwindling supplies. It was a real test of moral and physical stamina and their despair when they arrived at the meeting place to find no "Beare" was complete. They feared that they had been abandoned and only Jobson's stout defence of their Admiral forced them on to Port Peregrine.

When they had rested, they were wined and dined with the best the ships' companies could provide. Blue smoke curled from pipes full of magic tobacco, mingling with the succulent smell of roasting pigs. The last of the good wine was broached and the local Indians, smelling a party, shook out their best feathers and danced to the beat of their drums and their small bird-like pipes. They were accompanied by Ancient Barrow with his fiddle, all present being greatly revived by home-brewed liquor which the Indians generously shared in exchange for food.

Robert now had a difficult choice. He could wait for Raleigh's arrival, as planned, in the hopes that he would be allowed to attach himself to his expedition, probably taking orders from him and playing second fiddle to one whose fleet was four times the size of his own, an idea that did not appeal in the least. Alternatively, he could sail north now and try to intercept the reported Spanish Silver Fleet, as suggested by his Queen. Pride and the advice of Captain George Popham won the day. Having "claimed" Trinidad for the Queen, he wished to be the first to tell her so. He would have to leave "El Dorado" to Raleigh despite the fact that their combined experience might have brought better luck and that Raleigh would be most annoyed at their premature departure.

On 12th March, having waited eight days for Raleigh and in company with Captain Popham's vessel, they sailed north west from Trinidad. Robert had already sent the two caravels, under Captain Wood, northwards in search of further Spanish shipping. They negotiated the difficult "Dragon's Mouth", a series of islands, rocks and racing tides, at the north western end of the Gulf of Paria, Robert's navigation being wholeheartedly praised by Kendal and Wyatt, then, blown apart from Captain Popham, they headed for Puerto Rico. The following day they spotted, and attacked, a Spanish ship outward bound and carrying a cargo of wine, iron, linen, hats and other luxury home comforts for their colonists. Having overcome the ship, they transferred everything they wanted to the "Beare". They then burnt the Spanish ship, and, with great courtesy, conducted the unfortunate crew, among them several "persons of quality", to Puerto Rico, and left them wailing but supplied with iron rations and within reach of a likely village. They were kindly treated but firmly told to suffer the fortunes of war with a good grace.

From the pilot of this vessel, they learnt, with a little persuasion, that the Spanish fleet, reckoned to be "150 sails and the richest fleet ever out of the Indies", had already left Havana bound for Bermuda and Spain. This sounded promising and Robert directed their course between the straits of Puerto Rico and Santa Cruz, then altered course: "and bare for the coast of Florida to lie in wake of the Fleet of the West Indies bound for Spain". This they missed, much to their annoyance; it would have been the perfect end to their venture in Trinidad had they caught a straggler or two from this massive fleet.

Robert recorded ironically that: "I now caused the Master to bear for the Meridian of the Isle of Bermuda, hoping there to find the Fleet. The Fleet I found not, but foul weather enough to scatter many Fleets."

This turned out to have been an understatement. Having headed north they were engulfed by a storm which blew them up the eastern coast of America. Helpless, they could only run before it. Tough old soldier Wyatt, at the end of his considerable tether wrote that: "hell is no hell in comparison of this". He proved a mine of information nonetheless and described how they had gone as far north as Labrador and Nova Scotia: "which we know by the great abundance of whales". They were spared nothing. St. Elmo's fire flickered in blue and orange balls of flame on masts and yard arms, which was no reassurance since it was known to presage disaster, and the sight of icebergs appearing like phantoms in the mist and murk did nothing to reassure them. It was bitterly cold.

Kendal and Robert managed to get the ship back on course but the weather, out in mid Atlantic, became even worse. "The Beare", however, proved her worth and the soundness of her construction. She clawed her way up mountainous waves, hung suspended, then plunged or slid to the bottom of the troughs and, almost submerged, slowly heaved tons of water off her bow and painfully began to climb again. Men could not move about the ship without being battered to pieces or swept overboard and several were lost in the execution of their duties. It was icy in the screaming wind, there was not a dry inch on the ship and every man aboard thought each day would be his last.

Robert and Kendal, lashed to the structure securing the wheel, took turns to command, relieved or re-inforced by Jobson, Wentworth and Michell. Wood had gone with the caravels and Heaven alone knew where they were. The ship's company were exhausted beyond endurance, grey with fatigue, and their sunken eyes were beginning to play them false. This elemental battering by wind and wave seemed endless and the only consolation was that they were travelling at a speed never experienced even by Kendal. After almost three weeks of storm, the wind began to drop and he was able to assess their progress. They limped in to the Azores on 28th April having made the journey at such speed that, deceived by their appalling passage, Robert and Kendal were some fifty leagues out in their reckoning. The "Beare" had proved herself beyond doubt. So also had her Admiral.

They rested the crew at the Island of Flores, taking on water and foodstuffs, grudgingly given them by the islanders who had news also of the Spanish Fleet and were far more interested in supplying such a vast horde. They then set sail for England.

On 6th May Robert, who was on the quarter deck, saw a sail and realised that they were in luck. The quarry was a Spanish galleon of over 300 tons, battered, like themselves, but separated by the storms from the big fleet. She was no merchantman but a man-of-war, well-armed and soon approached by the fast-moving "Beare".

What followed was the stuff of Robert's dreams. When hailed and ordered to dip her topsail both as a sign of surrender and in respect for the Queen, the galleon "very stoutly never budged", opened fire, and a five-hour bludgeoning began much in the tradition of Drake and Grenville. Robert's Gunnery Officer, Michell, warned that much of their powder was damp despite his efforts and some of the guns had suffered in the storms. Come nightfall, they were still at it. Robert ordered up "a good store of cartridge against the morning to give this our proud consort a warm breakfast, keeping them waking in the night now-and-then with a cross bar shot." He was taut with excitement; sleep was out of the question.

In the morning, Robert, who, like his father, possessed a keen sense of drama, "came forth unarmed, having only his leading staff in his hand, saluted, and took his standing on the open deck where he might best see and be seen of his enemies". This kind of bravado being much appreciated by the crew, a cheer was raised and Captain Jobson then hoisted the Dudley colours with those of England to the tops, poops and shrouds of the ship. The galleon opened fire, the "Beare" blasted back and the slogging match continued all day. It was no picnic and during this, his first battle on land or sea, Robert's coolness, combined with his seamanship, was exemplary. At one point, when the Spaniards were "making many and dangerous shot, especially exceeding near the very face and head of our General.......

one struck the very blade of his leading staff into many pieces, going within a handful of his head, having before torn the sails, cut the shrouds, and pierced the ship very near the place of his standing; yet would he not budge or move by any means". This suggested that, conspicuous as he was, the enemy was attempting to target him personally. Kendal wrote later "Our General fought the galleon always to windward, within musket shot"; the close shave was, therefore, not surprising.

Another hero of the day was young William Bradshaw who, with Ancient Barrow loading for him, fired accurately and incessantly at the closest possible range until his musket broke. Jobson, seeing it, grabbed him and his weapon and hauled him up to Robert for commendation, quoting lines from a popular play beginning "This is my son, gracious General" and finishing "Long may he live to serve my General". Steeped in chivalry as he was, this appealed greatly to Robert, who gave William unstinted praise and a new weapon: "one of his own for his better encouragement and well-doing and valiance".

Towards nightfall, with the "Beare" running short of ammunition (a lot of it, as feared, was too damp to use) and the galleon having had the worst of it, they fired "seven sound canvasadoes", attacks with every weapon they had, and withdrew, surprised that the galleon had not already sunk. Wyatt mourned, "If we had had but two barrels more, we undoubtedly should have seen their miserable end in short time". She was very much more seriously damaged than the "Beare".

It was, undoubtedly, a well-earned victory, with surprisingly few casualties. Michell, shot through the thigh while struggling with the cannon below decks, was sent down to the surgeon with a promise from Robert that he would be given an almsman's room in his hospital of Warwick when they reached England. This he arranged and Michell survived to fight again with him at Cadiz.

Robert's own version of events, written later, was, perhaps, a little exaggerated with the passage of time. The size of the defeated galleon grew from 300 to 600 tons and the number of his own men decreased from approximately seventy to fifty, suggesting enormous odds. According to his account:

"…a great armada…with whom I fought board and board for two days, being in no way able in all possibility with fifty men to board a man-of-war of 600 tons. And having spent all my powder, I was constrained to leave her, yet in such distress, without sails and masts, and hull so often shot through with my great ordnance between wind and water, that being 300 leagues from land, I daresay it was impossible for her to escape sinking. Thus leaving her by necessity in this miserable estate, I made for England, where I arrived at St.Ives in Cornwall about the latter end of May, 1595". He was not yet twenty one years old.

His own summing up of the ships taken or sunk was that: "In this voyage, I and my fleet took, sunk and burnt nine Spanish ships, which was loss to them though I got nothing". His reckoning included the two galleons taken earlier on by Muncke, the two caravels taken in the Canaries, the Spanish trader he took and burnt near Puerto Rico, his big man-of-war and three smaller craft taken or sunk by the enterprising Captain Wood and his crews on the caravels' return journey. They missed the Atlantic storm and Wood survived to sail again in Robert's ship.

They were in for one more adventure before they reached home. As so often, there was a thick sea mist over the Isles of Scilly where they narrowly escaped being wrecked on the abundant and needle-sharp rocks which had been the grave of so many ships in the past.

Having paid off his men and officers at St.Ives, secured his ship and bidden them all a fond farewell with the hopes that they would sail again together, Robert and Jobson set off on the long ride home. It was a wrench to leave this close-knit band of men who for six months had been his companions in exploration, danger and laughter.

They stopped to rest one night with Drake at Buckland Manor, his home in Devonshire, where their welcome was uproarious and where they heard, via Drake's agents, that the Spanish man-of-war had, indeed, sunk with all hands. Drake and Hawkins had gained permission to sail in the near future to Puerto Rico. Drake wanted Abraham Kendal to go with him and asked Robert to approach him on his behalf.

Someone must have got word of their arrival, because, as they crossed into Wiltshire, a messenger from the Earl of Pembroke met them with an invitation to spend a few days at Wilton and tell their story. Though longing to get back to Margaret in Suffolk, this was something Robert could not resist. They were bone-weary after the voyage and the ride from Cornwall, but the Earl was one of the most influential men in England and his wife, Mary, the writer, was a cousin of Robert's through the Sidneys. His interest and advice could be extremely useful.

They were warmly welcomed at Wilton and sumptuously entertained, but the wise and kindly Earl had news for Robert that he did not wish him to hear from others. Margaret had contracted plague during February and could not be saved. The child had died with her.

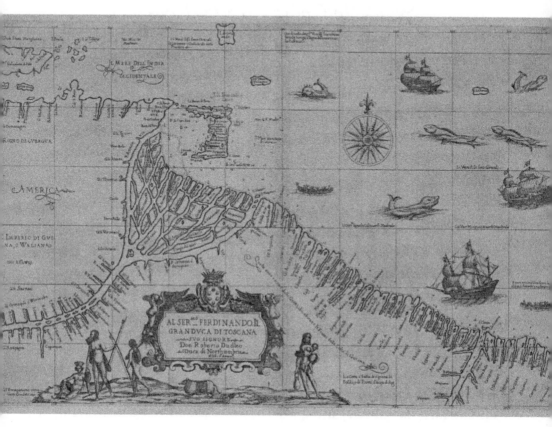

Robert Dudley's map showing 'Dudleiana'

CHAPTER FIVE

Prelude To Cadiz – 1595-1596

It was December, the year of our Lord 1595 and one of the most bitter winters in memory. Snow had lain on Kenilworth since November, falling softly at first, then in thick drifts, covering turrets and battlements like marchpane and freezing the Great Mere around the castle so hard that carts could be driven over it. Hunting became almost impossible. The village and outlying country folk were digging deeply into their stores and their livestock for food, and the gathering of fuel was a full-time occupation. The only sport to be had was hawking and shooting.

Robert Dudley stood by the window in his private library, gazing moodily at the snow swirling around the castle, blotting out the parks, lakes and woodland surrounding it and throwing mufflers around the tree trunks.

It had needed some resolve to take up residence here, alone but for a huge retinue of servants and the frequent visits of large numbers of his friends and relations. The castle had originally been built in 1127 and re-built over hundreds of years as a royal or semi-royal residence. Robert's grandfather the Duke of Northumberland, given Kenilworth in 1553 by the boy-King Edward VI, and subsequently executed by Mary Tudor for his machinations concerning Lady Jane Grey, had built the stable block and widened the magnificent tiltyard, constructed as a causeway over the mere to the orchards. Robert's father, when the house was restored to him in 1563, had gone much further. Like a bird adorning its nest to attract a mate, he had set about providing modern accommodation for Queen and Court. His great reconstruction in the Inner Court, known as Leicester's Building and designed for the Queen's use, was four floors high and included a tower.

She and her entourage had been frequent visitors. He also built a loggia leading to new gardens beside the Great Keep. His spending had been colossal and it culminated in the lavish nineteen day entertainment of Her Majesty in July 1575 which, sadly, did not have the hoped for result. The bird made full use of the nest and departed.

Robert had chosen to use part of the modern wing as his own quarters. It was warmer and nearer the kitchens. The vast quadrangle of buildings could accommodate as many guests as he chose and these included large numbers from his home county. He made them very welcome, as his father had not, and began to take an interest in county affairs. With the tiltyard, which served to keep his own jousting skills honed, a tennis court, and acres of chase for hunting, there was plenty to amuse them all. His Warwickshire neighbours, finding him more approachable than his autocratic father, had been quick to offer their sympathy for the loss of his wife and to gather him to the bosom of the county with generous hospitality. He was seldom alone. There was, also, a certain amount of interest and speculation regarding the future mistress of Kenilworth. Those with marriageable daughters began manoeuvres in that direction.

At his feet flopped two enormous dogs, sired by his beloved Kuvasz who had lived to a great age with no flagging in his powers of procreation. They were not pure-bred; their dam had been a mastiff, but the combination had produced two very powerful and handsome animals with whom no one argued. They were paler than a mastiff with longer, waving coats and the dark muzzles and ears of their dam; both were disinclined to allow Robert out of their sight and they covered great distances with him when he rode out, travelling with the long-reaching, tireless lope of their sire.

In Robert's hand was a rolled parchment and his gaze, directed at the gathering snow, was intense. He was enraged. The grey eyes were as wintry as the scene outside and the firelight danced on a face that belonged to no youth but to a dangerously angry man.

George, Earl of Cumberland, had sent him a copied version of Raleigh's publication on his voyage to Guiana, undertaken immediately after Robert's own. Raleigh had returned from Trinidad and the Orinoco in August this year and had now written his "Discoverie of Guiana". It was a descriptive and flowery account of his achievements; his capture of de Berrio, the Governor of San Paracoa, and the razing of the town. Then his journey up the Orinoco with a hundred men to a point far higher than that reached by Thomas Jobson, and his description, based only on native reports, of El Dorado, a shining golden city by a lake purportedly only sixty miles on from where they stood. He had been unable to reach it but believed that it truly existed. He had ignored all of Robert's achievements except to sneer at "Master Robert Dudley" who had mistaken marcasite for gold, which Robert had not done for long.

Worse than this pettiness, and when he heard that Robert was planning, and indeed, had applied for, another expedition to Guiana, Raleigh had written a stinging letter to Robert Cecil, now Secretary of State in the place of his father, Lord Burghley: "What becomes of Guiana I much desire to hear, whether it pass for a history or a fable, I hear Mr. Dudley and others are sending thither; if it be so, farewell all good from thence, for although myself, like a cockscomb, did rather prefer the future in respect of others, and rather sought to win the kings to her Majesty's service, than to sack them, I know what others will do when those kings come simply into their hands. If it may please you to acquaint my Lord Admiral therewith, then let it succeed as it will."

The Lord Admiral referred to was Robert's uncle, Lord Howard of Effingham and this was a spiteful piece of mischief on Raleigh's part. Perhaps because he felt Robert had forestalled and stolen a march on him, he had suggested that his behaviour to the natives of Trinidad had been savage when, throughout, he had treated them with humanity and courtesy. Raleigh's sack of the Spanish town hardly matched his own sanctimony on the matter. The other reason was that he also hoped to get permission to take a second fleet to the Orinoco and, this time, Raleigh wanted to get there ahead of Robert.

This letter, however, had done Robert no good. On the Earl of Pembroke's advice, he had been corresponding dutifully and respectfully with Cecil. Most particularly, this had covered the subject of a further voyage to the Indies, and he noticed a coolness and lack of progress following Raleigh's comments. He was also angry because Raleigh had been a friend of his father's. He could, of course, apply directly to the Queen, but any attempt to over-ride Cecil would be a mistake. He was eager to start gathering ships and crew again, but clearly could not do so until a licence was granted. The cost of keeping them in idleness would be prohibitive. "A Winter's Tale", indeed, he reflected, and not a good one. It would have been some solace had he known that Raleigh was having the same difficulty in obtaining permission for his expedition and that events had turned in a direction which preoccupied Cecil almost to the exclusion of all else.

Robert had some rumour of this through correspondence with Essex, knowing that his step-brother was running the Ordnance Office and was, therefore, deeply involved with the defence of the realm; in the likely event of another invasion by Spain, there might well be a role for Robert. He knew also that there was truth in the talk of another huge armada gathering in Spanish ports and that the King of Spain had already landed large numbers of troops in north-western France, the expected use for which would be an attack on England. He did not want to miss a battle on land or sea as he had at Tilbury.

One of the dogs rose and pushed a cold nose into his hand. He glanced down at its square, worried face and smiled. He would forget this pettifogging business with Raleigh, ride up to London and discover from Essex himself what was afoot. Christmas at Essex House would be more entertaining than in snow-bound Warwickshire and there would be friends at Court to feast and joust with, theatre and dinners at the Inns of Court and beautiful girls to distract him. Margaret's sad little ghost lay heavily on his mind as did the fact that, after nearly three years of marriage, there was no son to succeed to his estates. He missed her sorely, her adoration and her prettiness, but love had not yet truly touched him. Marriage did not necessarily have much to do with it and women would always hold a fascination for him.

He found Essex House full of guests, presided over by Frances, Countess of Essex, and with many of his friends and contemporaries either staying there or constantly visiting. It was a focal point for the young and talented from every calling and a vibrant centre for the arts, the military and the theatrical. It was also the centre of Essex's intelligence operations, seamlessly taken over on the death of Walsingham and now mainly directed by the gifted Bacon brothers, Anthony and Francis, though Robert Cecil remained the prime mover. Information of all kinds could be gleaned here, and straight from the source. The house drew the brightly shining stars of the generation like a magnet and, at Christmastide, it was overflowing. It was also far more amusing than the Court, ruled by an ageing Queen who had lost touch with her people and was doing little to alleviate their misery this bitter winter. Essex was their hero.

The vast hall and dining chamber of Essex House were crowded with people and the kitchens seethed from early morning onwards. Far into the night, the great house shone like a beacon on the north side of the Thames; singing, dancing, debating, music, quarrelling and laughter ringing out into the snow-filled dark.

Under flares set at either side of the entrance, Robert handed his horse to William Bradshaw, who had come up with him from Kenilworth, trod up the stairs to the outer hall, and passed into the huge galleried inner hall. Fires roared at either end of the chamber, yule logs stacked by them, and the whole length was hung with evergreen garlands. He stood for a moment surveying the scene with interest, not noticing the sudden hush around him, the pauses in conversation or the avid curiosity in the faces turned to him. No one had told him that he had a presence very like his father's and the looks that matched it. His gaze ranged round the hall, then lit up as shouts of welcome greeted him. Out of the mass surged the young Earl of Southampton, Henry Wriothesley, and Roger, Earl of Rutland; Wriothesley with his arm around Elizabeth Vernon, a pretty cousin of Essex's, who could barely drag her eyes from his face to greet anyone else at all. Behind them lounged the tall form of Richard Clanricarde, over from Ireland, his blue eyes laughing at Robert as he handed him the large cup of spiced wine always given on arrival. They were soon joined by Fulke Greville, who had helped evict Lettice from Kenilworth, and the Earl of Cumberland, Robert's comrade of the joust. Others quickly gathered round them, the wine, the warmth and the welcome easing the heart and cramped muscles.

He did not see Essex or his Countess until the hour of dinner by which time he had been able to wash and change his travel-stained garments. He was as richly dressed as any among that brilliant company though he did not favour the extremes of fashion or the very bright colours flaunted by some. Tonight, William Bradshaw had worked wonders. Like Ancient Barrow, they were less master and man than comrades in arms and William had fast learnt the arts of a gentleman's gentleman; in matters of dress, he was not above constructive criticism if he felt the need.

Essex gave a roar of greeting when he spotted Robert and enveloped him in a bear-hug. They were now almost the same height. With him came the Countess, small, exquisite and clearly pregnant. Nothing could detract from her grace, however, or the sweetness of the smile and the kiss of greeting she gave Robert. She was an unspoken ally in his dealings with Lettice, her mother-in-law. No woman would have been good enough for "Robin" and Lettice had tried, without success, to denigrate and to dominate the new Countess whenever and wherever possible. Not for nothing, however, was Frances the daughter of Sir Francis Walsingham, raised in diplomacy from the cradle and with a very much better brain than any of the Devereux who charmed or fought their way through most obstacles. Frances had managed Lettice to perfection and now stood on good terms with her, without giving an inch of her own authority; something Robert Dudley was unlikely to achieve. Too much lay between them, not least being Lettice's attempt to claim Kenilworth. He was happy to hear that she and her husband were spending Christmas in their manor at Wanstead.

Essex promised private talk with Robert later and the huge company flocked in to the dining hall and sat down to supper, directed by the stewards. The noise and shouts of laughter rose high as the wine went round. Robert found himself next to Christopher Marlowe, the young poet and playwright sponsored by Thomas Walsingham, a cousin of the Countess. His pale, boyish face had a closed look, but his tongue carried barbs of wit and gentle malice; the soft voice caressing one moment and ripping to shreds some plagiarism the next. Robert had not seen any of his plays but had read "The Jew of Malta" with fascination and recognised a man of mixed sexuality and enormous talent. He was working, he said, on an epic, full of mystery and witchcraft, which might advance him far beyond the fame of William Shakespeare. He called it "Dr.Faustus". Understandably, he did not mention his several brushes with the Law and the Church or that he was currently working as a spy for Thomas Walsingham. He was a street brawler and, in the past, had also been accused of heresy.

On the other side of Robert sat a lady well-known to him, Essex's younger sister, Dorothy, of whom he was extremely fond. She embraced him delightedly, clearly unworried by any family feuds, and embarked on a sprightly description of her second husband, the Earl of Northumberland, that erratic gentleman being well out of earshot. Her life had been quite turbulent. She was the same age as Robert, and, because of her recent marriage and the good offices of Essex, she had lately been allowed to return to Court after a long period of disgrace. Her first husband, Sir Thomas Perrot, wild as a hawk, had carried her off to church (perfectly willing) in the face of her guardian's prohibition. They were married by a terrified priest at sword point, the church being guarded the while by the bridegroom's friends, all armed to the teeth. This exploit had not appealed to the Queen whose Maid of Honour she was at the time. Her Majesty had refused to have anything to do with her for some while, despite a violent quarrel with Essex over the matter.

Dorothy was very nearly as beautiful as her sister, Penelope Rich, with the same fair hair and dark eyes and, like her, possessed all the Devereux outspoken charm and magnetism which ran like a golden streak through the family and blazed in the person of the Earl of Essex. She and Robert soon had their heads together over the latest family scandals. Dorothy was anything but discreet and only too happy to regale a handsome relative with some pulverising private detail. Did he know, for instance, that yet another Maid of Honour, Elizabeth Southwell, had borne Essex a son just after the birth of his own heir, and had claimed that the father was Thomas Vavasour? The stupid girl had initially insisted that the pregnancy was a "lameness in her leg", but that did not last for long. Last May, as Robert returned from the Indies, the Queen had discovered the child's true identity amid terrible scenes, particularly as Vavasour had been wrongly imprisoned for fathering the boy. Dorothy knew, of course, that Robert had been involved with the sister, Frances Vavasour; even so far as a contract of marriage, she remembered? And, would he believe, the child, another Walter Devereux, had been taken by Lettice to be reared in Staffordshire on the family estates. Dorothy thought it was her mother's form of revenge upon the Queen who did not fancy the thought of her favourite scattering illegitimate children around the country, least of all when they were then gathered in by her hated cousin Lettice. His marriage to Frances Sidney, in 1589, had almost caused an apoplexy. What a scandal, indeed, and how many more of her brother's by-blows would end up at Chartley Castle? Essex was incorrigible. Here he was trying to save England, and now involved in a roaring affair with the Countess of Derby, one of old Burghley's granddaughters. As for herself; she too was pregnant again, but no matter, she was once more at Court and a Countess. So she rattled on, Robert laughing at her nonsense, until Essex banged on the table and shouted for silence.

There was to be entertainment, he said. Would they clear the centre of the hall, hush the noise and await what was to come.

What came was the Earl of Southampton, dressed as Titania and reclining gracefully on a long seat covered in greenery and unseasonal flowers. Having had time to absorb this vision, the audience was then stunned by the entrance of William Shakespeare, in a furry mask adorned with long ears. They embarked upon cleverly parodied excerpts from "A Midsummer Night's Dream", altered just enough to point the finger of ridicule at first one and then another in their audience. The play was the height of fashion, having only recently been performed in public, was well known to all and the players soon had the whole company rolling in the aisles. Henry Wriothesley made an uncomfortably beautiful Titania, his long, dark red hair streaming down his back and his brilliant blue eyes shining out of his painted face. He was a natural actor with a natural stage presence though Robert knew well that he was also a good swordsman who loved a fight. Will Shakespeare's wit led them from one excess to another and, as the bawdiness grew, so did the gales of laughter. After an initial stiffening by Christopher Marlowe on Robert's right at the sight of his rival, he also succumbed to their clowning and was soon splitting his sides with the rest. At one point they burst into song, joined by a young man striding down from his place to pick up the theme and accompany them on his lute. This was Daniel Bacheler, a long-time friend and protégé of the Countess. Music was in his bones, his work was almost as well-known as that of Thomas Tallis, and he took centre stage when the two comics had run their course, playing the best known airs of the season and some of his own composing.

One thing followed another and Robert sought his bed in the small hours of the morning.

The following day, he joined Essex and Charles Blount, soon to be Lord Mountjoy, for a long while in Essex's study. Blount was, perhaps, Essex's greatest friend and deeply involved with his sister, Penelope Rich, whose marriage was far from happy. He was, nonetheless, a charming and honourable man.

They briefed Robert on the state of affairs at the Ordinance Office. The Lord Admiral, his uncle, was indeed gathering as large a fleet as he was able and negotiating with the Dutch navy to assist him in a supporting role. But the aim, this time, was an offensive. King Philip, who had smarted for seven long years since the defeat of the Armada in 1588, had constructed a sleeker, more seaworthy and a deadlier fleet in and around Cadiz. His actions in North Western France were becoming increasingly aggressive and his aim was clearly the capture of Calais. From there, the next step would be an attack upon the southern coast of England, backed up by his second armada. This time there would be no waiting game. Cadiz was to be bombarded and the Spanish fleet destroyed before it sailed. Drake's sortie to "singe the beard" of King Philip in 1590 would be a mere frolic by comparison. The beacons along the Channel coast were, once more, being primed.

This news, the fact that they had taken him into their counsels, and that possible action was not far distant, delighted Robert as nothing else could have done. Particularly when Essex leaned forward, fixed him with a glinting smile, and enquired whether he was prepared to take command of a ship; they would be obliged if he postponed any plans for further exploration in the Indies. Drake and Hawkins had already sailed for the Caribbean, as he knew, taking Abraham Kendal with them. It was the highest compliment Essex could pay him. The success of his voyage, his seamanship and his reputation were acknowledged and the grin on his face spoke for itself. They believed the "Nonpareil", a 500 ton man-of-war, was in need of a captain and Essex would put in a word with the Lord Admiral. Robert could do no harm in approaching his uncle himself. Above all, he should remember that information on the proposed attack was, at the moment, a close and vital secret and must remain so. He went from the room on air.

Robert then paid a visit to his uncle, Lord Howard of Effingham, ensconced in Arundel House, upriver from Essex House. Howard was an austerely good-looking man nearing fifty, with an impressive career behind him; his wife, the former Catherine Carey, was a cousin and close confidante of the Queen. He commiserated with Robert on the loss of his wife and child, gave him a glass of extremely strong punch, and wondered that he should wish to stay at Essex House, such a noisy melting-pot of an establishment as it was, rather than with him. He had few good words to say of Essex, and it was plain that he did not relish sharing command of the coming action with him; Essex being in charge of the military and himself of the naval forces. He knew, of course, the extent of Robert's voyaging and that he had returned with nine ships to his credit, sunk or captured. Questioning his nephew, he soon became aware, and with startling clarity, that Robert knew every bit as much about the provisioning, building, arming and maintenance of ships as did his uncle, and probably more about sailing and navigation; here was no callow youth. They were at one in deploring the absence, at this juncture, of Drake, Hawkins and Kendal.

Robert then broached the subject of a command and asked specifically to be allowed to include Captain Thomas Jobson, Captain Benjamin Wood and Captain Wyatt in his crew should this be granted. The old soldier was busy gathering "a hundred men out of Kent" and nothing was going to stop him. The Admiral, who had caught a glimpse of steel and of Leicester's thrusting arrogance in his nephew, eyed Robert for a frosty moment, then raised his glass to him and said that he had already so considered. He would get his command and could choose whom he wanted to join him.

Robert then gave the Admiral a concise account, in his own words, of his voyage and his activities in Trinidad, repudiating Raleigh's unpleasant letter on his behaviour towards its people. He was still extremely angry about this, but was told to hold his peace as Raleigh, with his vast experience of naval warfare, would most certainly play a large part in the coming attack on Cadiz. He would probably be commanding one of the fleet's four squadrons as a Rear Admiral. Robert realised, at this point, that silence was golden, but hoped, privately, that he would not be asked to serve directly under Raleigh. He had his own ideas about how he would conduct himself in any forthcoming battle and they did not include taking orders from Raleigh. He smiled dutifully at his uncle and thanked him profusely.

In the following days, he visited his mother and stepfather, Sir Edward Stafford. They had their own extensive establishment in London though Lady Douglas was often in attendance on the Queen. Sir Edward, a charming and indulgent husband, was not short of a few thousand pounds. His mother suggested that Robert had been too long absent from Court and should immediately pay his respects, after which she would busy herself in finding him a second wife. She begged him to abandon any ideas about a further voyage to Trinidad, to China, to Manila or anywhere else. He embraced her fondly, remarked on her continuing beauty, and told her that the world was a very large place of which he had seen little as yet.

He presented himself at Court, as he had done after returning from Trinidad the previous summer, to find the Queen somewhat snappish and preoccupied. More than anything, she detested foreign wars and their effect upon her exchequer and was, as expected, strongly resisting any offensive project. Prevarication had increased with age. However, she smiled on Robert, warned him that he was not the apple of Raleigh's eye and enquired what new folly he had up his sleeve in the way of exploration; all quite genial and unaccompanied by any devastating snubs. He noticed the signs of age that even a few months had wrought; the almost mask-like covering of her face with the frightful concoction, "ceruse", and the gaps in the discoloured teeth. None of which, however, affected her ability to dance the night away, ride to hounds, fly her own hawks or travel great distances in a day.

The twelve days of Christmas passed in a blur of activity. Robert's hours were crammed with hunting, jousting, feasting and theatre. There was also a considerable amount of time spent carousing in taverns and stews among his close friends and in the company of many delectable ladies of the night. His companions on these forays and his greatest friends included William and Philip Pembroke, sons of the kindly Earl; ("The most Noble and Incomparable Paire of Brethren") to whom the First Folio of Shakespeare's plays had been dedicated. Also, Edward Denny and other fellow jousters, together with a host of young Howard relations. Though there were many temptations at Court and many blatant handkerchiefs thrown in his direction by young and lovely Maids of Honour, he managed to steer clear of entanglement. This was quite a feat. In the somewhat promiscuous hothouse of the Court, his fortune, parentage and achievements made him a clear target for any girl, single or otherwise. He was not going to jeopardise his plans for the immediate future, nor his relationship with the Queen, by following in Essex's footsteps and landing himself in any compromising situation. His head ruled his inclinations, unlike his stepbrother. It was safer to stick with the ladies of the night for the time being; the maids of dishonour could wait.

That New Year's Day Joust could not be counted among Robert's greatest triumphs. He had not brought enough horses with him, nor had time to devise a full presentation of his own, and pride dictated that he should not ride with Essex as part of his entourage, but on his own, making a solitary entrance with a bow to the Queen. He borrowed a charger of Southampton's as a spare mount and hastily decked himself out in armour and silks covered in golden globes, denoting his maritime exploits and successes, and sporting a deep blue banner adorned with a ship. He had reckoned without his borrowed mount, however, the first of his string for that day.

At his entrance, the horse, a great raw-boned brute from Ireland, unused to anything but the silence of its native bogs, took one look at the crowded tiltyard and the cheering crowd and made a bolt for the gate. The onlookers were delighted and yelled encouragement. One, George Peel, was so overcome by Robert's ability that he wrote: "he could not help but admire young Dudleyes chivallrie" and ran to several pages on the subject.

In a towering rage, Robert then treated his audience to an exhibition of horsemanship to be remembered. Trying every trick in its repertoire, the horse backed into the barricade, reared up and punched the air, then put its nose between its forelegs, bucking and plunging the length of the yard. When that failed, it tried to scrape Robert off against the railings. It had met its match, however, and after a spectacular battle lasting several minutes and hugely enjoyed by the audience, it subsided and was ridden out of the yard to prolonged cheering.

Blazing with anger, Robert changed to one of his own horses, grabbed his pennant and charged back to the tiltyard, slithering to a halt in front of the "Queen's Window", the horse on its haunches. She looked at the grim young face before her and waved her fan at him.

Good came out of bad that day. He had seldom performed so well and only lost one course; those thundering down the lists towards him were unnerved by the fury and speed of his attack. Even Cumberland, the "Queen's Champion", gave way to him. Robert Dudley did not care to be the object of mirth, even when it was mixed with admiration. The cheering and applause was prolonged.

By the beginning of March 1596, Robert's commission as a naval captain was confirmed and he was appointed to the command of the greatship "Nonpareil", a 500 ton man-of-war of the Queen's Royal Navy, which bore the distinction of having been one of Drake's squadron during the defeat of the Armada. It was also confirmed that Raleigh, who had been brass-faced enough to demand total command, was to sail as Rear Admiral of the Fleet under Robert's uncle, the Lord Admiral. The other flag-officer was to be Lord Thomas Howard, son of the executed Duke of Norfolk, and yet another cousin of Robert's.

The Fleet, including the "Nonpareil", was beginning to muster in the Thames estuary or down in Plymouth; speculation was flying around

London and the surrounding countryside. It was too great a secret to keep, with thousands of soldiers and seamen massing in the vicinity and quartered near and all over London. It was generally assumed that the Fleet was gathering, once more, for the defence of England in the event of a Spanish attack on Calais.

Sure enough, this came on All Fool's Day. Early in the morning guns could be heard from across the channel and 6,000 men, under Essex, with the required ships to carry them, gathered hastily at Dover to try to prevent the fall and occupation of Calais. The dilatory uncertainty of the ageing Queen then became disastrously apparent. Still haggling with the French King over terms, she three times cancelled the order to sail with the result that this vital port fell to the Spanish, bringing their force all too close to her realm, their looming presence creating the worst possible circumstances for the fleet mustering for Cadiz. Amid scenes of angry chaos the ships and men destined for Calais at once set sail to gather at Plymouth.

This was bad enough but, hard on the heels of the disaster at Calais, came dispatches from the West Indies with the news that, following a severe repulse at Puerto Rico, both Drake and Hawkins had succumbed to dysentery and died. For Robert, an even crueller blow was the fact that Abraham Kendal, his friend and mentor, had also died there and on the same day as Drake. Three of England's greatest seamen had been lost within a week and their fleet badly mauled. It was not the moment to mourn; his own ship was waiting.

Robert lost no time in taking command of "The Nonpareil" and augmenting the threadbare crew so far allotted to her with seamen and officers of his own choice. The first of these to arrive was the redoubtable Captain Wyatt with the men he had raised in Kent. His legs a little bowed and his back a little bent, he marched his troop up in famous order; big men from the smiling garden of England, hop-pickers and brewers with the brawn to move weighty barrels, and with some experienced soldiers among them. To Robert's delight, a few of his veterans from the "Beare" also presented themselves, having got wind of events, and demanded to be taken on. Among these was Captain Wood, who had managed to sail the caravels "Intent" and "Regard" back from the Caribbean with two Spanish ships in tow, a remarkable feat of seamanship in itself. Of Jobson there was, sadly, no sign.

They boarded the ship in the Thames estuary and sailed almost immediately for Plymouth. Robert was anxious to get his ship to the victuallers and shipwrights there ahead of the main fleet. There was much work to be done aboard, inside and out, and much discipline to be enforced among the existing crew. He was obliged to be harsh with them. He had seen the grins on their faces as he went aboard for the first time; incredulity at his youth and sly winks at the easy time they would have running rings around him. It took forty-eight hours and two floggings before they realised what kind of a captain they were dealing with. His men from "The Beare" could have told them, but they chose not to and awaited events with wide grins. Meticulous and knowledgeable, Robert was always several jumps ahead of them, inspecting every detail of their duties and their quarters, allowing nothing but his own standards to be observed. The quality of his seamanship became apparent as soon as they put to sea; he relied on no-one, invited no advice and expected his orders to be unquestioned and instantly obeyed. This was no aristocratic sprig in a pretty uniform and by the time they reached Plymouth he was reasonably satisfied that they had no further delusions. Wyatt's men, well indoctrinated by their leader, had few delusions either, and made sure there was no nonsense from the seamen. The journey to Plymouth was a good opportunity to shake-down soldiers and sailors alike. There were one or two brawls and a few more floggings.

William Bradshaw had accompanied his Captain and was delighted to be at sea again, admittedly not among the close-knit fellowship that had been forged aboard the "Beare", but with new authority to pass on and enforce Robert's orders. In view of his valour during the battle for the Spanish ship off the Azores, he had been given the rank of Lieutenant and displayed a quiet and impressive authority from the start.

Down from Kenilworth, also, came Ancient Barrow having refused point-blank to obey instructions and remain at home. He had spruced himself up in no mean way and was hardly recognisable in a smart new jerkin of forest green emblazoned with the Dudley arms. He had kept abreast of events by some mysterious bush-telegraph, begged, borrowed or stolen horses to ride to Plymouth and presented himself and his fiddle a few days after Robert's arrival there looking extremely smug. No one had the heart to send him home and the fiddle did much to entertain those below decks. McElvey had accompanied him noisily in a box on his horse's crupper, ready to do his bit for England among the rodents aboard the "Nonpareil". Of these there were plenty. Also joining the ship at Plymouth as Gunnery Officer was Peter Michell from Cornwall, restored to health and with only a slight limp to mark his heroism during the battle off the Azores. He had been given excellent treatment in Warwickshire under the Dudley wing and was not going to miss another outing with Robert. He brought with him two other members of the "Beare"'s crew, forming, with Wood and Wyatt, a solid nucleus of loyal veterans who quickly set the tone for other crew members.

The "Nonpareil" was not in the first flush of youth and the sailing to Plymouth had revealed that there was room for a great deal of improvement in her structure and her seaworthiness. There was hard work to be done and, with old Sir John Norris's words of wisdom ringing in his ears, Robert made sure the men were well housed and well fed before they set to. He wanted both them and the ship in fighting form by the time they sailed for Spain. The guns, in particular, needed attention and, on this subject, he was in his element. Ever since he had pestered the life out of the gunsmiths at Tilbury he had been fascinated by firearms and artillery: the bigger the better, and in Plymouth were to be found some of the best craftsmen in the gunnery business. He was glad to have Michell and his expertise at his elbow and they immediately got to work.

Essex and the Lord Admiral were on their way to Plymouth with the rest of the fleet by mid-April. There would be pandemonium once they arrived and a scramble to get the ships provisioned and armed. Waiting to be distributed among them were vast numbers of troops converging on Plymouth, mostly levies but also many seasoned veterans who had fought with Philip Sidney, Francis Vere and Essex in Flanders. Flocking to Essex's banner, in particular, were gentlemen volunteers and adventurers, looking for a fight and with high hopes of plunder. The destination of the fleet was officially still unknown and speculation veered wildly between the re-taking of Calais, another mid-channel battle with the new Armada, or an attack on Spain.

Sealed orders to sail arrived from the Queen on 24th May and, much to the credit of its Commanders, sufficient order had been achieved for the fleet to set out from Plymouth on 1st June, its destination still unknown to all but its most senior officers. It consisted of four squadrons, each with its Admiral and Vice Admiral. The Admiral of the Fleet, Howard of

Effingham, in his flagship the "Ark Royal", was also Admiral of the First Squadron with his son-in-law, Sir Robert Southwell, as his Vice Admiral aboard the "Lion". The Second Squadron was led by Essex in "Repulse", the Vice Admiral being Sir Francis Vere in "Rainbow". The Admiral of the Third Squadron, Lord Thomas Howard, in his flagship "Merhonour", was also Vice Admiral of the Fleet. He had, as his squadron Vice Admiral, Robert Dudley in "Nonpareil". The Fourth Squadron was led by Raleigh in "Warspite", his Vice Admiral being Drake's erstwhile flag-officer, Captain Robert Crosse, in "Swiftsure". Robert was, therefore, not serving directly under Raleigh, but under his cousin, Thomas Howard, and, to his great pride, as a Vice Admiral. This pride was fully justified. He was twenty-one years old, had a recognised reputation as a commander and a navigator and had already crossed the Atlantic with his own small fleet. The Fifth Squadron was composed of Dutch ships under their Admiral, Jan van Duyvenvoord. The Dutch Navy, supported by the English in the Netherlands campaign had grown and developed substantially.

Other leading officers included Sir Christopher Blount, the one-handed husband of Lettice, in "Lioness", the Earl of Sussex in "Vanguard", and Sir George Carew, Master of the Ordnance, in "Mary Rose".

In all, the fleet consisted of some 120 men-of-war, both English and Dutch, made up of 14,000 English, of whom 6,500 were soldiers, and 2,500 Dutch.

The "Ark Royal" fired the signal gun and the huge fleet moved slowly out of Pymouth, squadron by squadron, accompanied by swarms of flyboats, pinnaces and transports. Sadly, it was a false start. The wind switched direction off Cornwall and blew them every which way but mostly back to Plymouth Sound where they re-grouped and set off once more on 3rd June.

In order to preserve surprise and secrecy, the fleet seized every foreign vessel they met once past Finisterre and, with a good wind, arrived about twelve leagues north of Cadiz on 18th June. Among these vessels they had the luck to encounter a fly-boat and, after a hard chase, captured and discovered from her that just outside Cadiz harbour lay a valuable Spanish merchant fleet with few warships to protect it, many of them having sailed to San Lucar for re-fitting. This information was confirmed by an Irish merchantman who also stated that the town was poorly garrisoned, with work in progress on the walls, and with no suspicion of what was coming its way. There were few among the English fleet who did not now know their destination.

By any standard, Cadiz, perched on a rock at the end of a five-mile isthmus, was a hard nut to crack. Behind the isthmus, on its landward side, lay an outer harbour, giving on to an inner haven. Because of rocks and shoals, access to the harbour and haven was going to be difficult, covered, as it was, by the guns of Fort Puntal. This was where Drake had blasted his way through and laid waste nine years before. What he had done with a tithe of the ships now gathered, could surely be done again, more thoroughly and in his memory.

Tension was now mounting throughout the fleet. The Admirals and Vice Admirals met to confer aboard the Flagship, the "Ark Royal", rowed by tender in a choppy sea. Robert, included in this august gathering as a Vice Admiral, listened in silence to the debate alongside his Squadron Leader, Lord Thomas Howard. Later, he had brief speech with Sir Robert Southwell, second in command of the Lord Admiral's squadron, and his son-in-law. The naval side of the expedition was quite a family affair. Southwell was one of England's finest seamen and his piercing blue eyes had twinkled at Robert in recognition during the briefing.

Which should be attacked first while they still had the advantage of surprise, the town or the rich convoy guarded by a reduced number of warships? This was the point of debate. Total success on both fronts would depend on whether the Spanish defenders became aware of their presence, and for how long, before the attack began. The plan also counted on penetration to the calmer waters of the harbour in order to land troops on the isthmus for the assault on the city from the landward side.

Eventually it was decided that Essex should take full advantage of the element of surprise and land troops on the seaward side, attacking the town's citadel as soon as possible. Picked men would go ashore first to cover the landing of those who followed. The Lord Admiral would deal with the merchantmen, containing them in the outer harbour and fighting off their defence, after which troops could be disembarked on the isthmus, braving the guns of Fort Puntal, and attacking the town from the harbour side.

At dawn, on 21st June 1596 in a rising wind, the great arc of ships sailed within sight of Cadiz.

CHAPTER SIX

The Battle and the Burning – 1596

It was never going to be an organised or dignified battle that went according to an organised or coherent plan. Very few battles ever did, even if, as in this case, it was a total surprise for those attacked. The Spanish had no notion that such a fleet was anywhere near them. On sighting the huge crescent of sails, panic immediately set in. Yelling and shouting, crews rushed to man their galleys and ships. Townsmen ran to prepare their guns for action and church bells rang frantically.

The English fleet approached and dropped anchor off the western side of Cadiz and the assault on the town, directed by Essex, began as planned. Soldiers, fully armed, were loaded into barges, lowered and headed for the shore but the Atlantic surf, rising all morning and thundering down on the beaches, was too much for them. Two boats capsized and the occupants, weighed down with equipment and ammunition, drowned horribly and in full view. Spanish cavalry and infantry appeared on the beach, taking cover behind stacked wine barrels. War galleys, rowed by slaves, appeared on the eastern side. The surf continued to rise, wind whipping spray off the waves, and a landing was clearly not going to be a success, but Essex, determined to spearhead the assault, was most unwilling to abandon it. Raleigh, moving rapidly between Essex and the Lord Admiral, managed to convince his commander that an attack by sea through the harbour, as Drake had done, would be a better plan. The wretched soldiers, still heaving about in the surf, were re-embarked in their ships, wet and seasick.

During this exchange, and while the Vice Admiral's back was turned, Raleigh had also persuaded the Lord Admiral to allow him to lead the harbour attack, accompanied by Southwell, Vere and Robert Dudley. Lord Thomas Howard, when he heard this, icily insisted that as second in command of the fleet, the honour should be his. Because he considered that his own ship "Merhonour" drew too much water to safely navigate the harbours, he transferred himself, some of his officers and his flag, to Robert's "Nonpareil".

79

This did not suit Robert at all. He would no longer be in command of his own ship and he would have to take orders from both Howard and Raleigh.

Before Howard came aboard, however, he went around every corner of the "Nonpareil" like a dervish, assuring himself that the men were not only at their stations but had been well fed and issued with a tot of rum. They would get a double tot before they went into action in the morning. He checked, with Peter Michell, the running out of each gun, the ammunition for every piece, including an arsenal for muskets, and each coil of rope. He heard reports, through Captain Wood and William Bradshaw, from those responsible for the sailing of the ship, on the state of masts, spars, colours, the battle positions of soldiers and the condition of their muskets. By now, his crew had his measure and appreciated not only his thoroughness but his concern for their welfare. The fact that he had only two sea battles under his belt had ceased to matter. He was their Captain and the Vice Admiral of their squadron. They were to have the honour of leading the attack with the Second in Command of the whole fleet on board to boot. There were grins of pride on many faces and Ancient Barrow struck up a jig.

All this preparation and re-deployment had given the Spanish time to withdraw their merchant fleet, laden with riches, together with many of their war galleys, to the inner harbour on the landward side of Cadiz and, therefore, out of reach of an immediate attack.

Sunrise was the signal for the assault and precedence for the advance had been agreed among the commanders. There was nothing orderly about what actually happened.

Raleigh, determined to be the first into the havens at all costs, weighed anchor while the sun was still below the horizon and charged across the outer harbour towards Fort Puntal. Enraged by his brazen disregard of orders, Lord Thomas Howard ordered Robert to follow him immediately and as closely as possible. After them came Southwell in "Lion", Carew in "Mary Rose" and Clifford in "Dreadnought". As with the start of a yachting race, the ships had to manoeuvre with the greatest skill to avoid hitting rocks, the shallows, or each other as they entered the harbour below the fort. It took every ounce of Robert's expertise as a navigator and the words of Abraham Kendal rang in his ears with truth that "he had learned enough navigation for an admiral". He felt that bear-like figure at his shoulder in a very real way, flung back his head and roared with laughter; action was imminent, there was a score to settle with Raleigh and they would not fail. Infected by his reckless enjoyment, those around him at the helm, even Lord Thomas Howard, laughed with him. Fortunately, there was enough wind to keep them moving; without it, the whole attack could have been fouled.

As he entered the harbour, Raleigh saw that his way was blocked by the four largest galleons of the Spanish fleet, known as the Apostles: "St. Philip", "St. Thomas", St. Mathew". and "St. Andrew". They were moored head to stern across the navigable water, presenting their broadsides and bristling with guns. His arrival was greeted by a terrifying barrage which was backed up by the guns from the fort, the three frigates and the seventeen galleys supporting the galleons. Raleigh immediately dropped anchor as did those behind him; all except for "Nonpareil". Robert pushed his ship past Raleigh's "Warspite" and took up the lead under the full blast of the enemy fire. Refusing to remain in second place, Raleigh then weighed anchor again and elbowed his way past both "Nonpareil" and Vere's "Rainbow", slewing his ship across the channel so that he could not be passed without risk of going aground. What the Spaniards made of this extraordinary scramble can only be guessed; they were so bemused that their fire temporarily slackened giving Essex, who had come up in "Repulse", time to shove his way to the front alongside Robert. He loathed Raleigh, was enraged by his behaviour and he refused to be left in reserve as ordered by the Lord Admiral.

It was at this point that Lord Thomas Howard, observing that "Merhonour" had made it into the harbour and had opened fire, decided to return to his ship. He did not appear concerned about the shot whistling around his ears and was duly taken off, rowed in a barge by a terrified crew in the capable charge of William Bradshaw whose coolness under fire was remarkable as was his return through the mêlée to his own ship.

This left Robert in sole command of "Nonpareil", now among the four leading ships, and fighting the battle of his life. His 250 soldiers and sailors, 30 cannon and 22 quick firers were all at full stretch and his ship was his own again. He could not have asked for more. This was no one to one encounter with time to strut about the deck and direct the fire, but a fierce scrimmage at close quarters with enormous galleons beautifully positioned to rake any ship within range. He was here, there and everywhere, weaving in and out of range of the Apostles and playing a deadly game of "catch" with the other English ships while delivering accurate fire whenever he could position "Nonpareil" to do so. One gun had slipped its breech ropes and was crashing about below decks, injuring men and smashing timber. He could hear the yells of "loose cannon" as the gun crews struggled to control it.

The English were, at this stage, at a disadvantage and Vere wrote: ".....they held us to good talk by reason their ships lay athwart with their broadsides towards us, and most of us right ahead, so that we could use but our chasing pieces".

Raleigh recorded "......the volleys of cannon and culverin came as thick as if it had been a skirmish of musketeers........the ships that abode that fight were the "Warspite", the "Nonpareil", the "Lion", the "Mary Rose", the "Rainbow" and the "Dreadnought". To second these came up the Earl in "Repulse" and the "Swiftsure" and these were all that did aught against six goodly galleons, two argosies, three frigates, seventeen galleys and the Fort of Puntal."

The Spaniards were disadvantaged by poor quality powder and their cannonballs tended to bounce off their targets rather than penetrate them while the English ammunition had far greater fire-power and raked through the thickest timber.

For three hours the rival fleets pounded each other, the English ships manoeuvring in the restricted space, distracting the Spanish from each other and pouring in fire at every chance. Gradually the accuracy and force of their gunnery began to tell and they closed in like a pack of wolves and edged forward to board. Raleigh, seizing the opportunity, tried to get alongside the Spanish flagship "St.Philip" closely followed by "Nonpareil". The Apostles, having finally had enough, panicked, and slipped their cables. Caught by the tide, they were swept on to the shoals off the mainland beaches.

What followed was not a pretty sight. The Spanish fired the "St. Philip" and the "St.Thomas" both of which were soon blazing furnaces, gunpowder barrels exploding in crashing salvoes, and men diving off ships in hundreds like rats, some blazing torches, others already charred. "Heaps of soldiers, so thick as if coals had been poured out of a sack, some drowned and some sticking in the mud" recorded one onlooker. The Dutch added to the chaos by butchering any Spaniard attempting to find refuge with them. John Donne wrote of this horrible scene:

"Out of a fired ship, which by no way
But drowning could be rescued from the flame,
Some men leaped forth, and ever as they came,

Near the foe's ships, did by their shot decay;
So all were lost which in the ship were found;
They in the sea being burnt; they in the burnt ship drowned."

Essex, with great speed and presence of mind, boarded the other two Apostles before they could be set alight, manning and securing them before any further advance. The galleys and other Spanish vessels retired promptly to the inner haven, out of reach for the present. The Spanish losses, by now, were mounting rapidly while the English had not suffered greatly. Among the Commanders, only Raleigh had been hit, with a shell splinter in the leg. This did not appear to slow him down.

Still smarting from having been left in reserve, and before the sea battle was complete, Essex then turned his attention to a landing on the isthmus south of Cadiz. Robert, realising his intention and that there was nothing further to be gained from pursuing the Apostles, immediately followed him, yelling orders to Captain Wyatt to prepare the troops for disembarkation. With him went Sir Francis Vere, Sir Conyers Clifford, Sir John Wingfield and Christopher Blount in their respective ships. By four o'clock in the afternoon, they were landing 2,000 men at a point three miles south of the town from a flotilla of barges and flyboats rowed in time to the beat of a drum in Essex's boat. Here, Clifford and Blount with 1,000 men, turned south to intercept possible reinforcements coming up the isthmus, while Essex, Vere, Wingfield and Robert Dudley, with the other 1,000 men, turned north in strict ranks to attack the town and the citadel. They ploughed across the sand at a great pace until they spotted a force of some 500 cavalry waiting outside the town gates to deter them. Robert, in the leading column, could see the sunlight glinting on armour and spearheads. Essex then gave orders for the main body of his troops to conceal themselves behind the dunes, the short, sea-stunted growth giving some cover, while a small guard launched an attack under Sir John Wingfield. This included Robert Dudley with Wyatt and some of his men. The cavalry charged the small group who fought hard and convincingly, then fell back upon the hidden majority. This was the first hand-to-hand fight of Robert's life, but years of fencing stood him in good stead and manoeuvres at Tilbury had taught him what to expect from a cavalry charge. He managed to parry the sabre cuts aimed at him and cover some of the less experienced soldiers as he fought his way back to his comrades. The Spanish cavalry were slowed by the sand and when Wingfield turned to face them and Essex's hidden column rose up at his back, they scattered and fled back to the town. They rushed through the gates, which were then shut, with such speed that many of them were left outside. Fortunately for these, the walls were in the process of being repaired, and they managed to bolt through the gaps, leaving their horses outside.

Essex, closely followed by Wingfield, Robert and as many men as could keep up with them, rushed after them through the holes (still strewn with tools) and proceeded to hack their way through to the centre of the town. With more forethought, Francis Vere gathered the remaining troops into a body, opened the main gates, and proceeded to fight his way methodically through to join them in the market place. It proved well that he did. Essex's heroes had been checked by a determined defence of the main Town Hall and were outnumbered. Having outstripped most of their following, they might well have been killed or driven out of the town. They were exhausted, some badly wounded, including the gallant Sir John Wingfield who died very shortly afterwards. Old Wyatt, frantically trying to keep pace with Robert, who had moved with deft and savage speed through the town, caught him with relief, scolding his foolhardiness and binding up a sword cut that had escaped his notice; blood was running down his left arm and dripping off his fingers. Dressed in the splendour of an admiral's uniform, he had been a near perfect target for anyone shooting from behind grilled doors or windows.

Hard on the heels of Vere, the Lord Admiral himself marched through the gates of Cadiz with most of the remaining English troops, ensuring its complete capitulation. He had not waited long to land his men and, in order to be certain of the town, he had ignored Essex's message proposing that he should first secure the merchant fleet, now withdrawn to the inner haven, and had followed him ashore. It was victory and at no very great cost for only about 100 Englishmen had been lost on land and at sea. They buried Sir John Wingfield with all honour in the captured cathedral; his courage in the face of the Spanish cavalry had set up Essex's attack and assured their success. By nightfall, the Queen's flag flew over the citadel.

Several of the town's richest and most prominent citizens were identified, discovered and taken hostage. They would bring a good price in due course.

The sack of Cadiz that began the next day was curiously restrained. Before the soldiers and sailors were let loose upon the town, the women and children and over 1,000 monks, nuns and friars were evacuated and orders

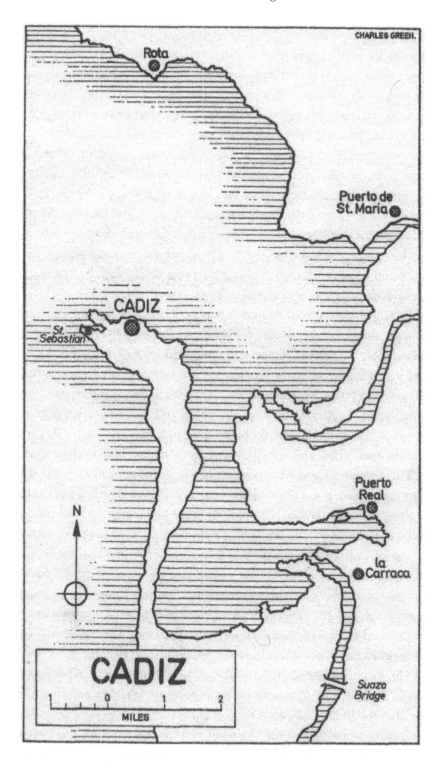

CHARLES GREEN.

Rota

Puerto de
St. Maria

CADIZ

St.
Sebastian

Puerto
Real

la
Carraca

N

CADIZ

1   0   1   2
MILES

Suazo
Bridge

given that the churches were not to be touched. The Dutch, in particular, were strictly warned against attempting reprisals on the Spaniards who had treated them with such barbarity over the years of the Netherlands wars. The long, sorry column of women, wailing children and clerics that wound its way down the sandy isthmus was a typical product of war although they were the lucky ones. A town that did not surrender was automatically ravaged by its conquerors and the inhabitants killed, made use of, or carried off. These had been reprieved by officers brought up in the chivalric traditions of Elizabethan high society. They would join their compatriots in Puerto Real on the far side of the Inner haven, from where the Duke of Medina Sidonia, of the 1588 Armada disgrace and now Commandant of Cadiz and Andalusia, had been forced to watch yet another spectacular defeat.

According to a Spanish report by a Lope de Valuela: "They treated very well the women, not offending them in any way."

Robert and Wyatt rounded up as many of their men as could be found and spent the night with Essex's troops in the Town Hall. There was plenty of good food and wine to be had and they drank deep. Knowing that Wood and Michell had charge of the "Nonpareil", and despite his stiffening wound, the Vice Admiral slept the sleep of the dead with his head on the pack of one of his Kentish soldiers. Little more than a boy and dead to the world, he did not see or hear his men raise their glasses to him with the toast: "To a man from his men." They had seen him in action and they all had stories to tell.

The despoiling of the town began before daybreak. Plunder was what many had come for and the soldiers were soon joined by sailors pouring off the ships in hundreds and, according to Raleigh's description: "all running headlong to the sack". He himself, determined to be in at the death, had been helped ashore after leaving the smouldering Apostles to their fate, but the wound in his leg got the better of him and he was soon carried back to "Warspite" and delivered to his surgeon. What he saw in Cadiz later prompted him to write, inspite of the moderation demanded by the Commanders, "If any man had a desire to see Hell itself, it was then most lively figured." This was a somewhat different tale from the Spanish report of Valuela.

The exodus to the town had left the ships scantily manned and in no state to complete their victory by attempting to seize the merchantmen retired to the inner harbour.

Cadiz was a rich city; the first landing place for many of the treasure ships from the New World, and its warehouses and shops, its palaces and mansions contained ducats, pictures and statues, gold and silver plate, jewels, silk, and every kind of merchandise, not to mention casks of wine and foodstuffs. The streets were soon strewn with opened trunks, broken bottles, sides of beef and mutton, furniture tossed out of windows and extremely drunk soldiers and sailors. The terrified inhabitants remaining in the city were only too happy to hand over their goods and valuables in return for their safety. It would have gone hard with them if they had not. What liquor was not running down the throats of Englishmen was soon running down the gutters and most of the heroes of yesterday were way past reasonable thought or behaviour by mid-morning.

Returning rather stiffly to his ship, Robert passed two of his crew astride a large statue of Cortez and his horse. Dressed haphazardly in women's clothing, they were singing riotously and without much tune and they cheerily waved bottles of wine in his direction; his uniform, perhaps, was vaguely familiar to their befogged minds. He ordered them to get down and they hurled the bottles at him, cursing and swearing. Wyatt, tugging at his sleeve, urged him on, saying that he would send in a force presently to round them up; it was pointless to try orders or reason for the present. They saw uglier sights than this on their way back to the boats. Two men had been impaled on a wooden door, thrust through by butcher's knives, clearly having tried to guard what lay behind it. When rescued, they were still alive and writhing, but their chances did not look good. They also saw some women being dragged screeching down an alley, one towed by the hair and another with her petticoats over her head. They had unwisely not chosen evacuation with the priesthood.

Booty was what the soldiers and sailors had fought for and they were stuffing their pockets and knapsacks with anything that might be of value and with little regard for the owners. Some of the Spanish residents, having heard of the ban on the raiding of churches, had been canny and quick enough to hide their valuables there, but the majority had not. Violence was beginning to break out among the drunken raiders as they fought over their trophies. An important quantity of sherry was "confiscated" during the raid which was reputedly the start of its popularity in England.

As Robert and Wyatt passed a large house standing in its own grounds, a servant came out to them, unlocking the heavy iron gates and giving them a large velvet bag. In good English, he begged them to put a guard on the house in order to spare his elderly employers, both in frail health and dreading an all too likely break-in. Wyatt posted men on the gate and Robert gave them signed orders to ensure the safety of those within. He returned the bag, saying that nothing could guarantee that the old people would be spared, but the man ran after him insisting that he take it.

Once back on "Nonpareil", the bag was found to contain two strings of immense pearls, one with a clasp of rubies and the other of sapphires, a necklace of aquamarines, an enormous cabuchon emerald of a deep sea-green hue, several heavy gold chains and rings and a curious brooch in the shape of a falcon composed of many-coloured precious stones. These were certainly the product of New world treasures fashioned by the goldsmiths of Cadiz. Robert gave Wyatt the gaudy falcon, knowing he would also do a little quiet plundering on his own account when he returned ashore for his men.

This had to be soon. The ships must be manned and the soldiers made ready to fight again if necessary. After a few days of wanton looting, commanders ordered the return of their men and sent the most reliable of their officers, boatswains and sergeants, still in a fit state, into the town. They erected a gibbet outside the Town Hall and went to work. It was a thankless task, but after a few hangings and liberal use of the lash, the men, in their hundreds, were marched back to the ships, surly, sick with drink, and mutinous. One persuasion given them to hasten departure was the fact that Cadiz would probably be burnt to the ground before long. They would be better off in their ships than incinerated in the town. Wyatt, William Bradshaw and Michell returned with all but two of the crew from "Nonpareil".

Medina Sidonia then achieved the one redeeming act of his career. Having watched two of the great Apostles go up in smoke and knowing how vulnerable was the treasure fleet now bottled up in the inner haven, he offered his former opponent, Lord Howard of Effingham, the sum of two million ducats if it was allowed to go free. Knowing he had him over a barrel, Howard refused and demanded four million ducats. It would have been game, set and match, had not Medina Sidonia, on the morning two days after the capture of Cadiz, set fire to every treasure ship, so destroying one of the richest cargoes to arrive in Spain. It was said that, for the first time since the 1588 Armada, a smile appeared on his long, pale face.

It was conflagration on a grand scale. The time wasted during the sack of Cadiz had cost the English marauders over twelve million ducats worth of ships and treasure. Their victory was, therefore, a somewhat hollow one and they had little to show for it but the two remaining

Apostles, a few valuable hostages, and the loot from the town, in no way comparable to the cargoes of the treasure ships. The original purpose, the destruction of the latest Armada intended for the attack on England, had not yet been fully achieved. They had, however, mounted a daring raid on Spanish soil, captured a key sea port and eliminated four of the largest enemy vessels. The Spanish losses were far greater than the English gains. They had lost Cadiz, the four Apostles, a ransom of 120,000 ducats to be paid shortly for the city, and thirty-six ships carrying twelve million ducats worth of goods, sent to lie at the bottom of the inner harbour.

Robert awoke that morning to see the huge columns of smoke rising, ever thicker, from the inner harbour and guessed what had happened. He had been too occupied since his return to "Nonpareil", dealing with his demoralised crew, to give much thought to the immediate future, but had assumed that they would proceed to the inner haven to secure the Spanish fleet as soon as possible. His officers had wrought with the men to the extent that they were in a fit state to man the ship, but not as he would wish. They were to be allowed to keep the valuables they had looted, a decision unlikely to please their Queen who expected that all such gains would automatically be passed to the Crown. Inevitably, a great deal of horse-trading was going on among the crews which gave rise to more feuding and fighting.

There followed a hasty and undignified rush to salvage anything possible from the scuttled Spanish fleet by those ships and smaller craft able to reach it through the narrow channel to the inner haven, but Medina Sidonia's men had done a thorough job. Only a few lucky ones braving the holocaust came away with any treasure and the only other valuables rescued were some of the guns.

Having reviewed the current situation, Essex and the Lord Admiral had now to decide a course of action. Essex was in favour of holding Cadiz with a sufficient force. They had enough provisions to last for around three months and a blockade could be set up. It was general knowledge that the annual arrival of the Spanish treasure fleet returning from the West Indies was shortly due and its capture would more than redeem the loss of the scuttled ships. He, personally, had decided to stay, and buoyantly declared himself Governor of Cadiz, immediately making plans for administering occupied territory. These included the knighting, in the Cathedral, of over sixty gentlemen who, he considered, had distinguished themselves in the fighting. Among them were his stepfather, Christopher Blount, and Gelli Meyrick, his steward. It was a repeat of the gall that had so enraged the Queen during the siege of Rouen. The right to dispense knighthoods lay principally with herself and it was setting his authority on a level with her own and cheapening what should be given after long, hard service. There would be trouble ahead.

His stepbrother was not included in this hysterical mass elevation. He lay sick in his berth on "Nonpareil" with an infection of the wound in his arm though he had received word from Essex that he was shortly to become Sir Robert Dudley. He was young, very strong and healthy and, thanks to Captain Wyatt following what medical lore he had picked up from Abraham Kendal, he was on his feet within a week. With the help of Ancient Barrow, scolding and cursing, Wyatt had applied hot fomentations of raw spirit directly to the wound and bound it tight. Robert's eyes watered, but the arm healed.

The Lord Admiral was of a different view concerning the immediate future of Cadiz. He knew, better than Essex, that setting up a base on foreign soil was not included in the Royal permission which had allowed the expedition to be commissioned, and that the Queen would never countenance such an expenditure. Furthermore, his experience of fighting men after a battle, particularly when enriched with the booty they had acquired, warned him that they would not be happy with anything other than a prompt return home. They had done themselves proud and were not likely to do any better unless the expedition could waylay the next Spanish treasure fleet. They were anxious to get themselves and their booty home before the tide of fortune turned.

Argument raged for several days between the two principals followed by more argument among lesser Admirals and Vice Admirals. Some, including Robert Dudley and Sir Robert Southwell, held that remaining in a somewhat precarious position on the edge of a hostile Spain with the threat of a counter-attack, would erode any will to fight among the fleet and the army. It would be better to give them a fresh objective whilst on the move for home; either to raid other Spanish ports with the aim of destroying shipping destined for an attack on England, or to prowl offshore in wait for the incentive of the big treasure fleet expected from the West Indies. Essex was reluctantly over-ruled. They would leave.

By lst July 1596, the destruction of Cadiz was being prepared. The engineers, whose skills had not so far been needed, went to work demolishing walls and fortifications, and transporting the city's cannon to the ships. On 4th July, two weeks after Cadiz was first sighted, the burning of the town began. The churches were deliberately not fired, those inhabitants remaining had been warned and a further stream of displaced people were making their way down the hot sand of the isthmus. Robert had sent early word to the old couple whose jewellery he carried in the hope they could find transport to take them to safety.

The last two people to leave the beach below Cadiz, and in the last boat, were the Earl of Essex and Robert Dudley. The roar of the flames racing through the town had, by now, become a familiar sound. First, it had been the Apostles, not a pleasant memory, then the Spanish treasure fleet, and now Cadiz itself. The wind was blowing inshore, carrying the shrouding smoke away from them and the noise from the blaze was so deafening that speech was impossible. Cadiz burnt to the ground. Robert hoped devoutly that all living things had been evacuated from the city. It was not a fate to be wished on any enemy.

The final acts of the expedition became somewhat frustrated by differing opinion and disastrous compromise. As the fleet sailed north, the commanders were still debating; there was unfinished business to attend to, but how to achieve it with Spain in uproar and news of their presence now widespread? Essex, foiled of his command of Cadiz, was in favour of remaining in the vicinity in order to waylay the incoming treasure fleet, or to sail to the Azores to find it there. Alternatively, they might raid some of the Portuguese ports they would be passing (long since occupied by Spain) in search of further booty or in the hope of destroying Spanish shipping. A trip to the Azores was vetoed, but an attack on the Portuguese town of Faro was agreed upon. The Lord Admiral declined this treat and remained patrolling offshore.

The expedition involved a ten-mile march inland in mid-summer heat only to find that every soul had taken to the hills with their valuables and livestock. On 14th July, accompanied by William Bradshaw, Robert Dudley, with a gathering of his men, made the journey, led by Sir Christopher Blount and, despite his strength and youth, found it hard going. His tight collar strangling him and the sweat pouring down his face he struggled into the town of Faro where they found the water fountains turned off and nothing worth purloining except one jewel of a find. The Bishop of Osorio had an exceptional library in Faro which had been abandoned, and they loaded this on to all available vehicles. Utterly frustrated, they then fired the town; yet another bonfire which added to the heat, and marched back to their ships without a sword being drawn. It had been an inglorious affair with only one happy outcome. Essex claimed the impressive collection of books on the grounds that it was he who had instigated the raid on Faro and accompanied Blount, and he had them loaded on to "Repulse". Much later, he gave the collection to Sir Thomas Bodley, who used it as the nucleus of the Bodleian Library in Oxford.

The wind changed suddenly as they sailed slowly northward and blew for the Azores, prompting Essex and Sir Francis Vere to again urge a dash to find the treasure fleet which must, by now, have reached the islands. Failing this, they advocated waiting for its arrival in the vicinity of Lisbon, a very likely landing place, or better still, attacking Lisbon itself. This was again vetoed by the Lord Admiral, who decided to head for home via Corunna in the hope of destroying further Spanish shipping there. They sailed at a good speed past Lisbon, to find, again, word of their coming had emptied the harbour at Corunna. Little did they know that two days later, the enormous Indies fleet, carrying 20,000,000 ducats' worth of treasure had meandered up the River Tagus to Lisbon blithely unaware of their proximity. It had been the worst of bad decisions. Essex had been right.

Unaware of this disaster, the English fleet sailed into Plymouth harbour on 8th August 1596, to what seemed like a rapturous welcome. The Queen had written delightedly: "You have made me famous, dreadful and renowned, not more for your victory than for your courage. Let the army know that I care not so much for being Queen, as that I am sovereign of such subjects." This was before she had time to assess the cost of the venture or to know what had been missed, both Medina Sidonia's fired treasure ships and the fleet from the Azores.

Very soon after their arrival, divine service was held in Plymouth to give thanks for the safe return of the fleet. Having seen "Nonpareil" safely bestowed on her mooring, Robert Dudley attended the service with his officers. Immediately afterwards: "In the open street, when the Lords general came from the sermon", he was knighted by Essex before a large crowd which included most of his own crew and those of many other ships. The same source also wrote of Robert that he had "so many good parts of a worthy gentleman as the like are seldom seen to concure in any". He was not yet twenty-two, a Vice Admiral, and had proved convincingly that he could command ships and men at the highest level, at sea and in battle. This was a far more impressive affair than to have been one of sixty in a foreign city.

CHAPTER SEVEN

Kenilworth – 1596

It might have been expected, after the rigours and excitement of the capture of Cadiz, that the tempo of Robert Dudley's life, driven though it was by such a restless spirit, might have slowed down a little. There was unfinished business, however, on two very different subjects; a second voyage and a second marriage.

He must have sons. The vision of canvas-shrouded forms slipping silently over the rails of "Nonpareil" was a reminder of the fragility of human life and still he had no legitimate heir. Kenilworth needed a mistress and he needed a successor.

A visit to Court soon after their return reflected how Robert's reputation had grown. He now rubbed shoulders with the greatest in the land; he had fought alongside Howard, Essex, Raleigh, Vere and Wingfield and been knighted for it. The illegitimate boy had become a very impressive man. Wealth, land, reputation and honour were his and his achievements in many spheres were well-known. He was a matrimonial prize and there were plenty of well-born beauties romping around the Court who would be only too pleased to step into Margaret's shoes and into Kenilworth. It was known, also, that the Queen looked kindly on him. At this early stage, she was delighted to welcome the heroes of Cadiz; the trouble would begin when she heard of the missed treasure fleet in Lisbon, the indecisions and the copious knighting in the Cathedral. Already there were rumblings on the subject of the fleet's vast expense and the lack of profit both for herself and the exchequer. These would increase when she realised that most of the plunder had not been handed in.

She rapped Robert smartly on the knuckles as he knelt before her, turned up his face and enquired how he enjoyed his knighthood. He grinned back at her and replied that all he had was at her service, now and always. She pinched his chin quite hard but she was smiling.

He now turned his attention, with real pleasure and amusement to the many girls being blatantly put in his way. Not many, even the great houses, would cavil at a union with the baseborn heir of Leicester, and he found he was meeting with nothing but encouragement. His stepsister, Dorothy, Countess of Northumberland, was extremely interested in his progress and introduced him to several ravishing beauties including young matrons who should have known better. He enjoyed them all; he loved women and their company and there were fewer rollicking evenings in the taverns with the Pembroke sons and other kindred spirits. It was now the turn of the ladies of the night to sigh for his company. He decked himself out with sober magnificence and attended routs, balls, the theatre and the famed evenings at the Inns of Court. He played the courtier for all he was worth, even writing verse or reading it if he had to. He had learnt to temper conceit, to play down the praise of others and transform it to jest. His knighthood had been earned and he was proud of it, but he could not help reflecting that it was a small honour compared to those he should already be holding; the Earldoms of Leicester and Warwick.

Then, quite suddenly, before the inevitable liaison began, he realised that this was not the place to look for a wife. He needed a country-bred girl who did not pine for life at Court but who would attend to Kenilworth in his absence. He immediately packed up his belongings, bade farewell to his mother, with whom he had been staying, gathered up his henchmen and his horses and headed for home.

The leisurely journey back to Warwickshire, stopping with relations, friends and at favourite inns was a pleasure to them all. They rode down lanes awash with wildflowers, the scents and sounds of midsummer a soothing background to the long, exhaustive re-living of their adventures. There were many memories to share with different views on their varied activities but between those who had known each other so long they could speak their minds and with pride, despite the yowls of McElvey. He had survived the battle but he did not appreciate his travelling box nor the movement of Ancient Barrow's horse. He was treated with respect as a veteran and for his work, through thick and thin, aboard an ageing ship full of rats and was given the best they could provide despite the racket he was making.

They reached Kenilworth one perfect summer's evening, as the fading light caught the ephemeral dance of butterflies and moths over the water meadows and the cattle standing with their feet in a gently rising mist. It touched the ancient sandstone of the castle, bathing it with a rosy glow which reflected in the waters of the mere behind it. It seemed older than time and Robert's heart lurched. This was his, as it had been his father's and would, in turn, be his son's. Compared to Leicester's great entourages, their company was a small, but a justly proud one. Robert's stewards stood gathered in the Base Court flanked by a horde of retainers. As they rode in through Leicester's gatehouse, a page let go his two great dogs. They had sensed his coming long before they saw him and raced forward making his horse snort and sidle. Their greeting and that of his household was joyous and unfeigned. News of Cadiz had spread rapidly.

Several days after his arrival, Robert sat talking to a neighbour who had ridden over to dine with him. Sir Thomas Leigh, from nearby Stoneleigh Abbey, three miles distant from Kenilworth, was a rich merchant whose father had been Lord Mayor of London, for which he had been given the estate and a baronetcy. Through his own city contacts, Sir Thomas had been one of the first to hear of the victory at Cadiz and of Robert's knighthood and had immediately come over to congratulate him. He was a dark, ambitious man who knew on which side his bread should be buttered. He had rushed to the assistance of Fulke Greville when Lettice attempted to retain Kenilworth castle after a very young Dudley had inherited it. Swords had been drawn and Robert had always been grateful to him. Sir Thomas was the father of a family which included several pretty daughters and he had allowed himself a little hopeful speculation on their future both before and after the death of Margaret.

The two sat in a comparatively small room between Leicester's Building and the entrance to the Inner Court. Formerly an antechamber, it had been taken over and converted by Robert to house all his own personal gadgets and inventions, and the books of reference pertaining to his own particular interests. It was known as "Sir Robert Dudley's Lobby". The vast library, containing books from the mists of time, had been founded by John of Gaunt and was situated some distance away. This room was bright and well-lit, facing, on one side, the Inner Court round which the castle buildings, from every age, were ranged. On the other side, it faced the larger Base Court and, at a distance, the new Stable Block, built by Leicester. The two were drinking some of Leicester's excellent wine which had survived the depredations of Lettice, though many valuable artefacts had not.

Sir Thomas was surprised and delighted when Robert suddenly leant forward and asked him bluntly whether any of his daughters were in a position to consider marriage. It is not often in life that a pipe-dream becomes instant reality. He had just been wondering how to bring the conversation round to domestic matters when the plum was dropped straight in his lap. He prevaricated a little because he did not want to appear too eager, but it was not long before the virtues of his daughters, their piety and their beauty, came out in a fulsome rush. There were two of marriageable age, Catherine and Alice, aged nineteen and almost eighteen. He could offer a well-educated bride who had been brought up to the management of large houses and would have no trouble taking her place in Warwickshire society or at Court. Catherine had been offered for but was not yet bespoken. Sir Robert could make his choice freely.

Sir Thomas was well aware that the Warwickshire aristocracy would be lining up their daughters for this son of Leicester as he was sure others had in London and he had had ample time to consider what he could offer Robert by way of incentive. His daughter would have a very generous dowry, followed by a large settlement on his own death. He was also aware of Robert's plans for a second voyage and he now proposed a donation to fund this. He had some idea of the costs involved; they would be enormous. In turn, Robert proposed that he should effect a jointure in favour of his wife on the Kenilworth timber, valued at around £20,000. The basic settlements for a marriage were then amicably discussed and agreed in principle, a second bottle of wine broached, and Robert was invited to ride over to Stoneleigh whenever he wished.

He did this about a week later, with considerably more composure than his hosts. He was as aware as Sir Thomas of his own worth and that he was in a position to choose a bride from almost any family in the land. This marriage would be very much on his terms and he had allowed just enough steel into the negotiations for Sir Thomas to realise it. Although this was primarily a business arrangement, a great deal would, of course, depend on the girl herself. The idea of marrying a near neighbour's daughter had been thoroughly turned over in Robert's mind on the slow meander home. There had been ample time to consider and, like all his conclusions, this one had been acted upon with decisive speed.

On hearing their father's news, the most exciting of their young lives, there had been a certain amount of strife between the sisters. Catherine immediately claimed that, as the elder, and despite the offer she had received, she was entitled to become Lady Dudley and the mistress of Kenilworth. Alice had very different ideas and hers was by far the stronger character. Since childhood, she had dreamed of marrying Robert and all that it entailed. Now was her moment and she was not going to miss it. She was dark, pretty and voluptuous, and very like her father whose ambition she shared. It was a foregone conclusion.

On arrival at Stoneleigh, Robert was met by Sir Thomas, his wife, Lady Catherine, and the three elder Leigh children, Catherine, Alice and John. They had, of course, known Leicester, though not well. He had stayed at the Abbey once after a bad fall from his horse but had been too high in the instep to take friendship further. The civilities over, Robert was given a chance to talk to his own generation. Despite the tension and embarrassment of the occasion, he was able to put them at their ease, gently teasing the girls and laughing with them and discussing hunting with their brother; anything that made them feel they were not up for inspection. And he was successful. An innate courtesy and kindness made him take Catherine's hand and tell her he could not trespass on another man's expectations, or hers, and that he was sorry for any awkwardness he may have caused her. He did not wish her to feel rejected but he had instantly preferred Alice and liked the covert invitation in her dark eyes and the decided tilt to her chin. Having once set eyes on Robert, Alice was now more than ever determined that nothing was going to prevent their marriage. She knew that he wanted sons and she was prepared to supply them by the dozen.

Amid much rejoicing, Robert and Alice announced their betrothal. The wedding was to take place in September, a matter of weeks away. Robert wrote a careful letter to his mother, asking for her blessing and her attendance, and an even more careful letter to the Queen. He well knew how she disliked the marriages of those she favoured; he would let the dust settle before he took Alice to Court. This would be the third time he had gone to her with a request for permission to marry.

He gave Alice, as a pre-nuptial gift, the string of pearls with the ruby clasp he had acquired in Cadiz. The stones were so big and so beautifully wrought that she wore them as a pendant on her breast. Such jewels had not been seen in Warwickshire since the last visit of the Queen.

Having resolved the first of his dilemmas, Robert turned his attention to the second, every bit as near his heart. The planning of the second voyage, at that time destined for the Caribbean, had been well under way when his energies had been deflected by the taking of Cadiz. He had sold the "Roebuck" and the "Leicester" after their battered return to Ireland from Cavendish's fated voyage. They were too old for a further expedition and his objectives had changed direction and were now far more ambitious. He was planning to take his ships round the Cape of Good Hope and across the Indian Ocean. The "Beare" and the "Beare's Whelpe" would be joined by the "Benjamin", at present under construction. The names were blatantly symbolic. The Bear represented Leicester and Warwick, the Whelp and the Benjamin represented himself, carrying their banner, their blood and their hopes to the far corners of the earth. Leicester and Warwick, passionately interested in maritime expansion, had invested huge sums in support of such seamen as Drake, Hawkins, Frobisher and Grenville, whose efforts had created the great seafaring nation that England now was. Robert's first voyage to Trinidad and Guiana, admittedly with the promise of gold, had brought him little but adventure and experience. His aims now were very different. His ships would sail, not for piracy or the finding of mines, but for trade. For years now the Portuguese and Spaniards and, more recently, the Dutch, had been trafficking with the Philippines, India, Burma, Ceylon and Malaya. What Cavendish had seized from the Manila galleons during his first voyage had been acquired by trade.

There had been only one English expedition, led by James Lancaster in 1591, to attempt such a thing and it had come to a bad end with few survivors. The London merchants who had invested in and financed the voyage, had lost heavily and fought shy of repeating the performance. Robert's aim, so far ahead of his time, was to establish a trade route of his own and gain a share of Far Eastern mercantile profit. Better and further still, and planted in his mind by Cavendish, was the lure of the unknown kingdom of Cathay. No other nation had so far succeeded in establishing trade there and Robert was determined to be the first. Travellers' tales told of a vast country full of gold, silk, dragons and shrouding mist.

With his usual ferocious energy, and despite his forthcoming marriage, Robert flung himself headlong into preparations for the coming voyage. The expense of fitting out a fleet of trading vessels for such a huge undertaking was going to be very high. Haklyut wrote that the voyage was undertaken "principally at the charge of the honourable knight, Sir Robert Dudley". Even if some of the charge was met by the proceeds, declared or undeclared, of his share in the spoils of Cadiz, he would be financially stretched. Sir Thomas's contribution might be welcome. He would have to pay for a patent to sail and trade, give an estimate of the profits expected, and the steps towards the granting of his Charter would involve the greasing of many palms, from Cecil upwards and downwards. The intricacies and dishonesties involved in this drove him nearly mad and he was hard put to it not to let the Dudley temper explode into unseemly rage. Those who tried to talk down to him soon discovered their mistake. The breadth of his knowledge was phenomenal by any standard.

He decided that Captain Wood, who had asked to sail with him, should be given the task of finding capable officers, particularly masters, for all three ships, and, in turn, allow them to pick their crews. Some of his veterans from the "Beare" and the "Nonpareil" came forward at once but not many; this was a very different expedition. It was one thing to set sail to attack Spain, part of a huge fleet, with the promise of booty and a quick return, and quite another to sail into the unknown for an unspecified time and with no promises at all; the reputation and records of far-flung journeys from England was not good. Wood might have to scrape the barrel of the maritime world to man his ships. There was also the military to consider. There should be man-power enough to repel Spanish, Portuguese and other corsairs. Sufficient guns and ammunition must also be provided and all vessels should be armed with long and short range cannon.

This being a trading venture, there was also the assembly of suitably saleable goods to consider. Woollen cloth of all kinds, brocades and taffetas, weapons, jewellery, guns, candles, and rope, all to be found and dispatched to the ships. It was a huge leap into the unknown. Cavendish had given advice on barter, but his aims had been piracy, not commerce. Captain Benjamin Wood had managed to persuade two adventurous London merchants to sail with him also, young men who shared Robert's vision. Richard Haklyut, wholly enthusiastic, presented himself, with his wife, at Kenilworth and proved invaluable. He was able to accompany Robert on expeditions to find trading merchandise, possible crew members and victuallers, in all of which fields he was very experienced.

Thomas Chaloner had been knighted by the French King, Henri IV for services in Northern France, one of only four Englishmen. He had then been sent to the Medici court in Tuscany by Essex on a mixed mission, including espionage, and was later to be transferred to France to report on the Edict of Nantes. He had, nevertheless, found time to advise on the construction of the new ship "Benjamin". His career was expanding rapidly but he remained in touch with Robert.

With all this frantic foraging and organisation, Robert was spending little time at home nor giving much attention to his forthcoming wedding. Hardly admitted, even to himself, was the question of whether he would be allowed to sail with his ships at all. It was only two years since he had been refused permission to accompany Cavendish, mercifully as it had transpired, and this latest venture was a far more personal affair. The conception, direction, aims and aspirations were his, as they had been on the West Indies run. He hoped he might escape the Queen's ageing eye this time, but even if he did, there were other problems to be faced.

He would be leaving a young and, hopefully, pregnant bride to manage Kenilworth. Her father would be only too pleased to step in and take over the castle on her behalf, but Robert had already sensed possible encroachment from that quarter and would have to make sure his chief steward was capable of dealing with it. It was always a possibility that his luck would run out and that he would not come back from this voyage. What then? Trustees would have to be appointed for an infant son with endless complications following. He lived from day to day, cramming each one with frantic activity while his mind leapt on to the next complex issue.

None of these possibilities had escaped Sir Thomas Leigh either. With permission, he was proposing to put his shoulder into proving Robert's legitimacy. As the trusted father-in-law of the Earl of Leicester, he would be in a powerful position both in the county and the country and a baronetcy might well be improved upon. Alice had made it clear that she would dearly love to be a Countess. She did not, however, relish being left a matter of months after her marriage with no idea of when her husband would reappear.

Not unnaturally, she could not understand Robert's gyrations, what drove him, or why he felt it necessary to travel to the ends of the earth. He had Kenilworth and he would shortly have a wife and a large family; what more could he possibly want? She barely knew him and little did she realise what kind of a tiger she had by the tail. He was charming and generous to her, made arrangements for her chaplain to be housed at Kenilworth, (she was deeply religious; well aware of how a black lace mantilla became her) and had apartments made ready for her own use besides those they would share. These would be within Leicester's Building, the most modern, grand and beautifully furnished in all the castle complex, though even they were more than twenty years old.

They were married on 11th September 1596, in the little church of Ashow, Lady Douglas and Sir Edward Stafford attending the wedding and Robert managing to put aside all business connected with the voyage for at least ten days. They gave a wedding feast for everyone employed by or connected with Kenilworth a few days later, introducing Alice to all Robert's people. This was a great success, no expense being spared, and several, including Ancient Barrow, having to be escorted off the premises in a state of total disrepair. It was a very proper feast, varied, lavish and prolonged. Leicester's massive entertainment of the Queen in July 1575 was recalled with fond nostalgia and it was agreed that his son had started on the right lines. Alice, looking demure and enchanting, rose to the occasion and was heartily approved by all. She and her family were no strangers to most present, excepting Robert's own friends who had made the journey, and a positive bombardment of his relations.

The following day, a joust was held for the entertainment of the guests in the long tiltyard which formed a bridge from the meadows beyond the mere to an entrance to the Base Court through the Mortimer Tower. It had been enlarged by Leicester and improved by Robert and it made an impressive setting for a favourite sport, water glimmering on either side of the ancient stone and great tubs of flowers blazing against it in the September sun. As the host, Robert made sure he did not outshine his guests and he kept his own appearances to a minimum. However, his skill was, by now, so well-known that Alice, suitably seated in a place of honour, could safely bask in reflected glory even before she saw him in action, and that fairly took her breath away. Taught by his godfather, Sir Henry Lee, the Queen's Champion, during the times he had stayed with him as a boy, and polished by Essex and Cumberland, there were few who could hold a candle to him, young though he still was. He bestrode a plunging charger as if he were a part of it and made the heavy lance appear a matchstick. There was a hell-bent accuracy in his fighting and a precise skill that even Alice, who had never before watched a joust, could recognise.

Meanwhile, at Court, the bubble of rejoicing and congratulation following the taking of Cadiz had long since burst. Reality had swept in and repercussions were felt, even in Warwickshire. The Queen was now aware of how narrowly the Spanish Fleet had been missed, the figures had been totalled on the gains of the voyage, or lack of them, and the full extent of what had been purloined by, or distributed among, the heroes of Cadiz could now be guessed at. A spectacular row was brewing. Essex was publicly vilified, the new fashion he had set with his square "Cadiz" beard ridiculed, and Her Majesty's fury at the number of those knighted was white-hot and taken as a personal insult. Being a woman, she could not knight her subjects for their courage on the field of battle, but the prerogative was hers and had been imposed upon.

The common people of England took a different view. Essex was a hero; he had more than "singed" the King of Spain's beard, he had taken and razed a Spanish city and, in their opinion, had deflected a second armada. A sermon of thanksgiving, preached at St. Paul's Cross by the Archbishop of Canterbury, John Whitgift, praised Essex and his companions to the skies, hailed them as England's saviours and criticized their detractors. The old Queen had never been less popular and was obliged to tone down her anger. All she could do was to state that as the proceeds of the expedition had been so mishandled, she proposed to appropriate, for herself, every penny gained from the hostages taken in Cadiz. This would be a considerable sum.

As a Vice Admiral of the expedition, Robert was well out of the maelstrom going on in London though even his uncle, the Lord Admiral, came in for his share of blame. Despite the charms of his young bride, he continued to roam the country, furiously hunting down material and men for his expedition and with frequent visits to Southampton to check progress being made on the ships. He avoided London for the time being, though Alice was longing to see and to be seen at Court.

In October 1596, and contrary to popular expectation, King Philip of Spain gathered the scattered fleet that had survived the English raids and sailed down the Tagus to attack England. It was the month of storms and his commanders went down on their knees begging him to wait. Warning reached London in November via a group of captured Portuguese and everything was forgotten but defence. There was no time to gather a fleet and man it as in 1588. Troops were marched to the four most likely landing places, and, if they failed to hold their positions, plans were in place for a "scorched earth" welcome for the invaders. Essex was put in charge of a Council of War and quickly climbed back on his pedestal. Men shouldered arms once more and waited grimly for what might come.

Robert, who happened to be in Southampton when the first news broke, could not resist boarding a reconnaissance vessel and putting out into what was already a very rough Channel. They patrolled the western half for ten days, saw nothing but English sails on the same mission and returned to report no sign of Spanish shipping. Greatly refreshed by this expedition, Robert went on to London where he found furious activity, much rolling up of sleeves and Essex very much in command. He offered his services in any capacity, though preferably at sea, sent a message to Kenilworth that his return would be delayed and remained, hopefully, in Essex House to await what action followed. None did, and the weeks slipped by in a strange, expectant lull.

During this time, Robert received the Queen's Commission for his expedition to sail at the end of the year. He was sent for and, his heart in his mouth, appeared before her and in front of quite a crowd of the curious and more adventurous members of the Court. Despite the tense situation and daily expectation of the next armada, there was considerable interest in plans for his voyage. These were not generally known except among his greatest friends and he had learnt that silence could be golden until preparations were complete. The hopes of the expedition were attested by a letter, in Latin, to be carried in the flagship. It was headed: "A Gracious Commendation by Her Majesty to the Great Emperor of China." The Queen's interest had been aroused despite the current danger to her realm; what the Chinese Emperor would make of the Latin remained a mystery.

Then the blow fell. Sir Robert Dudley was not to sail with his ships. He might shortly be needed to sail in defence of his own country. He was newly married, needed heirs, and should not leave his wife so soon. He was forbidden to go. The Queen had, once again, refused to give his freedom to all that remained to her of Leicester.

By the beginning of December, news filtered through from reliable sources that the latest armada, as predicted by its Commanders, had been caught by huge storms in the Bay of Biscay, fragmented and sent packing to home ports. The "Protestant Wind" had done its work again. Amid great relief, the English defence forces stood down and dispersed for Christmas.

A week later, standing on the foreshore with a heart of lead, Robert Dudley watched his little fleet sail out of Southampton under the command of Benjamin Wood. Nothing had prepared him for this; after all the frantic work and planning to see the sails fill and tilt and the bows begin to cream through the dark grey water was one of the bleakest moments of his young life. So much of his vibrant person went with those ships, so many dreams drifted into specks as he watched, his eyes narrowing to slits, until the last sail vanished into the grey murk. He remained there for a long, bitter time seeing the ships in his mind's eye, hearing the creaking of stout rope, the whack of sails and tasting the salt spray on his lips. Stiff and tired, he turned at last, retrieved his horse and rode sombrely north, William Bradshaw a few paces behind him.

They reached Kenilworth on a cold Christmas Eve to find the place alive and bustling. From miles away, across the water meadows, they could see a blaze of light in the distance, like a small town. Riding in from the dark, through the Gatehouse, was like stepping onto a stage. Flares and braziers reflected light sparkling on the frosty ground and a deep bell boomed from far within the castle. People poured out to meet them and hot, spiced wine, the cup of welcome, was handed up before they had time to dismount. The Stewards, under Alice's direction, had had the main rooms of residence hung with evergreens, huge fires blazed in every chamber and the whole place was lit with thousands of branched candlesticks and sconces. Music and voices singing rang out into the cold night. Guests, friends and family gathered to greet Robert. They had little idea when he would arrive, but he had been daily expected and their warmth did much to thaw the ice in his soul. Alice, round and excited, came running down the great stairs, curtsied and flung herself into his arms. She was big with news, and something else. An heir for Kenilworth was on the way.

CHAPTER EIGHT

Winds of Change 1599 – 1602

The month of March 1599 was coming in like a lion and it was a wild day. A northerly wind careered through the tree tops, some still bare and some downy with bud, and set them writhing and roaring in the blasts. Clouds scudded and chased each other across a pale blue sky, bringing spring sunshine one moment and a lowering greyness the next. Small daffodils bobbed and danced in field and woodland and the blackthorn was almost in flower. It was best to keep moving and that was not difficult for those hunting through Kenilworth's great Chase. Blasts of wind got under the tails of the horses making them sidle and stamp and those on foot found it hard to keep pace with them.

Men alone were involved in the hunt this day; they were after boar which meant it was *"par force"*. The weapons would be swords or long spears and the kill or *"mort"* would be a dangerous business and very likely done on foot. They had left their most highly bred and prized horses in the stables and, for the chase, most rode tried and tested veterans, steady enough to stand a charge without bolting. The scent hounds, the lymers, had done their work well early in the morning. A large boar had been located and report brought to Robert Dudley at the assembly, or breakfast party, held in a pavilion just across the long bridge which crossed the mere's water to the Chase. There was nothing frugal about this meal; it was a sustaining feast designed to keep the huntsmen going all day. Meat, hot and cold, pasties, bread, fruit, sweetmeats and mulled wine poured out of the pavilion kitchen in a steady stream, their huge consumption showing how young men could eat on a cold day.

Robert then decided the course of the hunt and sent relays of the heavier "sight" dogs, with their handlers, to positions on the route the beast was expected to take. He would not risk his own two dogs for this kind of work. They would almost certainly be the first to attack and no handler would be able to hold them. He had left them fuming and whining in kennels.

He ordered the huntsman to sound the Chase on his horn. To shouts of "The hunt is up", the company drained their cups and rushed for their horses, mounted and followed the "scent hounds", beagle types who would do the tracking.

One of the most exciting moments of the chase was always the first sighting of the quarry. This boar was huge, a solid mass, heavy as a horse, bad tempered and old. Its razor-sharp tusks curled upward from its snout almost to its eyes, and it was most unwilling to be roused or "unharboured". Once on the move, however, it showed quite a turn of foot, frequently going to ground in dense cover and refusing to budge. This gave the sight hounds and their handlers a chance to come up with the horsemen, to try and flush it out. It would then erupt, squealing and aggressive, before taking off again, usually through the thickest undergrowth. It took them most of the day to wear it down.

Eventually, late in the afternoon, the boar took up a position in a hollow surrounded by swampy ground and close to the edge of the mere. From the point of view of the huntsmen, this was not ideal. They and their horses could get bogged down and although the boar, unlikely to swim, was trapped, it was still in a position to do damage if provoked. It lay, partly hidden, in rushy cover; they could see the heaving flanks and hear the hoarse, grunty breathing.

Robert gave orders that all hounds should be leashed; it was their instinct to try and take the animal down when cornered, his own would have been the first to do so, and this beast was far from finished. There would be savage injuries if they rushed it. This stage of the hunt was known as "the baying" when the animal was trapped and exhausted and what was to follow could be dangerous and difficult work. Robert, as the host, would normally have taken matters into his own hands, but George Cumberland, his guest of honour, demanded that he be allowed first chance. He jokingly added that if he failed, Robert had better pick up the pieces and finish the job.

They both dismounted, giving their horses to grooms, and took from the huntsmen who carried them the long-handled, razor-sharp spears. These had cross pieces above the blade designed to keep the animal from running up the haft when stuck. They were not as heavy as a jousting lance, but infinitely sharper – the hide of a boar was notoriously tough.

George advanced, a little ahead of Robert, and yelled at the quarry.

There was a commotion and it charged a short way out of the hollow; they could see the little red eyes, smell the rasping breath and realised that this boar was not only massive, but still very mobile. Grunting, but thoroughly alarmed, it retreated into the rushes and settled back into the mud. They could only follow it, hoping that they would not get mired and so unable to move. They were now within yards of it and George, still on firm ground, flung the first spear into the beast's flank with all his strength. The boar, squealing horribly, charged straight at him in a fury, determined to settle the score, and Robert, carrying the second spear, flung it at its head, near the eye. He was lucky; it must have gone straight into the brain. Still in mid-charge, the boar's knees buckled though its momentum carried it forward, knocking Robert off his feet. Leaping up, he managed to grab the end of his spear and put his full weight behind it, up to the cross piece, slowing the animal to a halt, while George ran forward and, drawing his sword, stuck it up to the hilt in the boar's chest. Robert dropped the haft of the spear, and did the same, but into its throat, and that was that. Death followed in moments, the huntsman *"blowing the mort"* in triumph on his horn. The kill had been comparatively clean, without injury to men, horses or dogs, conducted in an honourable way, and with a huge beast to distribute.

As was customary, amid draughts of ale and wine brought up from the rear, and a lot of cheering and laughter, each member of the hunt was blooded; a smear of boar's blood on the face. This was followed by the giving of a portion of flesh to every dog involved, a practice known as the *"curee"*, beginning with the scent hounds, the lymers, then the beagles and finally the sight hounds who had not taken so large a part in proceedings. The rest of the carcase was then butchered and distributed, every person receiving a piece and some large cuts reserved for the castle kitchens.

This all took time and, at last, as the sun was beginning to sink into the scudding clouds, they turned for home, tired and stiff, but in tearing spirits. It had been one of many such hunting days, energetic, carefully contrived and immensely enjoyable.

Leicester had enlarged the Chase, the castle's own hunting grounds, by means of negotiation, mostly amicable, with his neighbours, and Robert had followed suit. If he was to be denied his voyage and obliged to spend more time at Kenilworth, he would make the hunting something out of the ordinary. Once more, he had approached those whose land marched with his and persuaded them to disgorge further acres, at a price, for the Chase. Among them was Sir John Throckmorton, from whom he had bought the Manor of Ladbrooke in 1598. The Chase now consisted of some 800 acres and was reached, from the castle, by the long bridge constructed from Leicester's Gatehouse entrance over the mere and directly into the hunting grounds. The Chase was also good ground for shooting parties. Robert had tramped over most of it since childhood, often in the company of Ancient Barrow, who had taught him much lore regarding game-birds, their rearing, feeding and habits. From this knowledge he had learnt the best way of driving them over guns and methods of handling the dogs who accompanied him. Some of his spaniels were firmly taught to sit until told to retrieve no matter what fell around them while others were trained to sweep towards huntsmen, driving the birds over them.

This evening, lit by an unexpected sunset which set fire to the low-flying clouds and left a rain-washed sky to turn slowly from rose to deep blue over their heads, they rode into the Base Court, dismounted, handed their horses to the grooms and entered the castle.

As Robert moved with his guests into the hall of Leicester's Building, he saw William Bradshaw coming quietly towards him. The look on his face would not have caused anyone but Robert to pause. He knew William too well to ignore it and turned to him at once to ask his news. The very slight jerk of the head informed him that it was important and private. Smiling, Robert excused himself and the two withdrew into Sir Robert's Lobby, his sanctum.

The news was bad. There had been a massacre of the Queen's troops in Ireland, on the Blackwater river. Two thousand men were dead, ambushed at Yellow Ford by the Earl of Tyrone. Ireland, like a torch, had gone up in flames, and Tyrone was pushing hard to gain control of the whole country. The savagery was appalling, even for the Irish, and Essex, who was in deep disgrace yet again, had been reluctantly recalled and was on his way to Ireland, accompanied by Fulke Greville, Mountjoy, Blount, de Burgh and a group of thoroughly irresponsible young lordlings. It was not a pleasant story but Essex was on top of the world, parading his troops through London with crowds lining the streets for miles, cheering him on. He was still regarded by most as a hero.

Robert stood very still, looking straight through William Bradshaw, while his mind followed Essex to Wales and across the turbulent Irish

Sea to turbulent Ireland. Should he go with horses and men to join his stepbrother in Dublin? Was permission needed from the Queen? His grey eyes fixed on far images and his mind racing, he began to line up what facts he had, whilst trying to prevent his personal feeling ruling his head. Essex had not called on him which was hardly surprising since the need for action had been so immediate. Had he done so, Robert would certainly have gone despite the fact that Ireland was the one battleground in which he wanted no part. It was, and always had been, running, dirty, guerrilla warfare against a people regarded by England as sub-human, and, worse, Catholic to a man. Atrocities on both sides were endemic. As a child, he had absorbed sufficient horror stories from Richard Clanricarde to have mentally crippled one of a later age, but Elizabethan children were not shielded from reality and many regarded an execution as a high treat. But who could forget the massacre of six hundred women and children hidden on Raithlin Island in July 1575, hunted like otters from the sea caves by none other than Sir John Norris, whilst their chieftain, the yellow-haired Surley Boy, was forced to watch from a hilltop on the mainland. Robert's ideas of chivalry made Ireland somewhere he did not wish to fight.

His own father, at that very time, was splurging recklessly on the Queen's entertainment at Kenilworth in a last attempt at marriage with her, while his mother was obliged to look on and his mistress and future wife bided her time.

Also lurking at the back of his mind, was the unwelcome thought that Essex's judgement and behaviour was becoming irrational. The ill-fated and muddled "Islands Voyage", yet another expensive failure, and his recent appalling behaviour at Court were not reassuring. The Queen had slapped his face during an argument and he had partly drawn his sword and turned his back on her which did not suggest a balanced mind. To draw steel against the Monarch was treasonable and Essex had been lucky to escape the Tower. After banishment and much furious sulking, only the posting to Ireland had resolved that contretemps. He appeared, at times, to be beyond reason. Robert was devoted to him, as he always had been, but his loyalties were now spread among many and could become divided. He would go to Dublin if urgently needed and this was the message sent with the small troop who had brought the news.

The years since 1596 had not been the most fulfilling or active of Robert Dudley's life. Baulked, after all his efforts, of his ambition to sail with his fleet to China and the Far East, his attention turned to two necessities; the proving of his own legitimacy and the begetting of heirs.

In the first of these he had the unstinting help of his father-in-law, Sir Thomas and, with the second, the enthusiastic cooperation of Alice.

Their first child, a girl, was baptised on 25th September 1597, almost exactly a year after their marriage. She was christened Alicia Douglassia in the chapel at Kenilworth and, for the next eight years, daughters continued to appear like clockwork almost every twelvemonth. Each time the disappointment was intense and Robert took to riding out for long hours, with only his dogs for company, whenever Alice was confined. The poor girl was almost constantly in a state of expectation, accompanied sometimes by tears and recriminations. She had never doubted her ability to produce sons or that Robert would, one day, become the legitimate Earl of Leicester. She passionately wished to strut upon the aristocratic stage, but what was the point unless she could produce an heir?

Robert had taken Alice to his mother in London and presented her to the Queen at Court. Her Majesty had been cursorily approving, her mind being much occupied with the "Islands Voyage" and yet another threatened invasion by Spain. This glimpse of Court life, however, and introductions to the highest in the land had given Alice an idea of what a great lady she might become as Robert's wife. She had been regarded with avid interest and had revelled in it. She had seen for herself that Robert's standing at Court was high, that he had the Queen's approval and that he was welcomed by most as a leading light and deferred to by many. She did not meet Lettice, still firmly barred from Court, but it was not lost on her that there was already one calling herself the Countess of Leicester and one that it would be hard to supplant.

Alice was also taken to see the house recently re-furbished by Robert in St.Giles-in-the-Fields. It had belonged to his grandfather, the Duke of Northumberland, and, in turn, to Leicester, but not until now had he felt the need for it. With a growing family, a base in London was essential, and Alice took an instant liking to the place, at once beginning to make plans for its decoration and its garden. It truly did stand in the fields, well away from the cramped and sometimes squalid conditions of London, but close to the village and church.

Although her father had been born a commoner and was conscious of the deep divide between the aristocratic and the plebeian, Alice was, through her mother, a distant cousin of the Duke of Sutherland, and considered herself to belong rightly in high circles. Sir Thomas was particularly anxious to see the divide bridged and was brutally blunt with his daughter on the subject of the Dudley propensity for shifting wives or husbands if things were not going their way. Alice genuinely loved and admired Robert as he was, but had he been a commoner with no Kenilworth, she would not have looked twice in his direction. Ambition kept her focused and her father likewise. She managed the domestic side of the castle, through stewards and housekeepers, extremely well and could always call on her mother, Lady Catherine, for help. She was not much given to physical exercise and, with constant childbearing, voluptuous roundness would become stoutness. Most ladies of her age and station rode incessantly, despite pregnancy, but she preferred a more sedentary way of life and a carriage to a horse. She liked pottering in the gardens, directing the gardeners; she spent long hours at prayer with her chaplain in the small chapel Robert had furnished near her own apartments, and she quickly acquired a reputation for piety. To Robert's mind, she was becoming unnecessarily devout and he detested the chaplain. This gentleman was small and plump with a determined smile and a habit of appearing when least wanted with a stream of sententious platitudes lacking either wit or point.

But, despite the sanctity, the longed-for son refused to appear.

Robert's genuine delight in women was as marked as ever and, at this stage of his life, it was unlikely that only one, a constantly pregnant wife, would keep him happy. He loved the chase, whether it was of beauties or beasts. While in London these small affaires were never a problem, but at Kenilworth, playing away from home was more difficult. He was a most attractive man with an aura of magnificence and a presence that made him hard for any woman to resist. He had a wicked sense of humour and a quick wit but he did not force himself on the object of his attentions; it was seldom necessary. He was as much at home in the bushes as the boudoir and his laughing sensuality made him an irresistible lover for any girl; he was as keen to delight as to be delighted. If by-blows resulted from his liaisons, he was generous in their protection. Several of the next generation at Kenilworth looked remarkably like him. Alice may have suspected but was too self-absorbed to probe or to worry. Lady Dudley was surely destined to become a Countess; little did she know how far her wildest dreams were to be exceeded.

Meanwhile, Sir Thomas was busily doing a great deal of background work on Robert's origins and the validity of Leicester's marriage to his mother. This was not easy because Lady Douglas was happy in her marriage to Stafford and, however much she would have liked to see Robert succeed his father, she did not want to rake over old coals. Her life was ordered and settled; she spent many hours in attendance on her cousin, the Queen, and she lacked for nothing. It was an imponderable problem because, if Robert were to be proved legitimate, she would have to admit that her marriage to Stafford was bigamous, as would be Lettice's marriage to Leicester. Lettice had no such purpose and was, in any case, still calling herself Countess of Leicester despite her seven-year marriage to Sir Christopher Blount. The Earl had dug a very deep hole for all three of them, Robert, Douglas and Lettice. There had to be at least one loser, if not two.

Robert, himself, was equally interested in the details of his birth. The Queen was ageing and the impetuous excitement of her early reign was slowing down; vigour and imperiousness were dwindling, though Essex did his best to prolong them with his ventures; perhaps the temper of her people was growing more humdrum. Those who had been behind her in the creation of a new and powerful England were gone. Her beloved and trusted councillor, Burleigh, had died, succeeded by his brilliant, crippled son, Robert Cecil. Also dead were Sir Christopher Hatton, Sir Francis Walsingham and many of Robert's relations including Sir William Howard, the Countess of Hertford, Lady Mary Dudley and Lady Catherine Howard who had served the Queen all her life. A chill wind was blowing. The rip-roaring adventures, when riches followed piracy, were fewer, succeeded by something more staid. Would the eye of the Queen's successor light upon Kenilworth, a semi-royal palace, and, knowing it belonged to an illegitimate knight only, purloin it for his own or for a favourite's use? This was how Robert's grandfather had acquired it. He was as anxious as Sir Thomas to prove his legitimacy; it would be much more difficult to dislodge a belted and established Earl from his home of three generations.

Meanwhile, events in Ireland had moved with horrible speed. Essex failed to subdue the Earl of Tyrone, whether by battle or by bargaining, and, after only six months in the field, deserted his army and raced back to the Queen with a few close comrades, in an attempt to convince her that it was no failure but a selfless act on his part. However, once assured that he was not about to bring the army back to threaten the Crown, she promptly locked him up in York House under the care of Lord Egerton. No one, not even the long-suffering Countess who had just given birth to a daughter, was allowed near him. His case was to be heard in Star Chamber and Mountjoy was given command of the troops in Ireland. Essex's future began to look very uncertain. He became so ill that no trial could be held and he was not freed for a further eleven months after a hearing lasting twelve hours. He then retired from London, stripped of all his offices and with ruin staring him in the face.

One of Robert's main concerns was, of course, the fate of his small fleet of ships bound for the East. Nothing had been seen or heard of them, either from friendly shipping or from any other source. Haklyut, almost as interested as Robert, wrote to him in 1599:

"We have heard no certain news of them since February 1597. The ships, we do suppose, may have arrived upon some part of the coast of China, and maybe there stayed by the Emperor, or perhaps may have some treachery wrought against them by the Portuguese of Macassa or the Spaniards of the Philippines".

The fleet was never to return. Robert's dreams, vanishing into the murk of the Channel that winter's day in 1596, were never realised. It was not until after 1601 that he discovered, in part, what had befallen them. He could never have learnt the full story because it was not until three centuries later that it was pieced together from scraps written in Dutch, Portuguese and Spanish. Sad enough that he never saw his ships and men again, but worse, perhaps, if he had known the whole truth. What he did hear was bizarre enough.

A Dutch ship, short of water, stopped in Mauritius to take on supplies. They were hailed by a French castaway, a soldier, who turned out to be the sole survivor from the three ships. This news came to Robert in 1601, but he was never able to trace the man or to obtain anything like a first-hand report: that was all he ever discovered.

What emerged, much later and after years of research, was that the ships were in trouble rounding the Cape of Good Hope, the "Benjamin" was lost, with all hands, in a storm, and the other two were attacked by Portuguese ships off Mozambique. They crossed the Indian Ocean to Ceylon and India where they captured and plundered two Portuguese merchant ships. They then continued to the Malacca Straits, arriving in January 1598, and were again attacked by a fleet of six Portuguese vessels which they fought off for eight days, withdrawing only when the gunpowder store aboard the "Beare" exploded. The crews of the two ships were now so depleted, with many sick and wounded, that they burned the "Beare's Whelp" off the Malayan coast, near Kedah, taking the remains of her crew aboard. Disease, also, was taking a terrible toll, to the extent that the "Beare" also could no longer be manned, probably because Wood and his officers had succumbed. The ship, badly damaged by the explosion of gunpowder, went aground and the seven survivors, with real heroism, made the journey across the Indian Ocean to Mauritius in a native canoe. Of these, the Frenchman was the only one left standing. It was an epic but tragic story and, of all people, Benjamin Wood should have been the survivor. He had risked so much in the Orinoco delta on Robert's behalf and brought his men back to safety in Trinidad.

October 1600 was a golden month, the summer holding for weeks of hot, hazy days and the leaves barely beginning to turn. Cattle and horses had a sheen on their well-plumped hides and the children a gilded gloss on hair, face and skin. Harvest had been late but spectacularly good; trees dripped with apples, pears, plums and gages. The barns and storehouses were bulging with the fruits of earth and tree and there was a rounded look of content on the faces of husbandmen, farmers and manor lords. The mornings were misty and the evenings cooler, but the days were bright as midsummer.

Robert was now the father of three daughters with a fourth child on the way and Kenilworth had acquired what it had lacked since Henry V and his many brothers and sisters had been brought up there; an aura of homeliness. He had just returned from London and he was always particularly aware of it when he had been away. Rather than serried ranks of stewards and servants, a swarm of small children and dogs poured out to greet him, his own and other people's; children generated other children and there were cousins, friends' offspring and a host of castle young who had never formerly appeared. Gone was the rigid grandeur of Leicester's day.

He had recently been on a quest for his lost fleet. He had combed every likely source for news, from greatest to least. These enquiries had even taken him to Raleigh's establishment, Durham House, on the Strand, which had formerly belonged to his own grandfather, Northumberland. Raleigh had suffered several years in the cold for his marriage to Bess Throckmorton, a maid of honour to the Queen whose pregnancy had not been well received and which had been the cause of a visit to the Tower, disgrace, and a cancellation of many privileges. Raleigh was not one to lie down under adversity, however, and was now restored to both the magnificence of Durham House and his position as Captain of the Guard. He either could not, or would not, give Robert any news of his ships and was clearly delighted by the downfall of Essex. They did not part the best of friends. Raleigh's efforts to patronise Robert were met with the cold indifference and hauteur of an aristocrat dealing with an inferior. Basically, they were, despite their differing backgrounds, remarkably alike in character; clever, courageous opportunists who would push their luck with no regard for danger.

The humming throng from every sphere of society to be found at Essex House, despite the absence of the Earl, could not yield any information either.

Robert then took a barge down to visit Essex himself at Barn Elms, a manor belonging to the Countess, which nestled in the big bend of the river near the village of Barnes. He was shocked to the core by the sight of his stepbrother. His height exaggerated by the loss of weight and muscle he had suffered during his imprisonment and illness, he was a wreck of the man Robert knew so well. Gaunt, grey and angry, he was politically and financially ruined. The grant on the Farm of Sweet Wines that had kept him in pocket for the past ten years, had just been revoked and his wife, Frances, was being forced to sell jewelry, pictures, property and carriages. His sisters, Penelope Rich, the mistress of Mountjoy, and Dorothy, Countess of Northumberland, were staying in the house with their children and exhorting him to work himself back to Court and into the Queen's favour. Though they both adored him, they were suffering the lack of privileges he had always been so generous in obtaining for them and both were vocal and outspoken on the subject. He had, for years, been the ticket to their success.

Robert tweaked the sleeve of Essex's doublet, firmly took his arm and marched him out to the serenity of the knot garden behind the house, where they could be private. There, among the sweet-scented flowering expanse, he demanded to know the full sum of Essex's troubles, financial and otherwise, what his plans were and how he could help him. The boot was now on the younger man's foot.

It all came pouring out; grievances against the Queen, the Cecils, the Howards, Raleigh and now Mountjoy, who, because of his position in Ireland, could not, or would not, any longer support him. Also, anger against James VI in Scotland, with whom he had been corresponding as the expected heir to the throne of England. The King would not commit himself in any way and Essex wanted assurances as to his position in the event of the Queen's death, and the chance to become his right hand man in a new monarchy. It was wild, dangerous talk, interspersed with vague threats smacking of insurrection and treason. Essex was clearly being urged on by the Devereux family, his stewards and advisors, and a lot of hot-headed young bloods such as Southampton, Rutland and his stepfather, Sir Christopher Blount, all now returned from Ireland. He sounded vengeful and poised for action even while the Queen still lived.

Robert listened in silence to the flood of invective and bitterness, aware that the man was not himself and, with deep regret, that he might never be again. He at once guaranteed specified drafts for money to be drawn from his own bankers by Essex and the Countess, but not for the benefit of the Devereux family as a whole; the other stipulation being that these funds were never to be used for anything other than their immediate, personal needs. He was not going to advance money for the raising of armies or supply of arms, either against the Queen or for the future King James. With gathering sadness, he had realised that he could no longer trust this man who had been brother, friend and mentor all his life. Failure was not anything Essex had ever contemplated and his anger was beginning to sound dangerous.

As he left, Robert also told the Countess what arrangements he would make for their help, kissed her small, anxious face with deep affection and wished her joy of the child she was carrying. Privately, he did not think there was going to be much joy, but her large, luminous eyes spoke her gratitude.

On his return to London, Robert proceeded to search through the dangerous and, sometimes, disgusting stews, taverns and inns along the south bank of the river, particularly those frequented by seamen and, often, their ships' officers. He was well-known in several of these, including the whore-houses of his youth where he was given warm welcome. He scooped one well-remembered Madame off his knee, sat her down with a glass of ale and asked her to search her excellent memory for any story told, boast made, or rumour she might have overheard concerning his fleet. After much fond reminiscence, she called over a hoary old captain drinking in a corner, who swore he had seen the ships at Capo Blanco, bound for the Cape. Robert could not be sure that the clink of coins had not revived his memory, and he continued to spread the enquiry for his ships to every corner of this insalubrious quarter of London, asking that any news be sent to Dudley House where reward would be waiting. The maritime bush-telegraph was usually sharp. A ship's cook had seen the three ships off the coast of Portugal and one seaman had spotted them between Ascension Island and the African coast. After that, the trail went cold. It was not for another year that he was to hear of the lone survivor.

Having spread word through the docks, the taverns, Thames boatmen and any other likely source in the area, Robert returned to Warwickshire, heavy of heart.

He found Alice recently delivered of yet another daughter and, having kissed his wife and the small dark scrap in her arms, he retired, with his two great dogs and a bottle of his father's wine, to his "Lobby" to consider, in depth, his future movements.

He was more concerned than he would care to admit about the situation Essex appeared to be creating. It could not be ignored and, as with Ireland, only loyalty would involve him with it. He decided to visit him again in the New Year and hope for a less turbulent mood.

In the meantime, he would continue to search the sequence of events and the circumstances that had led to his birth, and to pick up any threads that might lead to an uncovering of the true facts. The scent had faded; he was now twenty-six years old and his mother's memory was becoming blurred. He was in no doubt that he was Leicester's true born son and had discovered from Lady Douglas, on this last visit, one or two overlooked facts which she had unwillingly dredged up.

Sir Edward Stafford wanted no aspersions cast on his wife and had become quite hostile at Robert's insistent questioning. He would have much preferred to see the whole matter dropped and the past left to itself. He knew, from Douglas's tearful recollections, that she had considered herself truly married to Leicester, a Countess, and with a legitimate son. She had consented to marry him only because Leicester had assured her that she was none of those things, and a combination of threats and cajoling had persuaded her to start life again with a man who loved her rather than hang on to one who had plainly tired of her. She had been prepared to forfeit her son's birthright and his place in the world in order to be comfortable; also, to convince herself that Leicester was right, that they had not been married, and therefore there was no case of bigamy to answer. What she, herself, felt about the matter would emerge later. The whole affair had been pushed firmly under the carpet and both she and Sir Edward were most unwilling to see it dragged out again. Neither had bargained for the force of Robert's will or the ruthless determination which drove him; there would be trouble ahead. This was only the beginning.

What Robert gleaned from his mother, on this visit, was that a certain Owen Jones, a long-time servant of Leicester, had reported to her a conversation with his master which occurred during one of Leicester's frequent visits to his small son. In an unguarded moment, Leicester had said: "Owen, thou knowest that Robyn my boy is my lawful son and, as I do, and have, charged thee to keep it secret, so I charge thee not to forget it, and therefore see that thou be carefull of him and forget not yet, when time serves, he shall remember you." There was a certain resonance in those words; they were hard to overlook and Jones was to reappear in Robert's life when they would be repeated to his own cost. Robert remembered Jones well and set store by what he had said.

The other tale she told him was of a terrible scene between his father and herself that took place in the gardens of Greenwich Palace in 1577, the memory of which time had failed to erase. It was a pre-arranged meeting to which Leicester had invited two witnesses and it became disastrously out of hand. He offered her seven hundred pounds a year if she would deny their marriage and give him custody of Robert, then a very small boy. She burst into tears and wept all over the gardens but refused. He then lost his temper with her, shouted and threatened her until she eventually capitulated, saying later that she feared he would have her killed. She had good cause, by that time, to know, or suspect, how ruthless he could be. Stafford was produced in quick time to breach any gap, and before she changed her mind. He was a rising courtier of great charm, and a friend of Leicester, whose late wife, Rosetta Robsart, was a cousin of the tragic Amy Robsart. There were many wheels turning within this torrid tale.

The story of the bribe in the garden was, to Robert, ample proof that he was Leicester's legitimate son. Why go to such lengths if he were not? Was it surprising that Sir Edward did not want any further revelations, particularly if they were to land Lady Douglas or himself in a court of law?

An even darker story emerged, during all this soul-searching, which explained why Lady Douglas, who had never mentioned it before, was so reluctant to dig up the past. Robert had no idea that the rumour existed and she swore him to secrecy and to a promise never to repeat it. Her first husband, Sheffield, had died in 1568. Just before his sudden death his sister, married to a Denzil Holles, had picked up a letter dropped inadvertently by Lady Douglas and written by Leicester, which implied that she knew there was a plot to kill Sheffield. Lady Holles probably suspected that Douglas was in love with Leicester and was eager to make trouble. She claimed that, in spite of all her efforts, it was, by then, too late to save Sheffield. Lady Douglas swore to Robert that there was not an iota of truth in this unsavoury tale, but the fact that it existed at all, even so long ago, still had the power to frighten her.

Robert now had a great deal to think about. While wishing to protect his mother from unpleasant notoriety, the truth must be found and told if he was to prove his legitimate birth and that would have to be in a court of law.

For the present, what was he to name a fourth daughter? The first three were christened, Alicia, Frances and Anne. He decided to call her Catherine as a polite nod to his mother-in-law. Sir Thomas, for whatever reason, had been extremely helpful.

CHAPTER NINE

Knight or Earl – 1602-1605

Robert Dudley did not attend the trial of Essex in February 1601, but he stood shoulder to shoulder with Richard Clanricarde at the Earl's execution on the square of green turf within the Tower of London where so many of the great, good and bad, had come by their end. They were both fighting men and death was no stranger to them, but this was a page torn untimely from their lives, a premeditated act of violence done in cold blood. The thud of the axe and what came after was not easy to witness. Essex had died as they knew he would, with a smile and a jest to the headsman, a wave of his black felt hat to the select crowd gathered, and a genuine prayer for pardon and redemption. Robert's own grandfather and two of his uncles had knelt here before the axe.

Neither he, nor Richard, had taken part in the ill-judged and panic-induced uprising, or the march from Essex House to the city on 8th February which had ended, not with the support of the pre-warned citizens, but with the arrest of the insurgents. This was followed by the surrounding of the house and the apprehension of all those involved. Clanricarde was still in Ireland with Mountjoy until a week before Essex's execution

Robert was taken into custody from Dudley House late on the same day. He had gone, with the Essex House party the previous evening, February 7th, to hear a special performance of Shakespeare's "Richard II" at the Globe Theatre across the river: this was arranged by the Earl of Southampton and intended as an incendiary manoeuvre and to raise support in the city. After that he had returned to his own house at St.Giles-in-the-Fields and took no part in the armed march the following morning. Indeed, he was not aware of it. This had been triggered, as it was intended to, by a demand from Robert Cecil the previous night that Essex should appear before the Privy Council at once to explain the reinforcement of men and arms at Essex House. Events then went from bad to worse. Although Robert was not involved in the insurgency, his name had been given as one of the theatre party. Combined with his known close relationship with Essex, this warranted his arrest the following evening. He was bundled, his hands tied behind his back, by two apologetic members of the Queen's Guard, into a stinking rattletrap of a carriage and taken to the Tower of London where supporters of Essex were initially detained. Resistance would have been easy, but foolish, and an admission of guilt. He saw the grey, bedraggled faces of Southampton, Rutland and Gorges peering out of the gloom as he was marched down long, cold ramps and passages with barred doors and he shouted out to them as he passed. The situation did not look good; neither did the cell into which he was thrust. Freezing cold, with water running down from the tiny barred window, and a pallet full of damp straw its only furnishing, it was worse than he had feared. He was furiously angry that he had been arrested, and at his stepbrother's rashness, but the only fear he felt was for Essex himself, who was now unlikely to go unpunished. He had been horrified to find Essex House almost on a war footing, a bare two miles from Whitehall and in full public view, but realised that Essex was beyond persuasion. Robert had refused point blank to throw in his lot with him and his equally deranged supporters, though many of them were his friends.

On his arrival in London, he still had hopes of moderating the direction Essex appeared to be taking, which looked very like insurrection. The play they saw, "Richard II", with its forced abdication, overthrow of a monarch and brutal implications, had convinced him that he wanted no part in their plans.

As dawn dimly lit his miserable quarters, he saw a scratching on the wall opposite the window. He rose to run his finger over the roughened surface and, with the hair rising on his head, recognised a crude carving of the bear and ragged staff, the emblem of his father, his house and himself. This was the cell where Leicester, with his brother Ambrose, had been imprisoned all those years ago, daily expecting execution following the fall of Lady Jane Grey. They had survived to live the fullest of lives. So, by God's Grace and his own will, would he.

What wheels then turned, operated by whom, he never discovered, but he was released within a week with the verbal advice that there was no case against him, but that it would be wise to remain at Kenilworth for a while with no appearances at Court. He, therefore, never heard the tortuous detail of the trials following the uprising until much later, nor the unhinged religious ranting of Essex, whose betrayal of his friends resulted in the prosecution of many others. Executed shortly after him were Sir Christopher Blount, his stepfather, Sir Charles Danvers, Sir Gilly Meyrick, and Henry Cuffe, his steward. Condemned, but not beheaded, were the Earls of Southampton, Rutland and Bedford. After paying enormous fines, they were eventually released, as were Lord Monteagle, the Pembroke brothers and many others. Penelope Rich, the Earl's sister, was put under house arrest.

Essex's own execution had been a foregone conclusion, although it was expedited by Francis Bacon whose reptilian eyes were firmly fixed upon the future. He and his brother, Anthony, had served Essex for many years, mainly in the field of intelligence, but he had turned his coat promptly and thoroughly soon after Essex's disastrous return from Ireland. Anthony remained bone loyal and died, broken-hearted, soon after the execution.

The only record to remain of Robert having been in London and involved in the Essex rising during those fateful days, came from an Italian diplomat, Ottaviano Lotti, the resident Florentine Minister in London, with whom he was to have many dealings in the future. Lotti reported the uprising to his master, the Grand Duke Ferdinand of Tuscany and, perhaps, made particular mention of Robert's name because of his connections with Thomas Chaloner, who, besides other activities, was working as a special envoy at the Tuscan Court at the time.

Despite the warning to stay away, Robert made the journey back to the Tower, joined Clanricarde, and said his farewell to a loved brother with no hesitation; Essex would have done the same for him. Whatever had gone amiss with Essex's mind towards the end of his life, his singular power to charm and hold the loyalty of those around him, had never failed. Robert recognised this gift, knew how Essex used it, but was not aware that he, himself, possessed it.

Richard Clanricarde returned to join Mountjoy in Ireland. He had fought with him at the battle of Kinsale and been knighted on the field for his courage. This was the decisive battle and Mountjoy then drove the Earl of Tyrone all the way to Ulster where he finally surrendered in December 1602. Robert was sorely tempted to join them, any form of action would have been welcome despite his feelings about Ireland, but a single rash move at this stage might jeopardise his planned legitimacy case. Following his arrest, he would plainly be under scrutiny. He was bored and frustrated and difficult to live with.

The horrified Alice saw her dreams of elevation to the peerage evaporating and became quite hysterical. She had no conception of the depth of her husband's feeling for Essex or the bitter grief at his loss; she railed at him for going to London at all at such a time or allowing himself to be involved with Essex in any way. Robert lost his temper with her, which he very seldom did, shouted her down and told her to go and say her prayers with her slimy little priest. He was equally short with his father-in-law's protestations and hand-wringing.

For Robert, the following months were extremely tedious. There were no grand schemes, no battles to be fought and no expeditions to plan during this rustication, though he and Alice entertained a great deal at Kenilworth and news of Queen and Court filtered through from friends and cousins. The death of Essex marked the slow decline of the Queen; it was a blow from which she never recovered and it seemed as if the royal flame was burning low and would soon begin to gutter. The greatest of the Tudor monarchies was drawing slowly to a close.

By the end of the year, Robert was back at Court again, with his ear still to the ground for news of his small fleet of ships. The story of the lone survivor from Mauritius had reached him through Richard Haklyut, via a variety of sources, and he was fully employed in following them up. Haklyut himself had also been searching and heard the rumour that the ships had reached the Malayan coast. Sadly, the lone survivor himself had completely disappeared, though they managed to get the story from an officer of the ship that had found him. It was the end of that particular dream.

Robert was saddened by the appearance of the Queen. She had aged a great deal since he had last seen her. Though she still rode to hounds and danced the galliard with verve, it was clearly an effort. She did not appear to be bearing any grudge against him and he could only guess whether her orders had been behind his rapid release after the Essex House uprising. He had been half expecting black looks and pungent remarks, if not worse. He was well aware how lucky he had been; many of his friends were still imprisoned. He might have spent months in that cell instead of days, and the stink of treason still about him on his release would have been no help to him in any future enterprise. He was still determined to establish his name and his honour and was prepared to fight for it in the courts. He particularly wanted to prove that he had inherited Kenilworth by right and not because of a last minute effort at reparation on Leicester's part to a base-born son of whom he had been fond. (The reiteration of the words "base son" in Leicester's will had bitten deep.) Many, he knew, considered that this was the case. Alternatively, many believed that he was indeed Leicester's legitimate heir, never acknowledged because of his parents' murky marriage arrangements. Pride dictated that the truth must come out.

Work had finished on Dudley House and it had become a pleasant base for Robert's family in London. Alice was particularly fond of it; the house seemed like a cottage after the vastness of Kenilworth. Compact, warm and pretty, it became her especial favourite. She was again pregnant.

The following year there appeared in Robert's life one Thomas Drury, a connection of his stepfather, Sir Edward Stafford. He was the son of Sir William Drury, married to Stafford's sister. Drury was to prove a money-grubbing rogue, but he had a proposition for Robert which sounded interesting. He gave assurances that he could produce three witnesses who would go far to prove that Robert was Leicester's true-born son. They were two of Douglas Sheffield's household who had, purportedly, witnessed her actual marriage to his father. One was her gentleman usher, Henry Frodsham, and the other, her gentlewoman, Magdalen Frodsham, now Mrs.Salisbury. The third was Leicester's proctor, a Thomas Ward. He promised to bring them to Kenilworth for inspection and this he did, after which they were lodged at Stoneleigh Abbey with Sir Thomas Leigh. They were joined by Owen Jones, his father's erstwhile servant, who had fallen on hard times and presented himself at Kenilworth seeking Robert's help which was most willingly given. Owen promised to testify in any court of law on Robert's behalf; Leicester's words to him concerning his son "Robin" had been prophetic: "I charge thee be careful of him and forget not, when time serves, he shall remember you." Owen had not forgotten and neither would Robert. There would, therefore, be five potential witnesses to his parents' marriage. These included an old friend, Lady Parker, formerly Mrs.Erisa.

Robert hesitated after hearing the depositions of these witnesses and assessing their reliability; a hesitation that was to cost him dear. If his claim succeeded, the effect on his mother's marriage and her reputation would be extremely bad and Sir Edward Stafford had made it clear that neither of them would stand as witnesses. But, if it did succeed, he would not only become Earl of Leicester and Warwick, but would also obtain the extensive lands that had been escheated and become Crown property on the deaths of his father and his uncle without legitimate heirs, including Warwick Castle. He would become very powerful and very rich. Given his own conviction that he was, indeed, their heir, his accepted status as a bastard had not bothered him unduly until now. After all, both the Queen and her sister Mary had been publicly proclaimed as such by the King, their father, and the Pope. But now there was another generation growing up at Kenilworth, hopefully to include a son, and it was most important that he, himself, should take his rightful place as a peer of the realm and insure that child's inheritance. There was too much at stake to draw back now for the sake of finer feelings, even his mother's. It was time to test his position at law.

But fate was to deal Robert a bad blow. He had hesitated too long. On 24th March, 1603, after stubborn refusal to do so, the old Queen died and the country, already in the grip of a fearsome outbreak of plague, became suspended by shock, while a deputation, led by Robert Sidney, galloped north to offer James VI of Scotland the crown of England. This was cruel luck for Robert Dudley. Not only must his case wait, but the future Monarch would not now be a familiar figure who had loved his father, known and favoured him all his life, but a total stranger, one of whose few graces was gratitude to those who had served him. James I of England had been in correspondence with Essex and the Sidneys for years, even if he had not contributed to the uprising, as hoped. It was Robert Sidney and Lettice, Countess of Essex, whom he would support. The old Queen would have done anything to crush her hated cousin and rival, Lettice, and declare her marriage invalid. Robert could look for no help from the new King of England; Essex, his link with the Sidneys, was gone. Robert was now in the other camp and viewed with increasing hostility.

Shortly before the old Queen's death, Richard Clanricarde came back from Ireland where peace of a kind had been achieved, and married Frances, the widowed Countess of Essex. He had carried a torch for her many years and it seemed that some real happiness had emerged from the Essex tragedy. Robert, who knew Clanricarde too well to have missed the way the wind blew, rejoiced for both of them. Richard owned huge tracts of land in Galway and the Clanricarde lives would be divided between the two countries. Ireland was never going to be easy.

While England reeled, then prepared to welcome its new Monarch, Robert reviewed the situation and decided first to approach the Archbishop of Canterbury. Using intermediaries, he wrote: "particularly desiring him to examine the witnesses himself". This the Archbishop declined to do, but he did authorise a Court of Audience to take the witness's respective depositions. The date of the award was 20th May 1603 and the fact that it was executed at Stoneleigh under the supervision of Sir Thomas Leigh and by his chaplain, showed how deeply his father-in-law had involved himself in Robert's case. The opening of the subsequent Commission was delayed by the ravages of the plague, sweeping like a scythe through southern England. The wretched Drury, intent on making money out of Robert, succumbed and died in August at the Swan Inn, Southwark. The Archbishop also died that month.

Because of the horrors of the plague, permission was granted for a Consistory Court to be held in Lichfield, in Staffordshire and happily close to Kenilworth. It was not until 27th September, however, that the witnesses, still lodged at Stoneleigh, began their testimonies. So far, so good, but on 18th October, Robert's cousin, Robert Sidney, now Lord Sidney, rode into Lichfield carrying a mandate from the Lord of the Privy Council empowering him to stop the Commission's proceedings in its tracks, to impound the depositions, and to bring them before the Court of Star Chamber in Whitehall. Unsurprisingly, he was not invited to break his journey at Kenilworth, cousin or no cousin.

Robert Sidney, a more ruthless character than the much-loved Philip, had deeply ingratiated himself with King James, and lost no time in obtaining a peerage. In 1588, it had been Sidney who was appointed to ride North carrying to Holyrood the Queen's grateful thanks to James for his refusal to help the fleeing Armada as it struggled round the north coast of Scotland. Robert Sidney was a personable man and James had not forgotten him; he was, indeed, scattering peerages like confetti from the moment he was crowned and Sidney considered himself the rightful heir to the earldoms of both Leicester and Warwick. On Robert Dudley's side, the Howards were also benefitting greatly from the King's bounty and not much help could be looked for from them. The Lord Admiral was now the Earl of Nottingham, Lord Thomas Howard, his Admiral at Cadiz, was now the Earl of Northampton. None of them would be anxious to disrupt the flood of honours pouring out of Hampton Court. The King had rushed there immediately after his coronation for fear of the plague and from thence he decamped to the Pembroke seat at Wilton, still dispensing peerages as he went. None of this was of comfort to Robert who was not getting the support he needed. The family was dividing into camps with Robert cast as the pariah, the upstart and the interloper.

Robert Sidney had been named by Leicester as his lawful successor to Kenilworth, in the event of Robert's own death, and he was most acquisitive. He already had Penshurst, a peerage, a very rich wife and the post of Chamberlain to the new Queen, Anne of Denmark. But he wanted Kenilworth and the earldoms as well. Urged on by the redoubtable Lettice, he was making full use of the King's favour to influence any outcome and he now persuaded James that their cause should be identified with the Crown, and therefore represented by the Attorney General, the aggressive and arrogant Sir Edward Coke, well known for his manipulation of witnesses and his penchant for taking bribes.

This was very bad news for Robert Dudley, now becoming more embattled than ever. But worse was to come. In February 1604, engineered by the guileful Coke and under his influence, Lettice, Countess of Leicester, brought a Bill against Robert Dudley, his wife, Alice, her father, Sir Thomas Leigh, and every person involved with the Lichfield proceedings, for a conspiracy to defame her. This counter suit was an astute move and it left Robert in an unenviable position. He had been transformed, at a stroke, from litigant to defendant. Lettice had an implacable hatred for Robert. She saw him as the upstart who had robbed her of Kenilworth, much of Leicester's wealth and the rebel who had escaped penalty when both her son and her third husband were beheaded. Worse, this bastard was now seeking to establish himself at the cost of her reputation. There were no bounds to the lengths she would go to crush him and his pretensions. The atmosphere of the case was becoming extremely ugly. The Queen had gone and Robert was fair game.

Robert, who loathed Lettice every bit as much as she did him, and had done since boyhood, immediately began to search for further authentic witnesses to his parent's marriage.

It was at this time that an encounter took place which was to change, forever, his life and the lives of those close to him.

On past visits to Court, he had occasionally noticed an exceptionally pretty child waiting on the old Queen. Loving women as he did, the thought crossed his mind that she would, one day, become a beauty. He promptly forgot her. Adolescents were of no interest to him, besides which he had an attractive wife and several children. Not that this would, or ever had, stopped his eye from roving, and there had been several highly enjoyable affairs over the last five years, both in London and at Kenilworth. Robert had no halo where women were concerned.

With strange little James I now on the throne, he put in a fairly prompt appearance at Hampton Court, avoiding the undignified rush of those intent on gaining favour, and noted the changes while paying his respects to their Majesties. The King appeared affable enough at this point. He had a phenomenal memory for faces and events and an eye for a good-looking man, despite his devotion to his family. He knew Robert's history well and was disposed to be friendly because of his connection with Essex. Looking at his pursed mouth and guarded expression, however, Robert sensed a difficult personality. Queen Anne, his plain, Danish wife seemed perfectly amiable.

Coming away from the royal presence at Hampton Court one lovely spring morning that year of 1604, Robert, crossing a quadrangle, heard a voice ringing from an open window which stopped him in mid-stride. He thought, to begin with, that it must be a boy's alto, so pure and unfeigned it was; perhaps some music teacher and his pupil. The notes flowed effortlessly, in one paean of joy, from high to surprisingly low. He found a door opening on to the court and followed the singing to its source. He was not particularly musical, but he had never heard such an arresting sound.

A girl, so slender he could have spanned her waist with his hands, was standing, completely relaxed, with her hands resting on a spinet, singing her heart out with no accompaniment except the beat of her fingers to the rhythm of the song. There were several other people listening to her in the darkly panelled room, but Robert was not aware of them. He stood in the doorway transfixed by what he heard and saw. The girl, caught in the shafted sunlight, was so arrestingly beautiful and so unlike any he had seen before, that he barely recognized the pretty child who had appeared behind the old Queen.

With the excuse of listening to her voice, he was able to stand in the doorway, staring intently at her face. She was enjoying herself immensely, perfectly at ease with her audience, as the bewitching sound poured effortlessly out of her. Robert had the impression that some other people in the room were enjoying the sight of her as much as her voice. There were several men known to him there, no music lovers, who would not normally be absorbed by melody. It was the singer who had drawn them, not the song.

The girl was shining fair, with a warm, creamy skin, unlike the deathless white in fashion for so long. She was vibrantly alive from the top of her gleaming head to the small feet just visible beneath her kirtle. The energy within was so great that the voice soaring from her was a release rather than an effort. Her eyes, half-closed with delight in what she was doing, suddenly opened wide. Robert received, full force, the blow from which he would never recover. They were the clear, piercing blue of aquamarines, a replica of the necklace given him in Cadiz and they were set, like jewels, in a face of such sweetness that he could not look away. No more did she.

The song came softly to an end, but the singer did not move. Then, she slowly smiled, straight at Robert, and his ruin was complete. It seemed as if sun shone out from the clouds and at him alone. She turned and curtsied in dismissal to her audience. Robert remained rooted where he stood, greeting those he knew, until they had all drifted from the room. There were no words spoken. She never took her shining eyes from his face but moved towards him and reached her hands to his. He felt as though he were wading through deep water and that drowning would be a small price to pay. He opened his arms to her as if she had never left them, like a happy child coming home, and he held this precious being against his heart and knew he could never, in this world, let her go.

Later, sitting close, they talked for hours. They were cousins and Robert, still drowning, could see the likeness in her lovely face to his uncle, the Lord Admiral, now Earl of Nottingham, whose granddaughter she was. Her name was Elizabeth Southwell, daughter of Sir Robert Southwell with whom he had fought at Cadiz, one of England's great mariners; her brilliant eyes were the colour of his. Her mother was Elizabeth Howard, the Lord Admiral's daughter, and she was, therefore, Robert's first cousin, once removed. The generations had slipped, one into another; she was eighteen years old.

She came from Wood Rising, the Norfolk family home of the Southwells. Many East Anglian families were descended from Norsemen whose blue gaze reflected the seas they sailed. Unknown to Robert, their paths had crossed many times in the past; she knew him, had watched him joust, and had learnt that he was forbidden to sail with his expedition. She had been a Maid of Honour to Queen Elizabeth since she was thirteen and had managed to avoid marriage by the simple expedient, when threatened, of appealing to her father who could refuse her nothing. Her mother would have had her betrothed by fourteen and the suitors had never ceased. Sir Rowland Whyte, the courtier and artist, had written to Robert Sidney on the day she appeared: "The young faire Mrs. Southwell shall this day be sworn Mayde of Honour". He had clearly been struck, even at such a young age, by her beauty.

She was the third generation of her family to serve the Queen, her grandmother, Catherine Carey, being a cousin of her Majesty and she had been with her mistress when she finally died. She was now a Lady in Waiting to Queen Anne who loved music and greatly enjoyed her unusual voice. At this time, she was being pursued by the immensely rich Sir Clement Heigham who could not understand why the flood of jewels and expensive trinkets he sent her were constantly being returned to him. She had watched Robert from afar, never speaking to him, knowing his reputation, that he was married, and with children. Today had proved too much for her and here they were, locked in each other's arms, all her dreams realised and their future in tatters.

They talked until long shadows crept into the little room, as if they had known each other all their lives, their close relationship and common family background making a natural bridge over any differences. Few explanations were needed; they spoke the same language. She knew, of course, about the case that was looming. Who did not? She understood how high were the stakes for Robert and that his life and honour were riding on it, and she was not prepared to think further ahead than that, nor how the outcome would affect her. Love was not something to be calculated, evaluated or planned for. It happened or it did not and would find its own way if it was strong. Today was enough; tomorrow would take care of itself. She was his from this moment on, and the smile that lit her face was quite unshadowed.

Robert, bewitched and unusually bemused, tried to drag his mind back to practicalities and failed. In his affairs, he had always done the choosing, then dictated the terms of any liaison embarked upon, and there had been plenty of them, but gazing at Elizabeth, he felt powerless either to plan or to promise. He had nothing to offer her in return for her love; no marriage or security, no protection from gossip or vilification, and no happy ending that he could see; only this tidal wave of his own love. There was no certainty anywhere and, knowing he had the power to do so, he was afraid of harming her, or of losing her. It was the first time in his life that his concern for another was so far ahead of his own interests or so fiercely protective. Love had hit him late, unpredictably and very hard.

All she did was to put her small thumb between his eyebrows to rub out the lines, laugh merrily and kiss away the frown.

Meanwhile, events were moving. Shortly after Lettice launched her Bill against Robert and his family, the King decreed an Act forbidding re-marriage unless one partner were dead. This would put an end to a great deal of laxness and ambiguity and it would certainly have put an end to the goings-on in Leicester's love life. It would also put an end to any future divorce proceedings. The Act pronounced that it intended to: "restrain all persons from marriage until their former wives and husbands be dead." Furthermore, bigamy would now be a felony, punishable, possibly, by death. Bigamous marriages, until now, had been merely unrighteous under ecclesiastical law, but never criminal. This appeared, at first brush, to favour Robert's plea that his mother had been legally married to his father and that Lettice had not, but what of Lady Douglas's subsequent marriage to Stafford? What, also, of any ideas on divorce that he, himself, might contemplate? It appeared that the King had focused his attention upon the Dudley-Sidney case, would like to make an example of it, and seemed determined that such a situation should not be repeated.

It was at this point that Lady Douglas came wholeheartedly to Robert's support. She had hoped that she would not be alive to see this trial. Sir Edward was ill and close to death, his end hastened by what he feared would be a landslide of scandal and recrimination and she may have felt that she did not have much to lose. Whatever the reason, she could not stand by and see her son charged with conspiracy by Lettice, the woman who had almost ruined her own life. She agreed to an interrogation by the Attorney General, himself, at her present home, Sudely Castle.

With real courage, she faced up to Sir Edward Coke, cast her mind back thirty years and told the story of her love affair and marriage to Leicester in full. She was scrupulously honest, admitted that they had been lovers before marriage, and stuck to her facts in the face of all Coke's ruthless questioning. She also appealed to her brother, the Earl of Nottingham, to support her in maintaining that the marriage at Esher in the winter of 1573 had been a legal one. Robert, who loved her dearly, was duly grateful. It was a gallant gesture, particularly when her present husband was dying.

Back in Kenilworth, life had become difficult. Alice, because both she and her father had been named specifically in Lettice's Bill of February 1604, was truly furious. She had not expected to be involved personally in any way and, while she would have happily watched from the wings while Robert strove to establish them as Earl and Countess, she was not prepared to take part in any of the proceedings, particularly cross examination. She was outraged and, to his present relief, refused him any marital rights saying she was expecting yet another child. She screamed at him, long and loud; that he thought only of himself and the getting of a son, with no consideration for his wife or the fact that she had always expected to become Countess of Leicester. No thought either for his daughters, whose future he should be considering. Since much of what she said was true, and his thoughts were taken up with a very different kind of woman, Robert was relieved to let her slam the door on him and to retire, with his dogs, to his private Lobby.

Another daughter duly appeared in August 1604 and was baptised Douglas, after his mother. Robert was fond of his little girls, but tended to regard them as one entity. They were so close in age and appearance that he had to consciously think who they were. Alicia, the eldest, was followed by Frances, Anne and Catherine. Mostly, they were dark and brown-eyed. Only Douglas was to show signs of being lighter, with the touch of red that appeared in Robert's beard, and with a hint of her grandmother's beauty.

During the brief meetings they had managed in Hampton Court, he and Elizabeth had agreed that they would stay apart, however painful this might be, until the case in Star Chamber was decided. Her mother, a widow of a few years, had recently married John Stewart, soon to be the Earl of Carrick, and was now a Lady of Queen Anne's Drawing Room. A number of the Howards were very close to the main seat of power, and Elizabeth, herself, was now one of the elite at Court. More pressure would soon be put upon her to marry.

Because of the dread of plague, London had been out of the question for the moment as a meeting place. They trusted it would not be for long, but the hopes and fears of clandestine trysts would make it much harder for Robert to bear his part in the forthcoming law suit and he would not risk involving her in any way. The future was a very blank page indeed though this did not appear to worry Elizabeth. Her life was put trustfully into his hands which was where she wanted it to be. Not for nothing had she been at Court for five years; she had learnt the art of maintaining a friendly neutrality, which kept her at a distance from intrigue and her own affairs quite private, while affording her a great deal of amusement. She had a keen sense of the ridiculous and she was, like Robert, afraid of very little. They were kindred spirits and she laughed much more than she cried. His longing for her grew no less and, in some sort, it spurred him on to face and to wade through the mire of Star Chamber, though what the green fields on the far side would produce was another matter.

Forty thousand people had died in England during the recent outbreak of plague. In 1603, at the start, one quarter of London's population had been wiped out. It had almost wrecked the King's coronation and the Royal household did not return to Whitehall until it had subsided. It was a foul disease, akin to, if not the same as, the Black Death of the fourteenth century. Bubonic plague had killed a third of Europe's population then, mainly taking the form of a swelling of the lymph glands into great boils, or buboes, accompanied by violent fever and several other disgusting symptoms, among them a horrible stench. Few survived unless the boils burst early and drained. Another form, pneumonic plague, attacked the lungs and was swifter and more generally lethal, sufferers often dying within hours. Folk carried bunches of herbs wherever they went. In some towns and villages, the dead lay heaped in filthy streets littered with the remains of rosemary, juniper, sage, lavender and bay; there was no-one left to bury them. To give the King his due, he had appointed officers to enforce the laws he passed to deal with the outbreak. Any afflicted family must be confined in their own home until they either died or survived a certain given time. His local officers had the power to prevent the traffic of people fleeing from an afflicted village which meant that many of them took to the countryside and tried to live off the land, unworked because of the lack of labour. Crops were lost and livestock died, as did many of those living rough. People turned on anything unknown or suspected of being a cause of the pestilence and many supposed witches and warlocks were summarily burnt or strangled. 1603 to 1605 were bitter years.

The hearing of Robert's case, therefore, did not open until 22nd June 1604 when the plague was subsiding and the King had returned to Whitehall. It opened with quite a bang.

A contemporary lawyer and chronicler, Sir John Haywarde, announced, of the opening in the Star Chamber of the Palace of Westminster, that ...."The greatest cause now of England between Lord Sidney and Sir Robert Dudley for the Earldom of Warwick and Leicester......a very great cause, and many honourable persons interested in the same in blood and right; and for that purpose, there came with Sir Robert Dudley and stood by him in the Court, the Lord Dudley, the Lord Sheffield and the Lord of Effingham."

The family had rallied. Lady Douglas and her brother, the Earl of Nottingham, had stepped in and the four men made an impressive entrance into Star Chamber that beautiful morning in June. Lord Dudley (not the Leicester branch) was Lady Douglas's brother-in-law, Edmund Sheffield was her son, Robert's half-brother, whilst the Lord of Effingham was his cousin and the son of Nottingham. They were all eye-catching men and they stalked into the Chamber as if they owned it.

The Attorney General bridled and sarcastically declared that: "it was a strange precedent that so great and honourable personages should come into Court to countenance and embrace any cause contrary to the law." He wanted it made clear from the start that Robert was the defendant and that the Crown assumed him guilty of trying to blacken the name of Lettice, Countess of Leicester. Also, that Robert could bring in as many of the great and good as he chose, it would not help him. The law, in this case, was going to be very one-sided, as it frequently was in Star Chamber, its transactions bearing little resemblance to later administration or notions of justice. It could function impartially, but it was exempt from common law and all too likely to conform to the wishes of the King and his favourites. The Attorney General could very easily take on the role of judge as well as prosecutor and it was known that he seldom refused a bribe.

He waded in very aggressively:

"That whereas the Earl of Leicester had named Sir Robert Dudley in his testament seventeen times bastard, whom he had by Lady Sheffield,

Sir Robert Dudley hath stirred up some to call him bastard, and in the Ecclesiastical Court, by the subordinations of Thomas Drury, hath endeavoured to prove himself legitimate, and the Lady Sheffield, his mother, married to the Earl of Leicester, to the great dishonour of that noble and virtuous lady, now Countess of Leicester; and that Sir Robert Dudley hath given the Ragged Staff to his men that work upon the Thames, and calleth himself Earl of Warwick and Leicester; that this was very dishonourable to the King, who is the life and fountain of all honours and dignities; and the Countess of Leicester had complained thereof to the King, who did much dislike the contemptuous and proud courses and attempts of Sir Robert Dudley, and willed the same should be examined and punished."

Coke was hitting as low as he could and implying that Robert's "guilt" was a foregone conclusion; reminding him of his father's will with its constant repetition of the word "base", inferring that Drury, of ill-repute, had stirred up others to call Dudley a bastard in order to invoke the Ecclesiastical Courts to prove him legitimate, thus giving the whole case a shady flavour from the start. Also, accusing him, erroneously, of adorning his Thames boatmen with the Leicester coat of arms. Added to this, he was making it pointedly clear that the King was on the side of Lettice.

It was more than Robert could stomach. Outraged at the repeated affirmations of guilt, he rose in wrath, interrupted the Attorney General before he could utter one more biased word, and told him furiously: "that Mr. Attorney did cast forth many scandalous aspersions and rumours to prejudice his case before it came to hearing." He also strongly denied the taradiddle about the Thames boatmen and that he had ever called himself Earl of Leicester and Warwick and he demanded that the case should be tried publicly. Also, that he had brought this case to prove his legitimacy, not to be tried for petty offences or for offending his stepmother. He had a deep, clear voice that rang and resounded round the Chamber and a presence that had nothing to do with pettiness. The Lord Chancellor, surprisingly, agreed, and the hearing was adjourned. Those present sat up with renewed interest; this case would be good entertainment for a long time to come.

And it was, indeed, to be a long time. It was not re-opened during the current term of the Court, but adjourned indefinitely. Coke had been given to think about the accuracy of his evidence.

This was extremely hard for Robert. Longing for the case to be over and longing for Elizabeth, he was squarely between the devil and the deep blue sea, so that when the opportunity arose to accompany his uncle, Nottingham, the Lord Admiral, on a mission to Spain ordered by the King, the deep blue sea seemed the perfect escape. The mission was to "take the oath of the King of Spain for the peace." After almost forty years of hostilities, peace had been agreed. The fact that the Earl had invited him was a gesture of family solidarity. Robert was delighted by the thought of being at sea again, despite the separation from Elizabeth, and of escaping the strain of waiting for the Crown to gather its forces; to escape also from the constant speculations and recriminations of his wife who, like a dog with a bone, could talk of nothing else. He was as gentle with her as possible but spent much time hunting and jousting with his friends. He was not so gentle with his father-in-law, whose ambitions were becoming transparent. Sir Thomas Leigh could see a barony slipping away and was not pleased, though he had, in fact, been most helpful in housing Robert's witnesses and organising their depositions for the Consistory Court in Lichfield.

Unfortunately, the mission to Spain with his uncle did not materialise, and Robert was denied any respite from the continuous strain and speculation. In January 1605, during the Hilary Term of Star Chamber, the Attorney General intervened and Robert was "stayed at the Attorney General's motion, because the next term the cause was to be heard." Coke was determined to win this high profile case and had mustered his resources with good effect.

The Court assembled again on May 1st, 1605 and included some of the greatest in England. It consisted of the new Archbishop of Canterbury, the Lord Chancellor, the Lord Treasurer, the Lord Chamberlain, the Earls of Northampton, Devonshire and Northumberland, the Lords Knollys, Zouch, and Cranborne (formerly Robert Cecil), the Lord Chief Justice and a variety of other justices. The fact that Lettice's brother and Robert's relations were among this august gathering did not appear to matter. Haywarde avidly reported that: "The great case between Lord Sidney and Sir Robert Dudley and others, defendants upon the Attorney's information, was opened by the Solicitor General."

The Solicitor-General, Lord Ellesmere, was the first to rise and after five minutes of speech made apparent the plan that had been laid. "The civil law", he declared "that all chamber, clandestine or secret marriages should be confirmed by the oath of witnesses present at the same." There were five witnesses ready to testify to the Esher wedding that winter of 1573, but their written testimonies on oath had already been given and this gave the Crown the right to dispose of them as it would. Coke's strategy then emerged clearly as the Solicitor General proclaimed: "There are five witnesses to prove the first marriage, all not worth a frieze jerkin". These vital, authentic witnesses were to be vilified by the Crown, bullied, and blackened in character. They were to be shown capable of any perjury, so that their word, in fact, would be of no value to the Court or to Robert Dudley. The future of the case was looking very uncertain.

The attack began with the Solicitor General requesting the King's Sergeant to read out evidence, far-fetched as it was, to prove that the witnesses had all been procured by Robert for large sums of money, this included the housing of the five most important at Stoneleigh by Sir Thomas Leigh, the father of Lady Dudley. He alleged that the witnesses, had, in fact, been bought and their testimonies were not worth the paper they were written on.

On May 3rd, when the Court re-assembled, the entire proceedings were taken up in presenting Sidney's case, establishing his descent from the Earls of Leicester and Warwick, none of which had ever been in doubt, followed by an exhaustive account of Leicester's marriage to Lettice, with its many witnesses, at Wanstead, intended to prove its authenticity This was a blatant assumption that the Esher marriage was not authentic and had already been discounted and it showed how steeply stacked already were the odds against Robert Dudley.

On May 4th, yet another nail was hammered into Robert's coffin, one that was an open affront, almost an insult. King James created Sidney, Viscount Lisle of Penshurst. A second peerage, granted actually while the trial was in progress, left no one in doubt as to where the Royal partiality lay, and it had an added sting in its tail. The Lisle barony was a subsidiary title of the Warwick earldom and it would have gone to Robert Dudley had his legitimacy been proved. Worse still, Sidney had, earlier, petitioned Queen Elizabeth for the Lisle barony as "the next male heir" and she had refused point-blank. On the same day, Robert Cecil, the Secretary of State, already Lord Cranborne, was created Earl of Salisbury. The pieces on the chess board were being lined up.

That evening, in the long warm twilight, amid a gentle mist rising from the Thames, William Bradshaw flung himself on his horse and careered through London from St.Giles on a series of delicate missions. He was no fool and he knew what he was being asked to do. Absolute secrecy was needed, as he was well aware, and a certain amount of diplomacy. Therefore, he went alone. Living at close quarters with Robert and deeply involved with every aspect of his life, there was little he did not know of him or could not anticipate. He had been in Star Chamber all day and he was cold with fury at the way his master and friend was being treated. They had sailed, adventured, fought and laughed together for over ten years and he now stood on the same footing as had the old poacher, Ancient Barrow. He knew Robert's conviction that he was Leicester's true son, that he believed his mother's word on the marriage, and that he would fight to the last ditch to prove it, no matter what the odds. In fact, the odds against were assuming vast proportions, but that would not stop him. Only Royal interference would, and William was aware that it was coming to that, the way the wind was blowing; he was aware, also, of what the effect would be upon Robert. Like his father, he would not tolerate insult, and the reaction would be savage and unexpected. William went on his way with urgency and did not return until dawn's early light. It was the first of many such missions.

The Court re-opened on 8th May, Sidney, Cecil and Coke all basking in the sunshine and evidence of Royal favour. It was Robert Dudley's turn to present his case and from his mother, Lady Douglas, came the full story of her love affair and marriage with Leicester, supported by Magdalen Salisbury and the other witnesses, among them the former Mrs.Erisa, a close friend, now the wife of Sir Nicholas Parker. Lady Douglas's sister, Mary, Lady Dudley, Sir Edward Horsey, an old friend of Leicester who gave her away, George Digby and the dubious Dr.Giulio, who had all been present, had either died or disappeared. Of these, Lady Parker was the strongest witness, but thirty years on, her memory was a little hazy and lacking in detail. Magdalen Salisbury gave her statement boldly and clearly, insisting that there had been a marriage that winter evening in Esher. She was dismissed as: "an infamous instrument, procured for pay". Owen Davies was equally stalwart. He was described as: "a lewd fellow" who could easily be "laid out in his true colours", the prosecution pointing out how unlikely it was that Leicester, with his great position, would ever have deigned to confide in him.

Sir Edward Stafford had died recently, on 5th February, but Lady Douglas gave her evidence with dignity and courage. There were, however, vital details missing, or which had escaped her. She could not remember the exact date of the wedding or who had performed it. She had been presented with a diamond ring by Leicester on the occasion of the marriage, a table diamond surrounded by five pointed stones. It had originally been given to him by a former Earl of Pembroke on the express condition that it should be bestowed on none other than his wife, but she could not now produce it. The secrecy with which the whole marriage was shrouded, she explained, lay in Leicester's declaration that: "If the Queen should know of it, I were undone and disgraced and cast out of favour for ever." This was plausible enough, and later confirmed, by the fury vented on him when he eventually married Lettice, Countess of Essex. In support of her contention that the Earl had initially regarded their marriage as valid, Lady Douglas produced letters, including one in which "he did thank God for the birth of their son, who might be the comfort and staff of their old age" and signed it ..."Your Loving Husband." This had been written when news was brought to him of Robert's birth and was his instant reply.

She then recounted the meeting with Leicester, as described earlier to Robert. Having finally tired of her and intent on fixing his interest with Lettice, he had tried to repudiate the marriage altogether. He had arranged the meeting in the Close Arbour of the garden at Greenwich, where he offered her, before witnesses, £700 a year if she would disclaim the marriage. When she refused, she was threatened and dissolved into frightened tears. She capitulated eventually in order to "secure her life" because she feared that she was being poisoned, "having had some ill potions given her which occasioned the loss of her hair and nails." The fact that Leicester had gone to such lengths to procure her silence, pointed squarely to the fact that there had, indeed, been a lawful marriage. To corroborate this was the widely read "Leycester's Commonwealth", the appalling little pamphlet circulated since its publication in 1584, in which Leicester's reputation was hauled through the mud with a murder on almost every page, very often by poison. It did however, include the assertion that: "My Lord of Leicester was contracted at least to another lady (meaning Lady Douglas) before, that liveth, and consummated the same contract by generation of children." It also asserted that Lady Douglas had given birth to a child at Dudley Castle, the home of her sister, Mary, before the birth of Robert, and this was raised by a witness. It was strongly denied, by Robert, his mother, and his uncle, the Earl of Nottingham, amid calls for the prosecution of the witness for such a slander.

The Attorney General then went to work on Lady Douglas's five main witnesses to the marriage. He could not denigrate Lady Parker, but the other four he tore to shreds, stressing the "baseness and meanness of the defendant's witnesses." They were described as: "a poor carpenter, a common drunkard, a lying tailor, and infamous instruments of Drury". It was strange that every one of these ordinary people, by reason of their association with Douglas's marriage or her son's upbringing, should suddenly be found to be of ill-repute.

There remained, however, the vital question of why Lady Douglas had re-married herself if she believed her wedding to Leicester to be valid. This was more difficult to answer. She stated that Leicester, having already tried to poison her and: "Life being sweet", she determined to marry Stafford "for safeguard of her life." She also insisted that it was fear of contradicting Leicester's wishes that had driven her into Stafford's arms, but, considering that she had the whole of the powerful Howard family behind her and well able to rise in support, the only realistic conclusion to be drawn was that she had wished to re-establish herself, and forget the whole miserable business, thereby leaving her son's future in the balance. He had, by then, been claimed by his father. She had certainly restored her reputation, both by her success in Paris as the Ambassador's wife and the fact that the Queen had made her a Lady of the Bedchamber on her return. Lady Douglas stuck to her guns with great fortitude despite her grief. She had found happiness with Stafford, and she appeared in Star Chamber in deepest black. This sorrowful beauty had a profound effect on all who saw her.

To have to listen to the cross-examination of his mother, her distress, and the whole questionable story of his origins aired in such a public way, did nothing for Robert's pride. He had known how unpleasant it would be, but the reality was worse than he had feared. He knew, or was related to, almost everyone then present in Star Chamber; he was among his peers, quite literally, and that made the lurid disclosures even worse. Running his eye around the Court, there were few faces that were not familiar. He would very soon find out who was friend and who was foe.

He was being roused to such rage at the biased conduct of the entire proceedings that it would be hard to control it or to find an outlet. He had, at least, expected Star Chamber to be just.

The Crown then made a great deal of the fact that the marriage at Esher had never been entered in the Archbishop's record, but this was irrelevant because it was not compulsory to do so at the time and, obviously, those involved had no wish to advertise a secret marriage.

The Court sat again on May 10th and Robert's case, as defendant, was concluded. Lettice had called over eighty witnesses and Robert over a hundred, though few of these had been heard. They had been required to answer a series of pre-arranged, written questions, a questionnaire in fact, in order to save the Court's time.

Star Chamber was, on this day, as full as it could hold and speculation of all kinds ran like rats around the crowded seats. "And so", wrote Haywarde excitedly, "was this great cause at six o'clock at night sentenced, but, I fear, not ended."

Sir Edward Coke, glossy with self-satisfaction, began his final speech with the words: "My Lords, this is one of the greatest causes that ever came into this Court". Probably because he knew how many would sympathise with her, he then paid tribute to Lady Douglas and delivered: "great protestations of how he dearly affected the honourable lady, Lady Sheffield, and how willing he would be to speak or do any good for her." Weasel words, indeed, and not intended to include her son. Coke would not forget his humiliation at Robert's hands on the opening day of the case.

He next stunned the Court, all except those who suspected the King's intervention, with the astonishing claim that all the evidence given concerning Douglas's Esher wedding: "should be damned" and that all her witnesses should be "debarred from giving testimony in this, or any other, Court", adding that they should also be drastically punished. A complete "volte face", in fact, delivered with all the drama and venom he could muster. So much for his unctuous sympathy with Lady Douglas.

Robert, sitting in a prominent position and flanked by Dudley, Effingham and Sheffield, could feel the almost palpable tension in the overheated chamber and hear the indrawn breath around him; he could see the many eyes sliding in his direction. The verdict was no longer in any doubt. He returned the stares until they flickered and fell, his grey eyes hard as ice, and he searched the phalanx of people, as he had every day, for Elizabeth's beautiful face, and was relieved that it was not there. They had agreed, long since, that she would not appear in Star Chamber. His own face expressionless, he awaited the judgement which was to be given at six o'clock that evening. He knew that he had lost, and by unfair means, that the question of his legitimacy had not been properly judged, if at all, and his mind was seething with alternatives.

The Lord Chancellor rose and delivered the final verdict. He "acquitted" Robert Dudley, his mother, his wife and his father-in-law and the majority of his many witnesses, but, most unjustly, fined Magdalen Salisbury, Frodsham and Owen Jones together with several others of "the base and poor" brigade, up to £100 each. Much worse, and quite outrageous, was the Court's order that they were to be publicly disgraced and never allowed to testify in a Court of Law again, and that the Court ordered that all the defence depositions and all other related papers were to be "sealed up and suppressed until the King should order the enclosure to be broken". The case could never be re-opened and, the final blow, all lands escheated to the Crown were to remain escheated. Robert's reputation was tarnished, he had almost been denounced as a rogue for trying to prove his own birthright, and it was implied that he was lucky to escape punishment for making the attempt.

As Rowland Whyte, a great gossip, wrote to the Earl of Shrewsbury: "The matter of marriage was not handled at all; only the practice was proved in the proceedings." The practice referred to Robert's attempt to get a hearing through the Ecclesiastical Court. The issue of legitimacy had been smothered, the witnesses to his parent's wedding had been ruthlessly suppressed and dismissed, and the King had precluded any re-opening of the case. Robert and his family had been victimised for "conspiring" to redress Leicester's wrong. The real conspirators had been the King, his current favourite, Robert Sidney, and the Crown Officials; the chicanery had come from their side.

Robert left Star Chamber, before anyone had a chance to comment or commiserate, and went immediately to his mother's house. She had not stayed to hear the verdict. He owed her an enormous debt for her courage and constancy in facing this ordeal so soon after Stafford's death, for seeing the distant past so painfully dragged before the eyes of all who knew her, and for so disrupting her life in her later years.

He marched in, flung his arms around her and thanked her from the bottom of his heart. She had done all within her power to help him, to right the wrong that had been done him, and at her own heavy cost. Her eyes full of tears, she begged him to forgive her, and his father, for the injury they had caused. It had now come home to roost with a vengeance. Then she suddenly raised her head and smiled through her tears straight over his shoulder. He spun on his heel as the door behind him opened and Elizabeth came softly into the room. She moved across to them, took Douglas's hand in one of her own, and Robert's in the other and kissed them each in turn. Douglas withdrew her own hand and joined both Robert's over Elizabeth's. She knew love when she saw it and, with an insight born of her own experience, would try to ensure the future happiness of her son, and redress the grief caused by this day's work.

The means by which she had stumbled on their secret were simple; a glance that strayed too long, a flicker of a shared smile. She had known Elizabeth all her young life and been instrumental in securing the position of Maid of Honour for her. She had guided and guarded her great niece in the overcharged environment of the Court since she was thirteen, and it was her own intuition that enabled her to guess how things now stood between these two. However great their discretion, she knew them both too well.

She had seen the glint in Robert's eye and knew he would never go tamely back to Kenilworth, plain Sir Robert Dudley after such a defeat, any more than his father would have done. He had one more rearguard action to fight; a last-ditch effort which had to be made. On 7th June he appealed to Star Chamber to mitigate the judgement on his reviled witnesses and pleaded that his father's escheated lands should not revert to the Crown. Robert Cecil, now Lord Salisbury, was among those who heard the appeal and made quite sure that it failed. Robert Dudley would recompense his witnesses generously in his own way and make sure not one of them should suffer, particularly the faithful Owen Davies who would remain a pensioner at Kenilworth to the end of his days.

On 25th June he obtained a licence from the Keeper of the Records at Greenwich: "for Sir Robert Dudley to travel beyond the seas for three years next after his departure with three servants, four geldings or nags and £80 in money with usual provisions."

On 30th June 1605, a small party rode out of London, heading south. Three of them were mounted on exceptional horses. The other led sumpter mules carrying a large amount of baggage. There was a ship waiting at Dover and, on 2nd July, they embarked, headed for Calais. Sir Robert Dudley and William Bradshaw were accompanied by a servant and a slim page boy who rode like a gypsy and laughed as the wind whipped his hat off and blew his hair about his face.

CHAPTER TEN

The Birds Fly South – 1605 – 1609

The big man standing in the shadows of the magnificent chamber remained with his back to the heavy double doors opening behind him.

The big man making his entrance, and lit by the long window beside him, also remained where he was, relaxed and still, his grey eyes narrowed and alert.

Ferdinand de Medici, Grand Duke of Tuscany, was curious to meet this traveller about whom he had heard so much but would take his time in assessing what he found. He was a notoriously shrewd and powerful ruler of his State and not given to rushing into any situation. There was much to be considered during this initial interview; what he saw and heard must be aligned with what he already knew.

The Duke was dressed with awe-inspiring richness; the long fur-trimmed brocade coat shimmered as he turned with deliberation towards the light and towards his guest. Report had not lied. The man by the doorway was equally impressive. Taller and younger than his host, he was the epitome of an English aristocrat: stance, dress and bearing suggesting an inborn assurance, bordering on arrogance. He was outstandingly good looking; his grey eyes shone out of a tanned face – he had, of course, been travelling – his figure was magnificent and there was strength in the breadth of his shoulders and the muscles of his shapely legs. This man was not one for sitting still, nor one to be trifled with. Did the brain, reputedly so precise and wide-ranging, match the looks of this paragon?

The Duke was amused to realise that whilst he was inspecting the stranger, he was, in turn, being scrutinised every bit as closely. Since he was accustomed to lowered eyes, deep obeisance and a clear desire to please, the Duke suspected that this man was boldly, though graciously, evaluating him, with an eye on the main chance.

Greetings and bows of precisely the right depth were exchanged and the interview proceeded on rigidly correct lines. The guest presented his credentials and a brief outline of his history and personal achievements. The Duke had already read these, and between the lines too. Any missing detail had been obligingly filled in by his envoy in London, Ottaviano Lotti, the Papal authorities in Rome, and interested gossip from Lyons. What was in writing was the bald truth but there was much that had not been dwelt upon and he was curious.

He clearly understood the outraged pride and defiance which had prompted a hasty departure from England, but the abandonment of a semi-royal castle, vast acreage and a wife and five children was another matter. The prompt conversion to Catholicism was also understandable as a means to an end. The man was partly Howard, as was his bride, and the family's Catholic leanings were well-known and accepted. He would be no stranger to the faith, though the Duke doubted he was religious in any sense; a quick gallop through the rosary would never be a problem. He also doubted whether the Pope knew much about the deserted wife and children when he had graciously given dispensation permitting a further marriage, and to a notably close relative at that. How much had been glossed over for the benefit of His Holiness and what arguments had been used to achieve these ends? It was all very intriguing.

Yet, here was Sir Robert Dudley, re-married, with, it was said, a child on the way, the essence of successful ambition, calmly assessing one of the most powerful men in Europe with a view to using him in order to make a name for himself in Italy. The Duke had a quiet chuckle to himself and began to ask some searching questions.

They were answered promptly and convincingly. The ground had been well prepared and there were no contradictions to what the Duke's careful investigations had already yielded.

By his own account, Sir Robert Dudley had left England in disgust at the slur on his name and the wrongful judgement given on his legitimacy and his titles. He had no wish to return. With him had travelled his cousin, Elizabeth Southwell, whom he had subsequently married in Lyons after obtaining permission from the Pope and following rapid conversions to the Catholic faith. The marriage was permitted on the grounds that his first three marriages were invalid. He claimed to have been contracted, without his realisation, at the age of seventeen, to a Mistress Frances Vavasour. He had documents to prove it. She had then married another, and, in ignorance, he had subsequently married Mistress Margaret

Cavendish and, on her demise, Mistress Alice Leigh. Mistress Vavasour being still alive at the time, both subsequent marriages were, therefore, bigamous. In any case, Dudley confessed disarmingly, none of these first three contracts were allowable on another count, though a somewhat flimsy one. They had been performed through the offices of Protestant heretics. Mistress Vavasour had conveniently died a few months before his departure, leaving him free to marry his cousin. The story was told with conviction though the Duke, a thoroughly worldly man, had trouble suppressing a smile. He knew much of Leicester and it appeared that the son boldly followed his own inclinations as had his father; blasting his way through the conventions and paying lamentably little heed to the precepts of any faith regarding marriage; these could be re-arranged to suit at will.

He knew that Sir Robert Dudley had eloped with his beautiful cousin, a jewel of the English Court whom no man could have resisted, leaving King, Queen and country aghast and shocked to the core. Worse still, she had travelled disguised as his page.

On their arrival at Calais, they had been questioned by forewarned authorities and had brazenly claimed that Dudley was escorting his cousin to be enrolled within the Order of St.Clara in Brussels. A likely tale, indeed, and the Ducal smile became quite broad. They had departed hurriedly for Lyons where, after lively correspondence with His Holiness Pope Paul V, and with the help of a Captain Robert Eliot, a contact in the Vatican, they had eventually obtained Papal permission to wed, despite the added complication of consanguinity. During the months this took to arrange, they remained in full public view of the interested population of Lyons, thoroughly enjoying themselves during the happy interlude before their marriage. The Duke understood that the girl was more beautiful than any yet seen in Tuscany and no threat to other men. She was, apparently, completely enthralled with her handsome husband. Clearly a spirited lady, she had ridden with him, in winter, across the Savoie massif from Lyons to Pisa where they were now living.

Sir Robert had come to the Tuscan Court to offer his services to the Duke as an expert ship builder, designer, engineer and cartographer. He had sailed to the Indies in his self-built ships at the age of twenty, battled at Cadiz, with the rank of Admiral, aged twenty-one, and outfitted an expedition to China by the age of twenty-four. He had the most innovative ideas on shipbuilding, navigation and naval warfare and the Duke was extremely interested in what he had to offer. He might even be considered a gift from God.

Ferdinand knew and liked Sir Thomas Chaloner who had spent some time in Florence acting as envoy, and, he suspected, doing some ferreting in an intelligence capacity as well. Sir Thomas had, himself, been extremely helpful to the Duke on naval matters and he had spoken very highly of the abilities of his former pupil, Dudley, whom he tutored at Oxford. By his account, Sir Robert was as sharp as they came, but utterly dedicated to any project he undertook and with a rare attention to detail. He had a strong sense of honour and he was a perfectionist. His achievements spoke for themselves, and his only failures, the scattering of his small fleet bound for China and the judgement on his legitimacy case in Star Chamber, had been events beyond his control. Chaloner's influence certainly had much to do with his decision to make Tuscany his destination.

The Duke had taken an interest in the Dudley case and was of the opinion that the judgement had been biased and wrong. As a true Catholic and a former Cardinal of Rome, Ferdinand accepted that the Esher marriage had been lawful and that Dudley was legitimate. He, therefore, recognised his visitor's right to the Leicester and Warwick titles. The Star Chamber had neither proved nor disproved Sir Robert's legitimacy and its verdict could be discounted. A ruler of the Duke's standing, on his home ground, could afford to ignore the findings of an English court. King James, having put his weight behind the Sidneys, was clearly backing his personal favourite and his own recent laws on the prohibition of divorce. This was not justice, nor was it surprising that a man of Dudley's mettle had defiantly turned his back on King and homeland. His rage at the outcome of the hearing had sought swift retaliation against the Crown. Later, he frankly: "protested he was driven into it by grief of mind". It did not, however, excuse his abandonment of a godly wife and five children, his estates and his responsibilities, in order to elope with, and then marry, his lovely cousin. There were clearly several sides to this man, among them a strong resemblance to his father, Leicester, and to his grandfather, the Duke of Northumberland. Both had been utterly self-interested and ruthless.

This first meeting gave the Duke a great deal to think about and it had certainly roused his interest. He was surprised, in view of all he had

Portrait of The Earl of Leicester by Steven Van Der Meulen.
By Courtesy of the Wallace Collection.

Portrait of Ambrose Dudley, Earl of Warwick
with his page (possibly Robert Dudley).
Reproduced by Permission of the Marquis of Bath, Longleat
House.

Portrait of Robert Dudley as a young man.
By courtesy of the National Portrait Gallery.

The Battle of Cadiz by Aert Anthonisz.
By courtesy of The Reyksmuseum, Amsterdam.

Image of Kenilworth Castle.
A reconstruction as it may have appeared around 1575.
By courtesy of Historic England Archive.

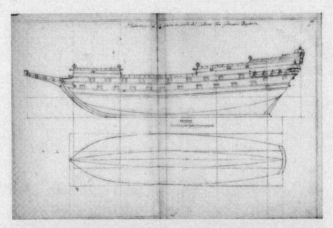

fig. 3 - ROBERT DUDLEY, *Il Perfetto disegno con pianta et profilo del Galeone San Giovanni Battista*, Londra, British Museum, add. ms. 22811

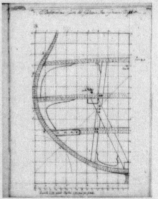

fig. 4 - ROBERT DUDLEY, *Il Perfetto disegno della Poppa del Galeone San Giovanni Battista*, Londra, British Museum, add. ms. 22811

fig. 5 - ROBERT DUDLEY, *Il Perfettissimo Garbo del Galeone San Giovanni Battista*, Londra, British Museum, add. ms. 22811

Print of Ship "San Giovanni Battista"
built by Robert Dudley in 1607.

Portrait of Robert Dudley with Dividers.
By kind courtesy of Clive Farahar.

Portrait of Teresa Dudley di Carpegna by Justus Sustermans 1564.
By courtesy of the Walters Museum.

heard about Sir Robert Dudley, to find that his first impression was one of immediate liking and trust. The Duke had seen no charlatan but a man with a strong sense of integrity. As for his recent private life, disgraceful as it had been, he found himself in some sympathy. The Medici, as a tribe, were no saints and as proud as peacocks. Dudley had come to him, not as a mendicant or a courtier looking for largesse, but as a highly qualified man offering his skills and with a request for work. He had asked for nothing else. These skills could be most useful in the furthering of several schemes uppermost in the Duke's mind.

As proof of his beliefs and opinion, he therefore wrote to Dudley's cousin, Henry Howard, now Earl of Northampton, explaining his views and asking for support for the Earl's wronged relative. He knew that Northampton was a well-disguised Catholic, as many of the Howards were, and he gave his own favourable opinion of Dudley to whom he now openly referred as "The Earl of Warwick." He was not likely to get much response as Northampton, at this time, was working hard for the post of Lord Privy Seal and doing his best to ingratiate himself with King James, but the gesture had been made and his stance declared. The word would be passed on.

Ferdinand I, Grand Duke of Tuscany, was an imposing and impressive man who had reigned over his State for twenty years. Before that, from the age of fifteen, he had been a Cardinal of the Roman Catholic Church and he would certainly have become Pope had he not chosen to take the Tuscan dukedom on the death of his brother. His long experience at the Vatican had given him insight and a capacity to judge men. Under his rule, Tuscany was now one of the richest, best-ordered and powerful of Europe's states and he, himself, was regarded by all with the greatest respect. He was a large, handsome, and heavily built man of considerable presence; not easily overlooked. It had not taken him long to get the measure of Robert Dudley, beyond his obvious charisma, and he quickly realised that his guest had too great a belief in himself, to want, or need, any deceit in presenting his history and his ambitions, though a little embroidery did no harm. His qualifications and experience could make him very useful indeed.

Further interviews during the next few days confirmed the Duke's opinion and saw the start of a genuine friendship between the two men based on mutual liking and recognition of each other's widely differing talents. As a result, Robert was to be given control of the expansion of the Tuscan navy, the construction and running of the shipyards and the arsenals both at Pisa and Livorno, employed and directed in these ventures personally by Duke Ferdinand. These were enormous undertakings and nothing could have pleased him more. Elizabeth was sent for from Pisa to meet their Highnesses and comfortable lodgings were arranged for them in Florence in the Via Strozzi.

The following week, having metaphorically rolled up their sleeves, the two men broached a bottle or two of excellent wine from nearby Verdigliana, and began discussion on those projects nearest to the Grand Duke's heart; they were soon completely engrossed. Foremost of these were plans for building a new fleet of ships to combat the threat from corsairs in the Mediterranean; then there was to be the construction of a large harbour at Livorno and the draining of that running sore, the Tuscan marshes alongside it, and already in progress. These were all vast undertakings and would need careful costing before any more work could be started. Money was not short but the Duke had no intention of wasting it. These projects were of immediate appeal to Robert, particularly the building of ships and the harbour at Livorno. He would begin drafting prospective plans as soon as he could do the necessary surveys. Livorno was, at the time, not much more than a fishing village with a good harbour. Elbows on the table, a bottle between them, grey eyes measuring dark ones, the ideas and conceptions began to flow, intent, dynamic, pushing the boundaries of possibility.

Robert's command of Italian, basic on arrival, had rapidly developed into something like fluency and would not be allowed to impede him for long. His French was excellent and the two men had no trouble understanding each other even down to nuances of language and quick repartee. They shared a rich, earthy sense of humour, all too easily translated, and when in doubt, they tried a different tongue, sometimes Latin. The Duke found that he was never obliged to explain anything more than once and that, often, Robert was one step ahead of him. His enthusiasm was exhilarating and boundless; his ideas poured forth in a steady and workable stream, many of them based on personal experience, and he appeared undaunted by the monumental amount of work being asked of him. When it came to precision or the mathematical side of things, however, Ferdinand could not compete with or follow him. Robert was in another league. Sir Thomas Chaloner had been right; this man was definitely the answer to a prayer, for the Duke, for Pisa and for Livorno. He would be delighted to work with him and to meet his wife.

This delight was fully realised the first time he set eyes on Elizabeth at a formal presentation a week later. His wife, the Grand Duchess Maria Christina was the daughter of Charles, Duke of Lorraine and granddaughter of Catherine de Medici. Though she had voiced her deep disapproval of Sir Robert and his bride, she was also curious to meet them.

It was a grand occasion, the guests in court dress and the huge salon in the Medici Palace as full as it could hold of the cream of society. The Tuscan Court was then one of the most elegant and civilised in Europe, smaller and more refined than King James's ramshackle establishment in London, and with higher standards of conduct. Stories had spread quickly and curiosity was intense at the chance to glimpse this notorious runaway couple from England.

They were both good at entrances. Under the unblinking gaze of Florentine society, and to indrawn breaths, they came into view at the head of a shallow flight of marble stairs. They made an arresting pair. Elizabeth's years in the English Court had taught her a great deal. She was a polished product of the old Queen's exacting standards. Poised, graceful and unerringly clad in palest blue, she drifted down on Robert's arm, hair and brilliant eyes shining and her creamy skin aglow with the faintest golden touch of Tuscan sun. She sank into a deep curtsey before the Ducal pair, rose and smiled with blinding sweetness upon the pair of them, her eyes reflecting the chain of aquamarines from Cadiz around her neck. The Duke visibly blinked and a long sigh of appreciation was heard to escape him. The Duchess inclined her head graciously, but her eyes flickered.

There were many lovely women there that evening, but Elizabeth shone them down; this slender sprite from a northern world. Her vitality, uncontrived and spontaneous, reached out to greet a new life and a new society. She was unbelievably beautiful and she took their breath away.

Robert, glancing down at her, felt a sense of unreality, enormous pride and, unusual for him, wonder. Of all the men in the world, why had she given up so much for him; her life as she knew it, her reputation and her family?

Remembering Christopher Marlowe's "Dr.Faustus", which he had taken the trouble to read at the poet's insistence, he could not help but be reminded of: "The face that launched a thousand ships." Elizabeth's would have launched a good number and might well, in reality, do so, in the near future. He had watched her during their travels; he found it hard to take his eyes off her at all, and he had seen the way she unconsciously used her beauty to confound and alter a situation.

He recalled one particular morning, during their long, hard journey to Pisa when he had seen the effect she could produce. Looking from the chamber window of their Alpine Inn, he saw her coming from the stables into the inn yard, her fur-lined cloak gripped round her; it was a bright, bitterly cold morning. She had been worried about her mare, after a hard ride the day before, and had slipped out to check her feet before starting out again this morning. She loved all animals and had a sound knowledge of horses and their welfare. She had not told him as she knew he would have stopped her and sent William Bradshaw to look the mare over. Robert was idly watching two men arguing in the yard, their altercation becoming increasingly angry. They were soon bawling at each other in earnest, one pushing back his cloak to grab a weapon. It began to look ugly. The other man immediately drew a dagger and Robert was about to rush down when Elizabeth emerged, her cloak wrapped round her and her face glowing from the cold. Horrified, he saw her walk straight up to the two enraged men, lay a hand on the arm of the one with the dagger and gently shake it. The man glanced down furiously, about to throw her off, but stopped, arrested and shocked by the lovely face looking up at him with unfeigned friendliness. She shook his arm again and turned to the other, pushing his hand from the hilt of his sword and smiling at the pair of them. They paused, completely mesmerised. One crossed himself, perhaps thinking of angels and heavenly intervention; the other stood with dropped jaw, gaping at her. Robert could only guess what she had said to them; it was quite irrelevant. She gathered her cloak around her and came into the Inn. Robert took her by the shoulders as she entered their room, shaking and scolding her with a mixture of anxiety and laughter. If he, himself, could never be accustomed to her beauty, how should he expect a pair of rough travellers to react? If they did not part the best of friends, at least they had not murdered each other.

It occurred to Robert that his bride was as fearless as himself and needed watching, particularly since she had just informed him, in the deep, cold, still of the previous night, that she believed she was with child. Her moonlit eyes, reflecting the snow outside, shone at him with luminous and tender intensity as she promised to ride with care and with less than her usual abandon.

News of the Dudleys' arrival and their reception in Italy was seized on with further shocked surprise in England and was passed immediately to Sir Henry Wotton, English ambassador to the Venetian Republic. Sir Henry was responsible for all English travellers in Italy, from aristocratic youths with their tutors to pernicious Catholic exiles, and he wrote immediately to a friend visiting Florence, Sir Edward Barrett, asking for a full report on "the arrival of Sir Robert Dudley and his Lady and the circumstances of their reception". Particularly, he wanted news of Elizabeth whom he had known well and avidly admired at the English Court. Wotton had no great opinion of their agent with the Vatican, Captain Eliot, whom he regarded as a dangerous rogue. "I had before understood, from the very fountains", he continued "how that business was conducted by Captain Eliot, whom the Pope is now likely to charge with surreption, or concealment of circumstances.......in the whole matter, I do much compassionate the case of the gentlewoman, whose mind, as her blood, was assuredly noble, but deceived. If you chance to see her, which methinks would be worth a step to Pisa, I pray you do me the honour to kiss her hand from me." He was, clearly, still quite besotted with Elizabeth and could not bring himself to leave her affairs alone. The "step to Pisa" spoke for itself.

Robert's fiscal arrangements before leaving England had, of necessity, been rapid and sketchy. William Bradshaw had done sterling service on his swift nocturnal rides round London in June, visiting bankers, friends and contacts, arranging transfers of the money, assets, and valuables necessary for immediate funding in France. He had also managed to tuck away 84,000 scudi in Lyons. Even so, expenses had been heavy, compounded by travelling, and Robert would be glad of the very handsome fee proposed by Duke Ferdinand. Officially, he was supposed to have taken only £80 with him from England. He was not used to counting the cost of anything personal having, since the age of fifteen, been very plump in the pocket. So much had been left behind in England. The Duke was offering an annuity of 2,000 ducats.

While in Lyons, he had the grace, in the midst of his many plans and contrivances, to make provision for his abandoned wife and family. He conveyed his entire estates to Alice's nearest relatives, Sir Thomas Leigh and her brother, Sir John Leigh, to hold as much of his property in trust for his family as possible. This was in the hope that Kenilworth would escape predatory Royal hands. It was the best that he could do for them. Alice still held the rights over the estate timber, her own wedding portion. He also left her sufficient funds for many years to come. She would, as well, have sole ownership of Dudley House in St.Giles.

Initially distraught at Robert's departure, Alice wrote an impassioned letter saying she would join him in Lyons with the children and was prepared, also, to change her religion; the very last thing he wanted and something that did not, in the circumstances, bear thinking of. She had borne him six daughters in the nine years of their marriage, the youngest of the surviving five only a few months old when he left and, of these, only four would grow to marriageable age. She was obliged to bear, also, the pain and ignominy of his desertion and, worse than any of this to her, she would never be the Countess of Leicester and Warwick. In the years of their marriage, she had seldom seen the ruthless side of Robert's nature and she found it hard to reconcile it with what she knew of him. The truth was that there had been little understanding or love in their marriage; it had been one of expedience, youthful attraction and the hopes of an heir. There was a ruthless streak in Alice also. The day after she heard of Robert's flight, she ordered the huntsman to take his dogs out and shoot them.

Lady Douglas, as she had promised Robert she would, again stepped in, this time to befriend and comfort Alice and her small granddaughters. She took them, initially, down to Sudely, her own home. She knew a certain amount about desertion and impetuous Dudley behaviour, and gave Alice the benefit of her counsel. It would be useless and undignified to pursue Robert and Elizabeth. The best Alice could do was to abandon all thought of social advancement, so long her aim and dream, and to concentrate upon the retention of her estates, her own comfort and the future of her daughters. Douglas, so long in the fore-front of Court and aristocratic life, would certainly help with their future and with the finding of suitable husbands in due course. Financially, she was well able to support them if need be, but, like Robert, she feared a Royal land-grab of Kenilworth. Alice hoped that King James would insist on Robert's return to render account of his behaviour but Douglas knew well this was most unlikely and that there would be no going back. She had seen for herself a new dimension in her son and recognised the overwhelming change so great a love had wrought in him.

Whilst in Lyons, Robert and Elizabeth had visited the houses of the silk merchants, for which the town was famous, and managed to replenish their wardrobes. True to form, he had taken a great interest in the manufacture and production of their wares, going over their weaving-rooms and warehouses and talking to their designers. All knowledge gleaned there had been stored in his versatile and enquiring mind for future use.

For the time being, the Dudleys, or the Earl and Countess of Warwick as they were now known, would remain in Pisa; more convenient for the work to be done there and in Livorno, but would retain the rooms made ready for them in Florence.

Florence was a magically beautiful city and they both hoped, one day, to build a house here for themselves and their family. Elizabeth, in particular, was enchanted with its mixture of ancient serenity, culture, and the sense of timelessness woven into its fabric. It was, under the rule of Duke Ferdinand, one of the best ordered cities in Europe. Clean, efficiently run, law-abiding and, according to Sir Henry Wotton, a magnet for his countrymen travelling abroad: "whither are drawn our English gentlemen by the beauty and security of the place and the purity of the language." This trend was to continue with increasing numbers down the centuries; Robert and Elizabeth were two of many who were cheerfully to exchange London for Florence.

It was the perfect setting, too, for their love for each other which had grown with each passing day. It was a deep, abiding and timeless passion which was the cornerstone of everything they did and enjoyed. Elizabeth laughed, loved and made light of difficulties and she brought to Robert's restless existence a peace and fulfilment his life had not known before. She was balm to the demons of anger and rejection which had haunted him since childhood. Not that this was to slow his activities down in any way. He was, already, deeply immersed in plans for ship and harbour building.

In the very sophisticated and critical society of Florence, the relationship of these newcomers was, after initial comment, recognised and remarked upon without malice. The Duchess, prepared to be extremely cautious with the unorthodox pair, found herself unable to do anything but enjoy their company. It was soon seen that Elizabeth's startling beauty was no threat to man or woman. She had eyes for no-one but her charismatic husband and, with the experience of years, she knew how to discourage advances from the susceptible Tuscan courtiers without giving the least offence. There were few moments in the lives of these gentlemen that were not enhanced by the sight of a beautiful woman. Almost to a man, they gasped, wondered and tried their luck with this golden girl, all to no avail; with well-chosen words and laughter she put them firmly aside. Her Italian was good; she had been brought up in a Court whose Queen spoke French, German, Italian, Spanish, Latin and Greek fluently, and who did not tolerate the under-educated.

The turning point in her acceptance came on the day before her return to Pisa, when the Duchess, having included her in a gathering of her ladies, heard her singing softly and decorously to her lute then, suddenly, strum the strings and burst into full, unbridled song, her voice soaring into the arches of the ornate chamber where they sat. Startling as it was, the music had a regrettably pagan flavour and beat, but the Duchess felt it might be tempered into something less passionate and more civilised. She was very fond of music and felt that the lovely Countess of Warwick might be an asset, after all. Quite apart from this, she could not help approving Elizabeth's charming manners and happy, natural personality, most unlike the rigidity of the watchful ladies of her Court who had been prepared, without exception, to give her the cold shoulder. Where the Duchess smiled, however, they could not frown. Later, when they realised that she was not trying to win favour at their expense or to impress their men, they began to unbend and regard her as a delightful, unsophisticated oddity. She was, in fact, an experienced courtier and quite content to let them think of her what they would.

It was during this visit that Elizabeth was approached by a Father Robert Parsons. Being new to Florence and the various groups of Englishmen living there, she could not be expected to differentiate between good and undesirable contacts among the many she met. Father Parsons, a fanatical Jesuit, was reputed to have contributed to "Leycester's Commonwealth", the pamphlet that had so viciously attacked Robert's father. While in Florence from Rome, he insinuated himself into Elizabeth's confidence through a series of introductions from people she had met and found unexceptional. Had Robert known of this, he would have been furious. Parsons knew exactly who she was, her family background, and that she appeared happy in her new religion; there was no need for proselytising. He also knew that she had been with the old Queen during her final days and he cleverly persuaded Elizabeth to give him a detailed account of every last word the Queen had spoken and the sequence of events that had led to her death. This he recorded, kept and, having quoted parts in his theological writings, passed down to posterity: a clear, concise account for historians to pore over for more than four hundred years. There were facts told in Elizabeth's account mentioned nowhere else. She had been there, she had seen and heard and she had not lied. Aged seventeen at the time, she was well able to produce such an account. From Elizabeth had come a record of several utterances made by the dying Queen. To Cecil, imploring her to go to bed: "the word "must" is not to be used to Princes. Little man, little man, if your father had lived, he durst not have said so much. But thou knowest I must die and that maketh thee so presumptuous." Also, when past speech and having refused to name her successor, the old Queen had pointed to her own, annointed head at the mention of James of Scotland, indicating that he was to succeed as King. There was also the unique description of the Queen's coffin bursting open during the watches of the night, according to Elizabeth: "with such a crack that splitted the wood, lead and cere cloth, whereupon the next day she was fain to be new trimmed up". No one else had recorded this unseemly happening but Elizabeth who had been keeping vigil over her mistress in Whitehall where she lay. The matter had been hastily put to rights and kept quiet for the sake of posterity and the dignity of the old Queen's departure.

When Robert discovered what had taken place, he exploded, threatening to spit Father Parsons, who had bolted for Rome like a rabbit, carrying Elizabeth's memories with him. He would take good care not to come within the Earl of Warwick's orbit again. Robert warned his wife to be careful in her dealings with English Catholics in future; some of them were malicious troublemakers who had hatched many a plot against the Old Queen.

Apart from Father Parsons, there were many English people living in Florence who quickly sought them out, among them a large trading fraternity which included both Protestants and Catholics. One couple in particular, Andrew Tracy and his wife, Mary, had been living in Florence for some years, and were shrewd and delightful people who went out of their way to make them welcome. They soon became good friends of the Warwicks. Tracy put Robert in touch with many who could help with the vast amount of work that faced him, while Mary introduced Elizabeth to mantua-makers, silk merchants, doctors and reliable servants. She was a sharp-faced little person with a quick wit and a kind heart who knew the pitfalls of Tuscan and Court society and she was to remain one of their greatest allies.

Elizabeth, possibly because of the rigorous ride from Lyons, lost the child she was carrying, to her great grief, but very soon became pregnant again, promising Robert that she would not ride, this time, beyond the early stages.

On their return from Florence, they had quickly settled down to life in Pisa. The house stood amongst orange and grapefruit trees and the heavenly scent of their blossom wafted through the rooms with every breeze in springtime. When Elizabeth could no longer travel with Robert to Livorno, she often took her lute out on the terrace in the evenings and sang. Before long a group of children with their parents quietly gathered under the trees in the garden, sometimes with a few patient little donkeys and dogs in attendance. She encouraged them to join in and accompany her, waving to one or another, and was surprised how many really beautiful voices responded. These musical interludes, usually at the end of a hard day's work, became a regular source of entertainment for everyone and the place rang with laughter. She learnt the local songs from them and the dances that accompanied them; her self-appointed chorus often brought with them loaves of bread, a few eggs or bags of polenta. Several offered to work in the house or garden and a small, friendly community gradually grew up around the house. Elizabeth soon knew them all, their families and relationships, and she employed three of their dark-eyed daughters.

Her steward, Philip, the "purveyor" of her household, was a native of Pisa himself. The product of an English seaman and a local girl, though usually very much upon his dignity, he unbent at the evening gatherings and was delighted to include these girls in the service of the house. He cast a fatherly eye over them and Elizabeth was tempted to wonder if those chosen were not related to him. Like William Bradshaw, his horizons had broadened dramatically when given employment with the Warwicks. Before long, he would be making the journeys to and from Florence with them. William Bradshaw's eye was also cast over the girls, but in a way that was not at all fatherly. The eldest of them, Seraphina, a seductive armful, was very much to his taste; the future looked promising.

Elizabeth had loved Italy from the beginning; the exuberance of the people, the warmth, the beauty of the building and art; above all, the carefree joyfulness that poured from every walk of life, despite the poverty, and the endless pattering of the donkeys' tiny feet as they passed her house. She was completely content in her new life even if the man she loved above all else was not constantly with her. The loss of her family, her high position at Court, her friends and her reputation had no power to hurt her even though she missed those she loved. Her mother's re-marriage to John Stewart, Earl of Carrick, had set her at a distance; it was her father, the big, blue-eyed Admiral whom she had adored and mourned.

Robert was spending much time travelling between Pisa and Livorno. After a while, when Elizabeth's pregnancy prevented her from accompanying him and he found he could not bear to be parted from her for long, he was often on the road. He had acquired a pair of trained Italian greyhounds who covered the ground with easy grace and assisted in a certain amount of hunting en route. While on these journeys Robert's fertile mind was busy with other schemes quite unrelated to ships or harbours.

To his delight, he was able to meet the ebullient Galileo who had retired to his birthplace in Pisa; he had been an idol of Robert's for many years. The scope of his erudition was enormous and varied and, until recently, he had tutored Duke Ferdinand's son, Cosimo. Robert listened, rapt, to his theories and inspected his numerous inventions. Galileo's championship of Copernicanism and heliocentrism had resulted in serious trouble with the Vatican, who regarded them as bordering on the blasphemous; he had even been imprisoned for a short time. He was gracious enough to listen to Robert's own plans as well, recognising a mind akin to his own and with as formidable a range of interests. He gave some excellent advice on the projects at Livorno and the continued draining of the Tuscan marshes. Galileo, despite his long white beard, was in fact, only ten years older than Robert; he possessed a keen sense of humour and his eyes twinkled, but he had tweaked the nose of His Holiness, Pope Paul V, to his own cost, and was later to refuse, under threat of torture, to deny any of his beliefs and theories. He was still busily employed in the construction of various new inventions, among them a high-powered water pump which was to be of considerable interest to Robert.

Robert was working, at this time, on a medicinal compound of his own brewing which he hoped would have a broad range of uses. He had experimented with it himself to see if there should be any dire side-effects and, so far, it had done him no harm. It was composed mainly of oxide of anthimony, tartaric acid, scammery and potassium, ground to fine powder and taken in water; a regular depth charge in fact, to act as a killer of pain, a purge and a restorative. Following what he had learned from Abraham Kendal on the control of sickness among his men at sea, he had moved naturally to the world of medical science. He had seen how disease could run riot in men living at close quarters with bad food and water, and how quickly they could recover when well-fed and sheltered. His voyage to Trinidad had taught him much, particularly on the subject of diet, and he did not agree with the universal practice of bleeding for almost any complaint. In cases of fever he believed that it only weakened the stricken body's capacity to fight infection and that it was better to boost the natural resources from within, and so aid recovery. Since he was now known universally as the Earl of Warwick, he had named his potion "Pulvis Warvicensis" and had no doubts as to its efficacy or its eventual recognition. Doubt was something that seldom troubled him and there were so many other avenues yet to explore.

The Medici had built up vast wealth through their banking houses over the last two generations; Duke Ferdinand was a serious and able economist and he would spare no cost in the development of his navy and his harbours. Robert worked relentlessly over the next eighteen months, his knowledge and his energy wading through, and over, many difficulties. He was able to employ known and trusted English shipwrights in modernising the Tuscan Navy and to man their finished fleet with many English seamen. His reputation in the nautical world was such that numbers of unemployed mariners in England hastened to Tuscany. He sent some of his plans to Thomas Chaloner, both for advice and for interest's sake. Sir Thomas was now tutor at Court to the young Prince Henry, a great advance in his career. Their friendship had survived the divergence of their lives and careers and Chaloner, according to Lotti, "showed me the design for a ship made at Livorno by the Earl of Warwick and another which he said was more perfect than any". This prototype warship was named the "San Giovanni Battista".

Incredibly, by the summer of 1607, Duke Ferdinand was able to send a fleet, manned largely by English sailors, to assist in an attack on Cyprus. This turned out to be something of a farce since the occupying Ottomans were warned and well-prepared for it. For Robert Dudley, however, it was a God-given opportunity to evaluate his work over the previous eighteen months. How could he possibly resist the temptation to test his ships and his own efforts and expertise; added to which would be the joy of being at sea again and the chance of a good battle? The raid was to be a joint endeavour by the Knights of St. Stephen, the Spanish, the Tuscans and a mongrel assortment of corsairs. The somewhat haphazard request for help had come from the Cypriot nobles, routed by the Ottomans in 1571, who were striving for a return to power.

Robert's main difficulty lay in persuading Elizabeth that he did not intend to walk into the jaws of death but to remain on stand-by in one of his ships and at the rear of any action. She knew him far too well. He was the heart of her heart, and he would never be anywhere but in the lead of any enterprise in which he was involved. He would instantly take command of any situation within his orbit and she could see him happily scaling walls in the dead of night with a sword between his teeth. She cried, she laughed, but she had seen the gleam in his eye and knew that she must let him go. He was back within the month.

The attack on Famagusta, indeed carried out at night, was chaotic and failed completely. Communication between the Cypriot nobles in the hills supposedly supporting the attack, the ships, and the landing forces was non-existent, no-one had the least idea where anyone else was or what they were doing and one flotilla of ships turned up two days too late. When it came to scaling the walls of the town, the ladders were found to be far too short. The guns of Famagusta, manned by the Ottomans, thundered impressively from the walls but failed to harm the would-be attackers, now landed and sheltering beneath them, nor could they reach the ships since they were out of range. The approaches, used mainly by galleys which drew little water, were too shallow and the harbour too small for the Tuscan ships to come within range of targets ashore and, as dawn broke, the whole raid was eventually called off.

Robert, on board the "San Giovanni Battista", the best of his new ships, enjoyed himself enormously. She was swift and responsive and a pleasure to helm. In command of the Tuscan force was Antonio de Medici, an illegitimate half-brother of Duke Ferdinand. He had no naval experience whatever and was more than happy to leave the handling of the ships in Robert's hands. They retrieved their landing parties with few casualties and sailed for home. It was to be Robert's last sea-faring expedition. He was now thirty three years old.

This first putative effort to establish Tuscan naval power was soon followed by a far more successful raid on the Barbary Coast corsairs, and later by a splendid battle with the Turks, during the course of which nine ships, scores of prisoners and jewels to the tune of two million ducats were captured. The Tuscan fleet was becoming a force to be reckoned with in the Mediterranean. Both Duke Ferdinand and his son, Cosimo, were delighted.

That same year, 1607, the first salvo of retribution from England was fired by King James at the Earl of Warwick. Until then, James had done little more than expostulate over Robert's departure in July 1605. Events at home, including Guy Fawkes's efforts to eradicate Parliament in November, with all the attendant shock and aftermath, had taken his mind off such a minor issue. His attack was not unexpected since Robert's leave to travel abroad had been granted for three years only. Nor was it unexpected that it came through the now all-powerful little Robert Cecil, the Earl of Salisbury, who had sided so blatantly with Robert Sidney and the King against Dudley in Star Chamber.

"We granted you leave to travel" stated the King peevishly, "in the hope that you might thereby prove the better enable to the service of us and our State, as you pretended. We do now certainly understand that you do bear and behave yourself inordinately, and have attempted many things prejudicial to us and our Crown, which we cannot suffer or endure." He then commanded Robert to return and to "yield and render your body to some of our Privy Council. Hereof fail you not, as you will answer the contrary to your uttermost peril." He was to come home forthwith and face his peers and his welcome would be anything but warm. This order was strong stuff, sent to Robert via Sir Henry Wotton in Venice in the form of a Royal Warrant of Privy Seal. He was well aware of its content since the messengers who brought it were a pair of garrulous gossips and he had, anyway, been forewarned by Sir Henry (still anxiously pining for Elizabeth).

Robert refused to accept or open the Warrant on the grounds that it was not addressed to him as the Earl of Warwick. He followed this up in a long letter to his cousin, the Earl of Northampton, saying that the lack of confidentiality had resulted in a widespread loss of character for him in Italy; "This is a great disreputation for me, to be published over Italy for a traitor and worse…. I hold the same course not very honourable to have bruited in his Majesty's name such scandals to a subject before trial……… if these be all the allegations my enemies have made against me to his Majesty, as I presume no man can be so horrible a liar to speak worse against me." There followed a lengthy justification of his flight, his change of religion, his marriage and the use of his titles as vindication of his legitimacy. He then asked to be allowed to remain at peace in Tuscany "to repair my reputation abroad and at home" and, as a parting shot, "to give my best assistance and service to the Great Duke of Florence." So much for the great King of England and any demands he might make for Robert's immediate return. Northampton, however, too busy toadying to the King over his own advancement, was putting no spokes in his own wheel in order to help Robert's concerns.

The second salvo fired was aimed at Kenilworth. Soon after his reply to Northampton, news came to Robert that the King had ordered all his estates to be sequestered to the Crown, in addition to those it already held. It was unlikely that his own orders to convey all his lands to the Leigh family could keep his Majesty's hands off the estate. There was little Robert could do. His contempt for the Crown had been all too clear.

It said much for his friendship with Duke Ferdinand, and for the respect he bore him, that he listened to the counsel given him at this time. The Duke had developed a deep affection for both Robert and Elizabeth. He was approaching sixty, almost thirty years older than Robert, and his long sojourn in the Vatican had given him insight and tolerance. He was anxious that Robert should not burn his boats with his native land, however much he appreciated the monumental work he was doing in Tuscany. He had proved Ferdinand's own initial judgement correct and was worth his weight in gold. The work on both ships and harbours had forged ahead at an incredible speed. But, quite apart from his worth, Ferdinand was concerned for his friend's future and he advised most strongly against an angry or provocative response. Robert's missive to his cousin, Northampton, had been quite provocative enough. He understood the fire in Robert's nature and the long-smouldering anger against the bastardy imposed on him but hoped that the recognition given him here in Tuscany had damped it down. In the interests of peace, the Duke asked Lotti, in London, to do his best to patch things up with King and Court, writing, himself: "Here he is known as a worthy knight, and of the utmost goodwill, and he could not possibly entertain any idea of disloyalty or ill-faith towards King James or his State."

Rumour swung back and forth. One story suggested that the King had again insisted on Robert's return, this time with the Earldom of Warwick as a promised sweetener, another that the Pope had annulled his marriage to Elizabeth. Lotti, with his ear to the ground in London, could not report any success regarding rapprochement, however, stating in February 1608, of Robert, that the King "disliked him heartily." Matters could only get worse.

The English Crown had no wish to sour relations with Duke Ferdinand; Tuscany was too valuable an ally. Yet, Robert Dudley was a thorn in James's flesh and the peevishness continued. "I should not wish to drive him out of His Serene Highness's State: yet that he could receive Dudley in his house, and honour him as he does, seems very strange to me. He has a wife and children here, the Pope has annulled his marriage to the woman he has with him and I, for my part, hold him incapable of any honourable action."

There was no love lost. King James was affronted and insulted. His character was a strange one, compounded of suspicion, bigotry, and somewhat confused sexuality. He loved his family and fathered many children but a troubled childhood had, perhaps, resulted in an over-ardent admiration of handsome, masterful men. He had a series of favourites, Robert Carr, later Earl of Somerset and George Villiers, Duke of Buckingham, in particular, with both of whom his relations were more than fond and which resulted in unseemly scandals. Guy Fawkes and his gunpowder had served to harden certain of his characteristics, leaving the King more suspicious and less forgiving. His fear of witches and warlocks, already pronounced, had become obsessive; they lurked behind every bush and must be rooted out. This led to the persecution of many innocent people.

This last reverberation from the King did strike home and had the effect of making Robert insist on a Papal confirmation of the legality of his marriage to Elizabeth. Here, Duke Ferdinand could most certainly help. After being so long a part of it, he was able to tread the corridors of power within the Vatican with ease. He knew Pope Paul V well and advised Robert on the presentation of a petition to verify the legality of the union. Robert still had in his possession, after all this time, written proof of his "contract" with Frances Vavasour which, purportedly, invalidated his other two marriages. This was a legal document witnessed in London in 1592, incredibly, by none other than Captain Thomas Jobson, his relative and shipmate of the expedition to Trinidad. It had been used in negotiating his marriage with Elizabeth and the fact that he had kept it was somewhat suspect and akin to some of his father's dealings. He had been seventeen years old at the time.

Elizabeth, naturally distressed and nearing the birth of their child, also wanted their marriage established beyond doubt before the baby's arrival. She appealed to Duchess Christina, whose piety was a byword, and it said much for that lady's belief in the validity of the Warwick marriage and her affection for Elizabeth that she personally wrote to Pope Paul V on her behalf.

A daughter was born very soon after this amid the greatest rejoicing. Robert had waited long for his heir but nothing could mar the joy of this arrival; time enough for a boy, and the house in Pisa resounded with celebration. Elizabeth's delivery was swift and easy for a first birth, assisted by the mothers of her young maids, and members of her "choir", who joined in the occasion with expertise and enthusiasm. They ruthlessly barred Robert from the house, according to custom, until mother and child were presented, suitably attired and composed and, as one emotional midwife insisted, looking like the "Santa Maria" and all the angels of heaven. Robert's cup was full as he took them both in his arms. They, indeed, christened the baby Maria and she was to be the first of a very large family. Robert's frantic anxiety during the birth caused him stirrings of guilt when he thought back on the arrivals of his many daughters at Kenilworth. Either he had not been present or he had ridden out fearing the advent of yet another girl.

The baptism took place in the Duomo of Pisa two days later amid much bell ringing and the lighting of many candles. Mary Tracy stood as godmother and the Duke and Duchess sent a beautifully decorated missal. Galileo produced a carved orb fashioned as a rattle and engraved with the contours of the known world.

CHAPTER ELEVEN

Under Tuscan Skies – 1608-1612

The Earl and Countess of Warwick were now well-established members of the Tuscan Court and held in great affection by both Duke Ferdinand and his Duchess. They found themselves in frequent attendance at the Medici Palace; both being natural diplomats and very decorative assets to proceedings. They were genuinely loved by the Ducal pair, and many others, for themselves and for the atmosphere of goodwill and vitality they radiated. They had proved excellent ambassadors, particularly when dealing with those from Northern hemispheres.

This became very apparent when the Duke's son, the nineteen year old Prince Cosimo, was betrothed to the Archduchess Maria Maddalena, the daughter of Archduke Charles of Austria. Maria Maddalena's brother, Ferdinand, was soon to become the Holy Roman Emperor and the alliance was an excellent one.

The bride, aged sixteen, duly arrived in Florence attended by an enormous retinue of courtiers and servants. She was red-haired and dignified but, surprisingly, she did not speak Italian, only German and Latin. The Countess of Warwick, who was known to speak some German, was immediately summoned from Pisa and asked to befriend her. There were, naturally, Italian speakers among her entourage able to translate for her, but few young wives in whom she could confide.

On arrival, Elizabeth was conducted to one of the enormous, pillared and painted reception chambers, so full of courtiers craning to get a glimpse of the Austrian Archduchess that she could scarcely follow her escort through the crowd. The girl, though poised enough, looked bewildered; her young bridegroom seemed equally ill at ease. They clearly could not communicate with each other even had they wished or been able to. The presentations were never-ending but, eventually, Elizabeth was asked to come forward. Rising from a curtsey, she smiled her lovely smile at Maria Maddalena, asked, in German, how she did after her journey and hoped she would have the honour to speak further in the future. The girl's face lit up; she had recognized a kindred spirit from the North, and she asked Elizabeth which country she came from. She then turned to one of her Chamberlains and asked him to note Lady Warwick's name. The Duchess Christina, soon to be her mother-in-law, smiled gently and nodded approval.

A few days later, Elizabeth was again introduced to Maria Maddalena and, after a few pleasantries, left to converse with her. They were only a few years apart in age and Elizabeth's German, though not perfect, was good enough to reach an easy understanding with her. The poor child confided that she was homesick, lonely in that huge throng of courtiers and her own entourage, and terrified of marriage with a total stranger, though this was the accepted fate of most royal ladies. Her upbringing had been rigid, she knew her duty, but her long Hapsburg face, inclined to melancholy, showed clearly how out of her depth she felt herself to be. Elizabeth's happy nature and the fact that she, also, had arrived as a foreigner in an unknown land, was a basis for the growing friendship which was to follow. She made Maria Maddalena smile, promised to help if she was needed, especially with the Italian tongue which, she assured her, was the easiest and loveliest of languages, and, unconsciously, imparted a little of her own buoyant optimism. As for the marriage, all would be well. Cosimo was a delightful boy and, probably, as apprehensive as she was. Having been treated to lectures from her guardians to the tune of "what cannot be cured must be endured", this was a pleasant change and Elizabeth was, in general, so enthusiastic regarding life in Tuscany that the young Archduchess began to feel more cheerful about her exile. She had only to look at that beautiful face to know that all, indeed, might yet be well.

Maria Maddalena had a passion for hunting and was an excellent horsewoman. She hoped that it was the custom in Tuscany, as in Austria, for ladies to ride out with their men and she became most animated when she began to describe some of the notable runs she had taken part in at home, sometimes even after boar. She had brought her favourite horses with her. Elizabeth shared her enthusiasm and promised she would immediately speak to her husband, the Earl of Warwick, who seldom missed a day out if he could help it.

Maria Maddalena's other passion was for dancing and she was a pleasure to watch. No one could fault her precision and, though taller than most of her entourage, her grace and elegance immediately drew the eye.

The marriage, which took place in the Basilica of San Lorenzo, the ancient cathedral patronized by the Medici, was attended, among hundreds, by the Earl and Countess of Warwick. What followed was one of the most lavish displays ever seen in Florence. It was set on a stretch of the Arno river between the Ponte alla Carraia and the Ponte Santa Trinita along which rows of allegorical statues had been set. The audience was seated in grandstands erected on the Lungarni. The theme was "The Argosy" and the heroic Jason, skirting enormous dolphins and fire-breathing hydra, sailed round a pre-constructed island, grabbed the golden fleece and presented it to Maria Maddalena together with six red apples, a Medici symbol. The weather held, nothing capsized and nobody drowned. It was a huge success.

That evening, a banquet of gargantuan proportions was held in the "Hall of the Five Hundred" within the Palazzo Vecchio. Robert was delighted to see that the Hall was decorated with a display of the treasures looted from the defeated Turkish fleet, taken by the Tuscan ships designed and built by him at Livorno and including the "San Giovanni Battista". She had proved her worth against the Turks in a very definite way.

During the feast, which lasted for hours, Elizabeth could see that, at the high table, Prince Cosimo was making a real effort to amuse and entertain his bride. They had fallen back on Latin as a means of communication. She was smiling, and even laughing, at something he was trying to demonstrate with the aid of several heavy gold salt cellars. She would never be a beauty, but she had charm and a sweet smile. No arranged marriage was ever easy, but the ice had clearly been broken; there was no established mistress in the wings, and every reason to suppose the union could be a happy one. Elizabeth, catching Robert's eye, which was glinting wickedly, knew that they were both thinking of their own courtship; it had been too speedy to need any help, let alone from gold salt cellars.

Elizabeth gradually became a trusted confidante of Maria Maddalena and, through her, Robert came to know Prince Cosimo, now emerging as his father's heir, and to establish the same position of trust and friendship with him, as he had with Duke Ferdinand. Increasingly, Cosimo was being included in his father's counsels.

The Earl and Countess of Warwick, inevitably, were not always universally popular. Their rapid rise among those favoured by the Medici, the impact they had made on the society of Florence and their glamour as a pair were bound to raise some jealous eyebrows. Robert, himself, stood half a head taller than any other man at the Tuscan Court and was not easily overlooked on any count. A bare fifty years ago, in this same Court, there may well have been murder and mayhem and a closing of ranks, both among the courtiers and the Medici family itself. During Duke Ferdinand's own youth there had been internecine strife resulting in the murders of the lovely Isabella de Medici and several of the Orsini family. There was often, too, a judicious pruning of the illegitimate children of ducal mistresses when the head of the house died.

By this same year, 1608, Robert had persuaded the marine-minded Duke to equip a 400 ton vessel, designed and built by himself, to sail, as he had done, to Guiana, the Orinoco and the Amazon for the purposes of further exploration and the possible establishment of a Tuscan colony in the fertile lands there. He had seen them for himself and he was able to give first-hand navigational information and maps of the topography of the area, including Dudleiana, the sun-drenched island of his dreams. El Dorado and Raleigh's expedition to find it still lurked in his memory. Duke Ferdinand was most enthusiastic about this venture and was supported by several influential members of his government; it was by no means a whim urged on him by Robert. It had caught his imagination; that which Spain, Portugal and England had achieved, was surely not beyond Tuscany, with its well-filled coffers, and he would be delighted to establish the first Italian colony in the New World. Robert, with his knowledge of the area and clear memories of his own expedition, was given a free rein and the ship sailed in September 1608 under the command of a Captain Richard Thornton, who had been working for the Medici in Tuscany before Robert's arrival. Thornton was now well known to him and he held a high opinion of him. Armed with minute instructions from Robert, Thornton arrived safely at his destination. He was extremely grateful for these, maintaining that he, his ship and his crew would have been lost without them. Forewarned of the sudden, vicious "bores", or tidal waves in the river mouths, most explicitly charted by Robert with the warning: "Beware of a bore at six hours and a quarter", he had managed to "warp his vessel with cables in a safer position, so as to receive the bore with his prow, and thus the vessel did not founder."

Thornton went on to discover the port of Chiana, later known as the French port of Cayenne, spending time there trading and becoming friendly with the native Indians. He was to bring back a good cargo of sugar cane, cotton, rosewood and, of course, pepper. Also, six men of the Carib Indian tribe, those cannibals encountered by Robert on his own voyage so many years before.

In December 1608, news arrived of Lady Douglas's death. This was a great grief for Robert, who loved her and owed her a great deal. He well knew, also, that he had disrupted the last years of her life. Despite the fact that he had been separated from her between the ages of five and fifteen, blood had proved thicker than water and she had guided him through his earliest days at Court with marked success. She, herself, had risen to the dizzy height of "Mistress of the Robes" in the Queen's household. During the ordeal of Star Chamber, she had endured much on his behalf and she had remained a friend to Alice and her daughters after his departure. By nature, she was compliant and, had she been less so, Robert's life would have been very different. A mother such as Lettice Knollys might have shaped another, more conventional character. Douglas's early weakness and reluctance to stand up to Leicester had made Robert's life, with its slur of bastardy, a battleground, from which a very remarkable man had emerged; an undaunted explorer of many fields, prepared for risk and with a mind unshackled by convention. In the end, she had given him all he had asked of her with generosity and courage and she had shielded and guided his deserted family to the best of her ability. She was not alone in her last years. Her Sheffield children and their families remained close to her and she had always been in constant touch with Alice and her granddaughters to whom she left generous bequests. She had also watched over Elizabeth from her arrival at Court as a Maid of Honour to the time of her flight with Robert and had managed to keep the interests of both his wives at heart. Both he and Elizabeth sincerely mourned her passing, regretting that they had not been with her in her declining years.

Robert's mountain of work in Pisa and Livorno, combined with increasing attendance at the Tuscan Court, now involved an even greater amount of travelling. The time had clearly come to establish a base in the heart of Florence somewhat larger than the rooms they had been given.

He approached a friend, the Cavalier Annibale Orlandini, a scatterbrained individual who also travelled extensively, and arranged to rent his house in the suitably named Via dell' Amore. Elizabeth dissolved into helpless laughter over the name and promised to do it justice, wondering whether there would be many ladies of the night similarly occupied in the vicinity. The house was well furnished and staffed and from there they planned, eventually, to find or build their own palazzo. Elizabeth was again pregnant and finding the constant travelling exhausting and Maria Maddalena, since her marriage, often asked for her company. She even shared the merriment over her friend's new address. Particularly, the young Duchess asked for Robert's company in the hunting field. Maria Maddalena was an intrepid rider to hounds, giving her entourage several nervous moments and she looked her best on the horses she had brought with her, some bred from the famous Spanish strain of Lippiza.

By New Year of 1609, the young Princess was also pregnant and, until nearly 1618, she was to present Cosimo with a child every year. Of her five sons, four died unmarried despite the fact that they survived to a good age; two were, admittedly, Cardinals of Rome. Only the eldest, Ferdinando, inheriting from his father, was to continue the Medici line in Tuscany. This first child, Maria Christina, was born malformed, a bitter shock to her mother which produced a sense of failure and a determination to give the Medici an heir at all costs. Despite this, the little girl was loved and cherished, lived with the family until she was fourteen and was painted by several artists. Within a year of this initial disappointment, the heir was born, followed by four further sons and three daughters.

Inbreeding among the European dynasties, despite the Papal laws on consanguinity, did not make for healthy or robust individuals, particularly where the Hapsburgs were concerned. Generations of territorial, family intermarriage had produced the "Hapsburg jaw", known later as "mandibular prognathism", manifested in a large, jutting jaw, a thick lower lip and an oversized tongue which made speech difficult. An increasing tendency to sterility was another characteristic. For years Hapsburgs had often married their cousins, uncles and nieces. This may have accounted for the unfortunate little Maria Christina and the fact that within the next three generations the Hapsburg Royal males would find it hard to breed at all. It may also have accounted for the fact that only two of Maria Maddalena and Cosimo's five sons produced children.

On 17th February 1609, the Grand Duke Ferdinand of Tuscany, the best, wisest and most provident of the Medici rulers, died. Never one to overindulge, it was believed that the prolonged wedding festivities accompanied by the huge feasts, followed, as they had been, with the Christmas celebrations, had been too much.

Elizabeth and Robert, dressed in deep mourning, and sincerely bereaved by the loss of this father figure, filed past his body as it lay in state in the Grand Ducal Palace and paid tribute to the man who had done so much for them and had become a true and trusted friend. He was eventually interred in the family mausoleum within San Lorenzo which he, himself, had begun to build.

He had achieved order, stability and huge wealth in Tuscany. He had put an end to the corruption so rife in the Courts of Justice and made Florence a centre of learning and, above all, the arts. During his long years in the Vatican, besides being a renowned patron, he had amassed a superb collection of classical art in his Villa Medici in Rome, and this he had brought to the Palace of the Uffizi in Florence. To music he had brought a new form, the Recitativo, later known as the Opera, which was first performed in the Great Hall of the Uffizi. With Robert's expertise and energy behind him, he had re-built the Tuscan navy and established its force in the Mediterranean, expanded the harbours of Pisa and Livorno, while further plans for the draining of the Tuscan marshes and their reclamation for agricultural land, were well under way. The two enterprises were closely linked. His like among the rulers of Tuscany would not be seen again.

Like a moth to a candle, Elizabeth had been drawn to the Recitativo and the performances given in the Uffizi. When in Florence, she attended every production possible and, galvanised by her energy and enthusiasm, the new Duchess Maria Maddalena also began to take a keen interest. She was amazed by the Countess's comparatively untutored, but inborn, knowledge of music and the pair were often to be found attending rehearsals where Elizabeth would join the singing, her voice ranging effortlessly between soprano and alto cantatas, both of which she could easily follow and enlarge upon. Not for many years would a woman be allowed on a stage, especially in an operatic role, but Elizabeth could indulge this gift of hers off stage and, at the same time, give inspiration and a lead to the singers, just as she had in her home in Pisa. Strangely, they bore her no resentment; not because she was clearly a friend of the Grand Duchess, but because of her natural enthusiasm and support for their art, not to mention her extraordinary beauty. Both ladies were almost constantly pregnant at this time and their participation and interest in the Recitativo gave them pleasure and occupation in the later stages when they could no longer ride or travel.

A Florentine band of dilettante musicians under a Count Bardi were often the performers and their repertoire included "Euridice" by Peri, and, as opera spread to Rome and to Venice, the works of Monteverdi also. Bardi, probably self-elevated, was a priceless caricature of the Italian singer complete with moustaches, plump silhouette and every theatrical gesture stretched to the limit. He wriggled with delight at the ducal interest, but it would never do to laugh. The female leading roles were sung by castrati, some quite beautifully, but few better than Elizabeth, their controlled and carefully trained voices lacking the vibrancy and spontaneity of hers. Robert, although he could not sing a note, loved to hear her, mainly because of the pleasure it gave her to sing. She was entirely unselfconscious, having been accustomed to perform since the age of thirteen, and a large audience held no terrors for her.

Maria Maddalena had stepped with assurance and dignity into the position of Grand Duchess of Tuscany and with rather more ease than did her husband into his role. It would take some time, if ever, for Cosimo to fill his father's shoes. He had neither the looks nor the presence of Ferdinand and his constitution was not robust. He was also caught between two women of powerful character, his mother, the devout Maria Christina, and his wife. Young as he was, he turned very naturally to a man of decision, strong will and a spirit of innovation; a courtier only of necessity, Robert Dudley, Earl of Warwick, would never take advantage of his trust, but would remain within reach, an advisor and an ally.

Cosimo had inherited from his father's twenty-two year reign an immense fortune, the most powerful state in Italy with its own army and navy, rich industry, and commerce which produced, yearly, an income far greater than that of England.

The young Duke had not failed to realise that some part of this success was due to his father's sponsorship of Robert Dudley. Neither had his mother, the Duchess Maria Christina, and both made sure that Robert retained his position of privilege and authority within the Tuscan

Court and the whole Medici family. He was too valuable an asset to lose or to be encouraged to return to England. From the outset, they had never held any doubts about the authenticity of his marriage to Elizabeth, and their children were always accepted as legitimate. Quite apart from anything else, they were not proof against the charm and vitality of the whole Warwick family. The Duchess Maria Christina was a stickler over religious matters and she had no fault to find.

The Medici, therefore, set about providing Robert with a "pension", over and above the retainer given him by Duke Ferdinand. This came betimes. Robert had now been forced to consider his own financial position more than he liked and, with a rapidly growing family, he could not remain in the scatty Orlandini's residence in the Via dell'Amore for much longer. There was no knowing when he would want it back and Robert was soon to be faced with the necessity of buying or building his own palazzo in Florence, always Elizabeth's dream. He had never been obliged to count cost in England and it did not come easily to him now. The "pension" would certainly help. The expense of constant travelling, added to the posting of horses along the route and the upkeep of carriages, was high.

More and more, the major coastal projects were being left in Robert's able hands. Their conception had been Duke Ferdinand's, but Cosimo's education was still being completed when they were begun. The new Duke was most interested in the work being done, nonetheless, and became particularly involved in the building of a large "mole" or pier at Livorno which he commissioned Robert to start at once. Happy though he was to have such a free rein, Robert realised that he could not remain in complete control of his projects and that some careful delegation was due. The role of these two ports, when completed, needed consideration, so that their uses could be expanded to fulfil their respective potential and their growth could be assured. They must be carefully planned with an eye to the future.

He had discussed with Duke Ferdinand the possibility of declaring Livorno, when complete, a "scala franca" or "free port". This would encourage merchants of every nationality to set up business there and to build their own houses and trading establishments. He knew that his influence and contacts alone would bring many English traders and friends. His friend, Andrew Tracy, was most enthusiastic about this. With unusual foresight, Robert had also suggested to the Duke that a law be passed ensuring freedom to all nationalities, including and in particular the Jews, which could have the effect of a very prompt increase in all trade. This aim was fully realised. Livorno became a haven for the embattled Spanish Jews and for many other political exiles. Robert aimed to make Livorno one of the best and biggest harbours in Europe and a great commercial city and centre. The Duke's decree, the "Livornina", declared that the port should be "a place of universal toleration", a gesture typical of this wise and generous ruler.

Already revolving in Robert's mind were plans for a harbour frontage of big, beautiful houses with others, set in their gardens, on the slopes behind. He was no dreamer and those plans would materialise and those houses would be built together with shops, warehouses and all possible incentives for international trade. Pisa would be used more as the naval base.

He had one more scheme up his sleeve. His knowledge of the manufacture of silk, acquired during his explorations in Lyons while waiting for Papal permission for his marriage to Elizabeth, must be put to use. Absorbed by his overwhelming love for her though he had been, he had not wasted his time there. Where better to build the first silk factory than in Livorno where merchants of every kind would be queuing on the doorstep and their ships in the harbour waiting to take their purchases on board?

Before the death of Duke Ferdinand, Robert had found they shared an interest in the making of silk in Tuscany. The Duke had, for some time, encouraged the growth of mulberry trees with this in mind, so that the raw materials would be easily available, but he had not carried the scheme much further. Robert's beady eye had seen, in Lyons, how the process could be improved upon and, furthermore, he had invented the necessary machinery for upgrading the manufacture and the quality of the silk. In October 1610 he was granted a patent for his invention and began its construction. He was also granted the right to profit exclusively from it for the next twenty years, which would ease his financial situation. It never crossed his mind that it was unusual for an Earl, or possibly a Duke, to be engaged in such occupations as architecture, shipbuilding and silk making, let alone the apothecary's trade. It had certainly occurred to Duke Ferdinand, with his shrewd business brain, and it had caused him some mirth; he laughingly called Robert an artisan and a tradesman. Nevertheless, due to their combined efforts, the silk trade in Italy, already well established, was to grow and blossom, giving employment to many in the country and in the factories that sprang up and flourished thereafter. Tuscan silk was to keep its reputation for centuries. Robert had often seen the mulberry trees growing along the roadsides, and he later made a point of finding further land for cultivation and investing in whole fields.

Before any of these grand dreams could be realised, and the ports be further expanded, the draining of the marshes between Pisa and Livorno must be completed. They hampered traffic to the ports, they were unsightly and disease ridden, and they stank. This work, long since in execution, had been high among Duke Ferdinand's priorities, and for personal reasons. He had watched his young brother, Giovanni, die of "mala aria", during a visit to Livorno in November 1562. He also had contracted the disease but had survived. Robert's vision and energy and his engineering knowledge were now directed at the final transformation into a fertile plain of the salty bogs around Pisa and along the Arno valley up to the Val di Nievole. He felt it was something he owed the old Duke.

Two other major projects begun by Duke Ferdinand were also occupying his mind. The first was to channel fresh water from Asciano to Pisa by aqueduct. This had been begun in 1592 with the aim of providing the citizens of Pisa, apparently always sick, with the pure, clean water from the Asciano hills, whose populace was always healthy. Modelled on the old Roman aqueduct, it consisted of nine hundred arches and ran six kilometres above the swampy ground between the two towns. A massive architectural work, it fascinated Robert at first sight and he was given permission to assist with its construction, (another good reason for draining the marshes). It was eventually completed in 1613 amid huge Tuscan self-congratulation.

The other major project was to link Pisa and Livorno by water, diverting the Arno River into a canal, the "Naviglio", which would eliminate the long detour by sea, increase trade and greatly benefit both ports.

Before further planning for these enterprises, Robert again consulted Galileo, with whom he was now on excellent terms, visiting him in the "Villa Arcetri", his home outside Pisa. Galileo, just appointed "Mathematician and Philosopher" to his former pupil, Duke Cosimo, had recently published his treatise "The Starry Messenger" which controversially stated that the Earth was not the centre of the universe, but revolved around the sun. This was to land him in yet more trouble; it did not accord with Rome's teaching.

Sitting in a studio of cheerful chaos, knee-deep in rolled parchment plans, with gadgets covering all available table space and prototype telescopes poised in every window, they were soon immersed in such subjects as mechanical pumps, sluices and canals. Galileo could switch his extraordinary mind from the infinite to the prosaic in a matter of moments; from the galaxy to the gangrenous marshes was a small step. Like a wizard producing rabbits from a hat, his deep-set, dark eyes lit up as he gleefully grabbed a pen and parchment and began to draw. Robert, mentally at the gallop behind him, was hard put to keep pace. There was already a pumping mechanism on his drawing boards which, expanded to a larger size, might well prove the answer to some of the problems confronting Robert. He and Galileo were made for each other and there were few places apart from this studio where he felt more at home.

Soon after the death of Duke Ferdinand, Captain Thornton returned safely from Trinidad and Chiana. He was full of praise for the charts, instructions and briefings received from Robert and his account was a testimony to Robert's own previous achievements. Another testimony was the six Carib Indians who had survived the homeward journey and were presented to the Grand Duke. Sadly, they did not live for long, falling easy prey to the diseases rife in Europe and unknown in South America. Before they succumbed Robert, brushing up his forgotten Arawak, was able to talk at length to them about their country, it's mineral wealth and their conviction that the great city by the lake, "El Dorado" or, to them, "Manoa" really did exist. One of them survived, learnt Italian, and remained in Robert's service at Court. The legend lived on in his mind, a mirage, clearly seen one moment and swept away by reason the next.

In Florence, the family front was expanding fast. His little daughter, Maria, was joined in July 1610, by the long-awaited son, a strapping baby named Cosimo, after the Grand Duke who stood as godfather, an honour which said much for the friendship between the two families. There was a strange prelude to this birth, which was to have a lasting benefit for Elizabeth.

In early spring that year, Robert and William Bradshaw were travelling as so often, from Livorno to Pisa, accompanied by his little greyhounds and hunting on the way. It was beautifully clear, the sun bright and the wind cold and they already had three hares strapped to their cruppers. Elizabeth and the baby, who had accompanied them from Florence, were awaiting them in Pisa. Robert had been coughing all morning and now noticed real pain on the right side of his chest and found his breathing was becoming difficult. Having ignored these unpleasant symptoms for some time, he also realised that he was burning with a heat that should not have been produced by mere hunting. He was almost never ill, but he knew a certain amount about fevers. They headed, at once, for home and by the time they reached it, William was seriously worried. Robert was on the point of collapse, bent, swaying, over his horse's withers, and coughing up discoloured matter. Elizabeth rushed him to bed, applying fomentations to the afflicted places and, at his instructions, William mixed a dose of his own powder – the Warwick powder – which he drank. He had guessed, rightly, that he was developing pleurisy, but did not know whether it was contagious or not. He, therefore, forbade Elizabeth to come near him again, since she was then expecting the second child, but got William to mix a further dose of his elixir later that day, followed by a third the next morning. Within three days he was on his feet again, without a doctor in attendance or any surgical bleeding. He felt unsteady, but delighted with the results of his powders. Elizabeth, suffering from morning sickness as never before and unfamiliar with its miseries since she had not been bothered in her previous pregnancy, insisted on taking a mild dose of it herself and found it so effective that she was never, thereafter, without it. The baby, Maria, then fell sick of a simple fever. She was also treated with a minute dose and recovered very quickly, the flush on her tiny face subsiding and her wailing fading into sleep.

Their steward, the faithful Philip, became seriously ill soon after this and was put immediately into a separate house for fear of infection. Horrified, they assumed that this time, and far worse, it was plague, since his whole body erupted in sores, besides the ravages of fever, and they feared for his life; he was not in the first flush of youth. He was dosed with Robert's powders at regular intervals, the infection subsided and he made a full recovery, sores and all, within a short time, returning to Florence with them at the end of the month.

People began to talk, and Robert was obliged to hire a team and premises to concoct and package the powder as demand for it grew. It was a complicated and meticulous process and his chemists needed careful training. Forearmed, Elizabeth always carried it and used it in early pregnancy thereafter. Within a few years, it had reached a popularity equivalent, centuries later, to Epsom Salts.

Dr. Marco Cornachini, a highly respected medicinal practitioner and associate of Robert, recorded these three incidents meticulously in his "Cornachini's Address to the Reader". He praised Robert to the skies for all his achievements, describing him as: "possessed of all virtues and worthy of every praise" and how he, himself, had regarded the "Pulvis Warvicensis" initially with scepticism, but had radically changed his opinion. Robert had given him the prescription and he was now convinced of its efficacy and willing to help with its production.

It was, perhaps, fortunate that Robert's lamented father, Leicester, had not possessed the same knowledge of chemistry as his son. He might easily have become too free with the use of noxious substances and his reputation, shady enough as it was, may have become dangerously accountable. Lady Douglas's description of her blackened nails and loss of hair was very close to home, not to mention the timely removal of her first husband, Sheffield, followed by the convenient demise of the Earl of Essex, wedded at the time to his rival, Lettice.

Five months after the episodes in Pisa, the safe arrival of Cosimo in the Via dell'Amore, after a hard birth, left Robert almost as exhausted as his wife. She took longer to recover than she had before and for just a few days the light went out of her eyes. It was a severe strain for Robert to leave her after the baptism, and go, again, to Pisa and Livorno. Their love for each other was as deep and constant as it had ever been, as remarkable for their time as Galileo's flying machines, and far exceeding the conventional. William Bradshaw remained in Florence with instructions to send word immediately if needful.

Nothing, however, could mar the celebration of this birth. Cosimo was a big, handsome baby with powerful lungs and had clearly been late in making an appearance; his head was thickly covered in waving hair and he looked, at birth, like a month old child. It was not long before Elizabeth was once more pregnant and a larger house was becoming a pressing matter. The following year, 1611, Robert's favourite child of all was born, Anna the beautiful, perfect in every way and the image of her mother. Even as a baby she had the artists reaching for their brushes.

It now occurred to both Robert and Elizabeth that they were going to need, in the near future, a country house within easy reach of Florence. Robert, in particular, remembered the freedom of his little daughters romping around the vastness of Kenilworth with their ponies and their dogs, and suffered, not for the first time, pangs of regret for the home and wealth he had left behind in England. This ever-increasing family in Italy would soon require a great deal more space if they were to be brought up in the same way. Reared in vast castles himself, Robert had no wish to see his children playing in courtyards and shut away behind high walls, no matter how beautiful the city in which they played.

This led him to consider, more fully, how he might be able to bring about some sort of reconciliation with his own King and country. It was never going to be easy to overcome James's intense dislike and distrust of him; he had hardly been conciliatory to his Monarch or to his minions in the past, but he did keep in close touch with friends at Court, members of his own family and, of course, Sir Thomas Chaloner, now tutor to the young heir, Prince Henry. His chances of salvaging anything from Kenilworth were, at this time, remote. The King had a tight hold on it since it had been sequestered to the Crown although Sidney already had his predatory eye fixed on some parts of the estate and was hoping for more. Robert had blatantly refused to comply with King James's orders to return to England and face retribution, he had broken the writ allowing him only three years away from his country, and he was to be heavily fined for it; it would take powerful persuasion to extract any kind of pardon although Duke Ferdinand, long-sighted as he was, had always advised him to attempt this. There was, of course, a convincing argument for remaining out of England. King James's new law against re-marriage while both original participants were alive. Both he and Elizabeth would be liable to punishment for bigamy as soon as they set foot in England.

Alice had not chosen to remain at Kenilworth with her daughters. Indeed, it would have been hard for her to do so. Robert's conveyancing of his estate to the Leighs had been resisted by the Crown which sought, at Law, to possess every part of it because of his contempt for the King's command to return to England. It was a foregone conclusion that judgement was given in the Crown's favour and a Commission was appointed to take possession of the estate on the King's behalf. It was hardly surprising that Alice removed to Dudley House at St.Giles-in-the-

Fields almost immediately after Robert's departure. It had always been her favourite house and to have shared Kenilworth with a Commissioner of the Crown, appointed to have charge of the estate, would have been impossible. It seemed that she had lost everything; her husband, her land, her possible title and her standing in society, always so important to her. Robert had left her, and the children, amply provided for, but her jointure on the woods of Kenilworth was all that remained to her of the estate, and that did not appear a certainty at this point. Her future appeared very bleak with four small daughters to establish and a mountain of anxiety and bitterness to live with. The youngest had died soon after her arrival in St.Giles.

She had her family in Warwickshire to support her and she had Lady Douglas also, until her death, but Robert's betrayal and abandonment was both a brutal shock and a subsequent hardship. Alice, however, was made of stern stuff and, as time passed, she devoted herself more and more to charity, the Church and the future of her daughters. She already had a reputation for piety and she would, in time, have her reward and her recompense.

Meanwhile, at the instigation of the erstwhile Admiral, Robert's cousin, the Earl of Northampton, now the Lord Privy Seal, Kenilworth was valued at the ridiculously low total of £38,554. Alice's jointure on the woods was valued at £11,722, where her marriage portion had been agreed at £20,000. Robert's fine for contempt, to be deducted from the whole, was £10,000, besides his being disinherited and deprived of his estate. There was a good reason for this gross undervaluation of Kenilworth.

Young Prince Henry, now seventeen, was a very different character from his father, so much so that some questioned the circumstances of his birth. He was highly intelligent, magnanimous and mature beyond his years. He had the presence and dignity so sadly lacking in King James and in May 1610, he was officially appointed Prince of Wales. Sir Thomas Chaloner was made his Lord Chamberlain, giving him a position of real influence. The Prince was a great admirer of Kenilworth and appreciated its wealth of history and its significance. He described it as: "The most noble and significant thing in the midland parts of this realm" and he now expressed a wish to own it. Negotiations were just beginning and the price would be a tithe of the value.

Other negotiations, already under way, were those concerning Prince Henry's marriage. He was a prize of the first order to any European Royal house. The King had favoured a union with the Infanta Anna of Spain, but this had been in the wind for some time and it was not going well, religion being the main obstacle. A French alliance had been suggested with a daughter of the Duke of Savoy, but this ruler was almost as impecunious as King James. Also considered, as long ago as 1601, was an alliance with the fabulously rich Medici. King James had burnt his boats at the outset by asking for part of the dowry in advance to ease his monetary needs. This had not impressed Duke Ferdinand and no further progress was made. Now, ten years later, Lotti was approached by Lord Salisbury suggesting a marriage between Prince Henry and Grand Duke Cosimo's sister, Caterina. This came with the concession that she would be allowed to practice her own religion. So far, so good; it would be a welcome boost for English Catholics. Sir Thomas Chaloner was called into action and his obvious contact in Tuscany was the Earl of Warwick.

The Earl of Warwick was perfectly willing, and able, to be that contact. He wanted to cultivate the friendship of the Prince of Wales with a view to a possible pardon in the future. Thanks to Chaloner, he had a fair idea of Prince Henry's outstanding character and he was well aware of how much this exceptional young man had achieved in his short life despite his regrettable father. He kept his own Court, had a good grip on European affairs and, thanks to Raleigh, a keen interest in the development of the New World. The three of them, the Prince, Raleigh and Dudley had a great deal in common.

Robert knew that he would never be able to achieve, in Tuscany, the status and wealth he had possessed in England. He had climbed to an incredible height in favour and position during the few years since his arrival in Italy and money was beginning to flow in as a result of his efforts, but a great deal of his fortune had been tied up in Kenilworth, and Kenilworth was no longer his. Thanks to William Bradshaw's hard riding around London just before the fateful day in Star Chamber, banking friends and their associate establishments had managed to get a considerable amount of that fortune transferred to safe monetary houses in France and Italy. It had been a swift and efficient operation, but the proceeds did not amount to the almost bottomless pit provided by his estates in England. He also needed friends in very high places in his own country for any chance of coming within reach of a pardon and the Prince of Wales would be a good beginning; the thin end of a wedge aimed at reacceptance. He had been given ample opportunity to observe how his own kith and kin had profited by the simple means of sycophancy. With very little effort and nothing like his own hard work and talent, his uncle and cousin were now Earls, one hugely rich as Lord Privy Seal, and both building their own edifices at Audley End and Charing Cross respectively.

Duke Cosimo knew of the Earl of Warwick's family links with the English Court. Also, that Elizabeth's younger sister, Margaret, was now a Lady of the Privy Chamber to Queen Anne and in a position to help support a Stuart-Medici match. While negotiations proceeded officially through Ottaviano Lotti, Chaloner and Margaret would be able to convey much more personal information to Prince Henry and Queen Anne, which they now began to do. Prince Henry, worldly-wise and quizzical, was greatly amused by all this, particularly as he had recently sent packing his mistress of some duration. Frances Howard, a cousin of Robert's and a thoroughly naughty girl, had been married to the young son of the executed Earl of Essex with little success on either side. Since the Prince's interest ceased, she was now kicking up her heels with the King's latest love, the extremely handsome but witless Robert Carr. The Stuart Court was messy and scandal-strewn; Prince Henry wanted no involvement with his father's indiscretions. He had been brought up away from his parents under the guardianship of the Earl of Mar and had scant respect for his father.

Back in Tuscany, approval of a marriage between the heir to England and her daughter, Caterina, was gladly given by the Dowager Duchess, Maria Christina, who immediately sent to Rome for Papal consent. When approval arrived, Duke Cosimo offered King James, as a basis for further negotiations, 600,000 ducats. The approval, however, carried conditions. The Pope would not sanction the match unless Prince Henry changed his religion and gave English Catholics freedom of worship. There were rocks ahead and, clearly, a great deal of careful manoeuvring to be done.

Robert Sidney's interest in Kenilworth was becoming marked and, encouraged by Chaloner, Prince Henry now made it clear to his father that he would like ownership given him in the near future. It had, for years, been a Royal residence and he considered it too good for the likes of Sidney.

Henry had already been able to prevent his father handing over Raleigh's estate to the beautiful Robert Carr, recently created Viscount Rochester. Raleigh, loathed by King James for his arrogance, was languishing in the Tower of London for no very good reason, his estate in Dorset escheated to the Crown which had now promised it to Rochester. Prince Henry had the greatest admiration for Raleigh, ignored his Royal father's disapproval and visited him often. His remark on the subject: "None but my Father would cage so fine a bird" was outspoken, to say the least. The Elizabethan spirit of adventure, exploration and conquest was very much to his taste. He had already outfitted, manned and sent an expedition to settle Virginia and was bitterly disappointed that he was not able to accompany them. He applauded the golden age of courage and swashbuckling enterprise and he now stepped in and demanded to be given Raleigh's estates, intending to restore them later. The King was obliged to defer to him and to compensate his avaricious favourite with £20,000.

Whatever their personal feelings towards one another, Raleigh's situation was very similar, apart from considerations of comfort, to Robert Dudley's; one in the Tower and the other exiled in Italy, and both with estates purloined by the Crown. It was easy for Chaloner to persuade the Prince how extremely similar, also, were the two men in character and achievement, and what an asset Dudley and his talents might be to him in the future; all perfectly true. Henry had only to consider what had been achieved in Tuscany; the re-building of the ducal navy reflected exactly what he wished to do with the wasted and outdated navy in England. What should prevent the Prince from restoring Kenilworth, also, to its rightful owner, in part and in due course, if he were so minded, and even if he, himself, were the owner by that time.

Chaloner was so successful in his mission that Prince Henry went much further and, having completely embraced Robert's cause, sent envoys to Livorno where he was currently ensconced, with an offer to buy Kenilworth from him for the ridiculous price of £7,000. This was clearly understood to include the price of a pardon and the mandatory fine for disobedience. Chaloner knew his Prince well enough to be sure that he would honour any agreement. Negotiations swung back and forth for over a year, complicated by the King dragging his heels, Sidney's avariciousness, and the Prince gallantly insisting that Alice should also benefit; she was to be given £300 annually. Eventually, Robert was made an advance payment of around £3,500.

Hopes of a pardon continued to ebb and flow but by July 1612 had reached a point where Chaloner was able to write a most encouraging letter to Robert although it did contain some hard raps over the knuckles for his past transgressions. It was the prelude to a pardon and contained specific conditions. This letter clearly had to pass the censorious eyes of the King, the Lord Chamberlain and Salisbury and did not reflect Chaloner's personal feelings for his old friend and pupil.

On the heels of the letter and as a clear mark of that friendship, a deep bond that went back to Robert's student days, Chaloner then sent his own son with a negotiator, Yates, to Florence where he was very warmly welcomed by both Robert and Elizabeth. There had been one paragraph in Chaloner's letter which touched, tactfully, on the subjects of both Alice and Elizabeth.

Of Alice he had written: "To your Lady's friends and allies here in England you endeavour to give present satisfaction, to the end that both herself and your children may have portions allotted to them, or some such assurance as you, in your fatherly care, are found to produce for them."

Of Elizabeth, without naming her, he had written: "Neither am I unmindful to put you in mind of what I presume you will not omit, that before your return to England, you will take order that some with you who have suffered loss of friends, and other prejudices, for your sake, be honourably settled with a convenient estate." What may have been intended by this tactful approach was that Elizabeth should be settled in Italy with his second family. To have re-appeared in England with another wife and yet more children would have been a grave embarrassment after the scandal of their departure, and a blatant example of the bigamous practices King James had been at such pains to eradicate and punish. His laws against divorce of any kind were very clear despite the shocking scandals with which his reign was littered. Robert's own behaviour was comparatively mild in relation to what was about to unfold in England. Elizabeth's return to her own country, however, under any circumstances, was not going to be possible with King James on the throne.

Finally, at the end of this momentous letter, came the vital promise: "By these endeavours you shall return a welcome guest to all your country:

and the Prince, whom you vow, next only unto the King, to honour and serve, shall not be ashamed to have such a servant. To which purpose, it hath seemed good to his Majesty and his Highness that I should enclose the articles herein, to the end that, upon notice given by you of your humble readiness to give way unto your own happiness by subscribing dutifully thereto, you may forthwith receive that gracious pardon which you so much thirst for."

Brandishing the letter, Robert charged into Elizabeth's room, swept her up in his arms and held her close as he read it out to her. She made light of the reference concerning herself despite the fact that it contained no encouragement for her own return to England. She did not expect admittance for herself or her children and it was not in her nature to wring her hands over anything so long as Robert was content. Her faith in him left no room for doubt; a way would be found and everyone could be happy. She had embraced life in Tuscany to the extent that, given a choice, she would remain here. It had become home to her.

With this passport to the future in Robert's grasp, they sat, handfast, on the window-seat, looking over the tiles of the many roofs of the Via dell' Amore, now turning the wonderful rosy red of an early Tuscan evening. Delicious odours of cooking; garlic, herbs, local pancetta, mixed with incense, lilies and much more earthy smells, drifted up from the street market below.

Robert, then writing to Yates, thanking him for his "extraordinary good respect unto me" and his efforts on his behalf, ended: "It cannot be unknown to you that I have given His Highness my estate of Kenilworth for a small matter, considering its worth. I have only reserved to myself and my heirs the Constableship of the Castle, so that I may have some command there under His Highness whenever I shall happen to come to England." The Prince was welcome to Kenilworth, if he and his heirs could have charge of it. Whatever else, he was ready for a return, in some part, to his own country.

With this letter came a treatise, written by himself to the Prince: "A proposition for Prince Henry, Prince of Wales" regarding the vital necessity of re-building and maintaining the English navy, which he now knew would catch and hold his interest. "For England, their good and safety hath always been upheld by their sea forces", he wrote, and furthermore, "Whosoever is patron of the sea commandeth the land". He knew he was echoing Raleigh's arguments and he knew, from his own wide experience, exactly what he was talking about. This was followed by a detailed description of the kind of ships, guns and rigging he had in mind. It was a masterly work, designed to fire Henry's imagination and interest. It ended: "Whereas, I have found no friendship nor favour in England but from your Highness, so do I renounce all other obligations (His Majesty excepted) but yourself. And when it shall please God, I may, with my honour, return to serve you, I can then promise divers other services, not inferior to this, as well as for your profit".

Not only would he be content to serve Prince Henry as Constable of Kenilworth, but he would also re-build his navy. Besides this, he was prepared to face down any antagonism in England.

Then came the third heavy blow in Robert Dudley's life. The letter and the "Treatise", written on 12th November, never reached the Prince. As a result of regularly swimming in the Thames, this exceptional boy died of a virulent attack of typhoid fever in St. James's Palace on 6th November and with him went the brightest hopes for England's future, paving the way for deadly Civil War and Cromwell's Commonwealth; with him also went Robert Dudley's hopes for any future in England.

CHAPTER TWELVE

The Medici Years – 1613-1620

The evening light was beginning to slant across the formal, but very beautiful, gardens of the Villa Rinieri at Castello, sending dark, pointed shadows reaching towards the house which stood against a low hill. It was a classic Tuscan country house, light and airy in summer but with shutters that could be drawn snugly against the cold in winter and with enormous fireplaces in every room. It had been given to the Earl and Countess of Warwick for their lifetime by a grateful Duke and Duchess of Tuscany.

Round the box hedges enclosing the flower beds a large number of children were chasing each other in what appeared to be an organised game. There were two teams, each ranging in age from ten to four years. One team consisted of the Medici ducal children; the other belonged to the house of Warwick.

Two very little people, with attendant keepers, staggered around on the grass lawn nearer the house. Francesco de Medici and Ambrogio Dudley tumbled over each other like puppies while their respective mothers sat chatting and laughing companionably and watching their offspring with one eye. Upstairs, and already in their cradles, were two babies, Anna de Medici and Giovanni Dudley.

One of the women was tall, handsome and red-haired, authority stamped in every line of her; the other, a golden creature of extraordinary beauty, undimmed by the rapid arrival of seven children. Her slenderness was still apparent though she was expecting an eighth; her movements quick and lissom as she rose with grace to rescue her son from the rose bush into which he had been shoved by his small friend.

The game around the box hedges and the many fountains was becoming exciting. At one end of the garden, the Medici team was guarding a small wooden lion, painted in the family colours. The Warwicks, by stealth and speed, were trying to steal it and carry it down to the other end; this involved skirting formal beds and splashing fountains with plenty of scope for both entrapment and evasion. Something, though, was unusual. Both sides were giving way to a tiny creature who moved at high speed though not in a natural way. She was dwarfish with short arms and legs but a fully developed torso and a head too large for her body. Maria Christina de Medici, the eldest of her family, though extremely mobile, had been born malformed. She scuttled, close to the ground, with a rocking motion, her small feet twinkling over the grass. It was clear that both sides deferred to her, shouting encouragement and applause whenever she grabbed the little painted lion for the Medici. This team, besides Maria Christina, consisted of the heir, Ferdinando, GianCarlo, Margherita and Mattias. The Warwick contingent were Maria, Cosimo, Anna, Maddalena and Carlo.

The respective families were easy to tell apart. The Medici all bore, in some degree, the Hapsburg stamp; a legacy from both their parents. The long faces and full lips, apparent more in some than in others, were particularly noticeable in the future Duke, Ferdinando, and his younger brother Mattias, while unremarkable in the tiny Maria Christina. This little child, now nine years old, who may have suffered deformity as a result of ancestral inbreeding, lived, much loved, within the family circle, until the age of puberty, when she became more difficult and was moved to a convent for the remainder of her short life.

The Warwick children stood out in any crowd. They were exceptionally good-looking, the boys big and sturdy and the girls already head-turningly beautiful. One in particular, Anna, at seven years old was so lovely that people would stop in their tracks and gaze at her.

There was no deference between the family groups, except to encourage Maria Christina. They knew each other so well and, already, lifelong affection between those of similar ages had developed. They were shouting at each other in Italian but slipped easily into English or German at will.

The sun had, by now, slanted still further, and the heat of the day was beginning to subside. The stately Duchess rose to her feet and called a time limit for the game to finish. It could be seen that she, too, was pregnant. She had more than assured the succession with four sons and had been discussing girls' names with the Countess. Her husband, Grand Duke Cosimo II, never robust, had fallen ill with a virulent fever four years before from which he had not fully recovered and he was reduced to a near-invalid state. Hers were now the hands that often held the reins, though sometimes in conjunction with Duchess Maria Christina, her mother-in-law.

Dudley House, and Loggia Corsi before the englargement of Via Tornabuoni, A. D. 1864.

With an ever-expanding family, the Earl and Countess of Warwick had found the Villa Rinieri di Castello, near Quarto, a great blessing. It was only a few miles from Florence, close enough for them to safely leave their children there if they, themselves, were required to attend the Tuscan Court. The house stood very close to the ducal Villa della Petraia, recently re-built by Duke Cosimo and originally a castle of the Brunelleschi. It was a testimony to the friendship between the two families that they were now such close neighbours, and there was frequent coming and going among them when both were in residence. The older ones rode out together, sometimes the bigger boys with the falconers and small hawks which they were taught to handle at an early age.

Elizabeth's dream of her own house in Florence had been realised too. Though still comparatively impecunious, the expansion of his family and his growing prestige in Florence, persuaded Robert, in 1613, to begin negotiations with the ancient Rucellai family for three small houses in the Via della Vigna Nuova. It was a wedge-shaped plot by the Palazzo of the Rucellai and close to the church of San Pancrazio. Here he designed and built a large, elegant house to his own specifications. For him, it was a short step from naval to civilian architecture. The main frontage was some forty-five yards long; there were four floors with ten windows to each floor. Elizabeth was overjoyed and much involved in the planning and, most of all, the decoration. As a family, they were now firmly rooted in a spacious house in Florence with an even larger and very beautiful house in the country. The immense amount of work and the achievements by Robert in Pisa and Livorno had been generously rewarded.

All this time and despite the work in the two ports, the Earl and Countess of Warwick were being increasingly drawn into the activities of Court life in Florence. Because of his jousting skills and outstanding horsemanship, Robert was now recognised as an authority when it came to tournaments and tilting and was often asked to organise or to judge such spectacles. By 1613, in the cooler month of February, he took a major part in one of the Duke's frequent entertainments; this one recorded by an interested spectator, on the 17th.

It began on the Piazza Santa Croce with a game of "calcio", a form of football, attended by the whole Court, and was followed by a ball at the Palazzo Pitti. The guests, magnificently gowned and jewelled, dined and danced until about 9.00pm in the evening when the fun really began.

According to a Bartolomeo Sermatelli who witnessed this, Robert Dudley took part as the herald. Translated, he recorded:

"A blast of drums and trumpets sounded and a herald in military uniform surrounded by torchbearers marched in to the hall. A wand in his hand and arrayed in a surcoat of cloth of gold with the arms of Eros and a broken thunderbolt beautifully embroidered on it. This herald was accompanied by ten pages carrying torches, and richly dressed in white and gold "Ermiso" with plumed caps of a new and bizarre shape. Having entered the room, with a proud and war-like mien, the herald spoke thus: 'The Knight Fidamante and the Knight of Immortal Love, Champions of omnipotent and insuperable love, moderator of heaven and earth, tamer of the fiercest beasts, have sent me to this company of famous heroes, to present a challenge which they are ready to support with the lance and with the pen.' With these words, he threw down some papers, which a dwarf, who was with him, presented to their Royal Highnesses, and the cavaliers, and departed. The challenge came from Prince Ferdinand de Medici and Don Paolo Giordano Orsini, who offered battle to any other knights, for "the Good Cause of the wrongs of Love, and of Venus who had come to Florence from Cyprus and found themselves neglected."

This tournament was held in the theatre of the Palazzo Pitti, a room about 25 yards square which was ornamented by statues and frescoes. It had a stage and scenery at one end and boxes and raised seats all round.

The knights, challengers and challenged, fought in the centre. Ten senators were deputed to elect twenty gentlemen as umpires, among whom Sir Robert Dudley, who was famous in all knightly exercises, was one. Two large boxes were erected at opposite ends. The Grand Ducal party were in one box, and the umpires in the other. Among these were Signor Francesco del Monte, General of the Ducal Infantry, Marchese Pireteo Malvezzi, Master of the Horse to H.R.H, and "Signor Conte de Veruich (Warwick) Englishman."

"Veruich" was another interesting variation on Warwick, of which there were plenty. Robert was taking part both as the Herald and as an umpire. According to this eye-witness account, the occasion was utterly resplendent with poems, dialogue, celestial beings, gods and goddesses, nymphs and shepherds, song and dance. After the "tournament" all those taking part made a torchlit procession through the streets, not going to bed till the morning. The Tuscan Court certainly knew how to enjoy itself.

By 1618, five years later, Robert Dudley and his wife were more firmly ensconced in their adopted country than ever. Since the cruel disappointments following the death of Henry, Prince of Wales, all doors opening to a lawful return to his own country had been slammed on the Earl in a series of metaphorical crashes. Any plans for the Constableship of Kenilworth, the re-building of the English navy and, above all, a Royal pardon had been abruptly curtailed by King James. He had dragged his heels in the face of his son's determination and, so far as he was concerned, Robert was guilty of bigamy, now a common law crime, apostasy, a canon law offence against the Church of England, and contempt against himself and the State. With Prince Henry's influence and persuasion gone, the King would not hesitate to prosecute Robert Dudley if he so much as showed his nose across the Channel. What riled the King more than anything else was that Robert had shown complete disregard for his own Royal person, while clearly demonstrating his respect and preference for the Dukes of Tuscany. The contract agreed on the sale of Kenilworth to Prince Henry had been immediately cancelled and the funds due to be paid were frozen. Prince Charles, only fourteen at the time, was now considered the legal owner, but lacked the authority to complete the transaction. This was no help to the Warwick family coffers. Robert, however, was seldom at a loss and his resilient nature immediately prompted him to assume, since he had not been paid, that he still owned Kenilworth and could, therefore, use it as collateral regardless of any claim Prince Charles might have. Such was his authority that he was able to borrow on that basis from several sources. With the building of his house in the Via della Vigna Nuova, he had a quiet helping hand from Duke Cosimo.

King James was not unaware of the sliding glances and the guarded whispers that had followed the death of his much-loved son. The Queen, herself, had been most unguarded, crying publicly that the favourite, Rochester, together with his friend, Sir Thomas Overbury, had murdered Henry, her first-born and best beloved. There were some nasty whispers, too, about the unconcerned manner in which, the day after the funeral, negotiations were opened by the King and Rochester for a marriage between the hapless Prince Charles and Henrietta of France.

Time passed and Robert, undeterred by misfortune and encouraged by Duke Cosimo, forged ahead with continuous shipbuilding, both for the Tuscan navy and the growing merchant fleet. One of his more innovative designs, the "St.Cosimo", was an oar-propelled galley suitable for Mediterranean use over which there was a certain amount of controversy, resolved with great firmness by Robert himself. He accused his critics of deliberately overloading the vessel in order to reduce its recorded speed. Among other pithy comments he wrote: "And further, I reply that even if it were true that it sinks so low as to impede its speed, I certify His Royal Highness that in two days I would remedy the defect by a stratagem of my own which has never been revealed."

By 1619, Robert had written his "Direttorio Marittimo", an instruction for the officers of the new Tuscan Navy. This was a comprehensive treatise, in Italian, which would later be included in his monumental work "Dell' Arcano del Mare".

Robert's reputation for design and construction had spread and his services were now in great demand from other Mediterranean states. The shipyards at Livorno and Pisa were constantly full; merchants from all over the Middle East, particularly the Spanish Jews, were arriving and beginning to establish themselves there. Some of these came to Robert for help in both ship and domestic building. His horizons were becoming broader and he was now an architect of houses as well as of ships. Livorno was rapidly becoming a major port with an air of prosperity and gracious living. Its harbour front was an impressive row of elegant buildings.

The unwholesome bogs and marshes lying between Pisa and Livorno had been almost completely drained. The aqueduct from Asciano to Pisa opened in 1613 and the Naviglio, or canal, connecting Livorno to the Arno river near Pisa was now in use.

His forty-four years lay lightly upon Robert and his rampant energy remained undiminished. Perhaps because of his own lonely, embattled childhood and his father's lack of progeny, the urge to become the patriarch of a large family had been fully realised. He now had two families with twelve children between them and a thirteenth on the way. He had done no more than provide financially, including handsome dowries, for the girls of his English family but, to his lasting shame, he appeared to take no further interest in them. He had ruthlessly closed that chapter of his life; unfortunately, it had included the ownership of Kenilworth and any dreams he may have had for a future in England were tied to it. This did not prevent him claiming possession when it came to its use as collateral.

His Italian family he frankly adored, planning their futures in detail and taking a keen interest in their activities. To these children he was no lofty, absent father figure but was already teaching his boys how to handle their ponies in preparation for hawking, jousting and hunting and he insisted they learn horse-management with their sleeves rolled up in the stables, as he had done.

His great love for his wife remained undimmed. It was as apparent as it had been when his mother, Lady Douglas, first understood that it was the lynch-pin of his existence, that he could not live without her and that he was prepared to break both God's and marriage laws in order to be with her for the rest of his life. It was recognised and respected by those visiting them, those they lived among and, after one or two initial pursuits of Elizabeth by hopeful Tuscans, it was known to her admirers. If she could not, Robert dealt swiftly and dangerously with any interlopers. When it came to his wife, he was as ruthless as his father had been. He could be both a very frightening and a very charming man.

The Warwick household, over these years and despite the constant arrival of children was a favourite destination for the many English visitors to Florence. They entertained constantly after the building of their own palazzo despite any fears their visitors may have had of possible reprisals on return to England. They were a curiosity and a magnet for travellers, besides being a very charismatic couple who welcomed their countrymen warmly and lavishly. They also entertained a positive flood of young English aristocrats and their tutors on the "Grand Tour" of Europe. Florence was always included on the well-trodden trail and some of these hopeful youths, whose aims were to enjoy a great deal more than works of art, needed a firm hand.

Lord Cherbury, an old friend of Lotti's and a noted philosopher and historian, visited them on his way north from Rome. He was most impressed with the hospitality he received and, like many, he was overcome by Elizabeth's charm and beauty; also by the notable feast he was given the night before he left. Agog, he later wrote: "I saw Sir Robert Dudley and the handsome Mrs.Sudel whom he carried with him out of England and was there taken for his wife". Robert, recognising Cherbury's worth, had offered him a position in Tuscany if he were so minded. His Lordship had clearly not thought it wise to refer to Robert as the Earl of Warwick or to recognise the marriage; "Mrs.Sudel" was the nearest he could get to Southwell.

Hard on the heels of Lord Cherbury came Inigo Jones, then on a tour with Lord Arundel from which would result the popularity of Palladian architecture in England. Inigo Jones had been the surveyor sent by Prince Henry to value Kenilworth before his death and had much to tell. These two, with Robert, sat late over their wine discussing ways and means, attitudes and possibilities. Inigo Jones's activities in the theatre and at the major Court masques of the day made him of instant interest to Elizabeth. He was fascinated by the Recitativo, attended several performances, and promised to encourage and send word of any progress it might make in England.

Having recovered swiftly from the unravelling of his plans after the untimely death of Prince Henry, and having bided his time, Robert was quite prepared to try the process of pardon again, should opportunity arise and, perhaps from a different angle. Opportunity did arise.

There was to be an element of glee in his next attempt, a deliberate tweaking of King James's tail. He did not seriously think any action of his would now result in a Royal pardon, but the effort was well worth the entertainment it gave him and, of course, there was always a faint chance of success. This next episode arose from the devastating scandal about to engulf the Court of James I.

Following her liaison with the late Prince Henry, Frances Howard, daughter of the Earl of Suffolk, and a cousin of Robert's, pursued her scandalous career by snaring Viscount Rochester as her next lover regardless of the unsavoury fact that she shared him with the King. This impassioned affair became more intense until nothing would do but marriage. Frances, besides having the soul of a courtesan, was well able to discern that her path to fame and fortune lay in securing the King's favourite. She was still married to the young Earl of Essex, son of Robert's beheaded stepbrother, and it would take a drastic bending of the rules for her to gain a divorce under the stringent new laws. However, what was sauce for the gander did not prove sauce for the goose. That which Robert Dudley had been reviled for, his cousin achieved with impunity. Divorced on the grounds of young Essex's impotency, she married Rochester in December 1613 amid a blaze of publicity, her husband being created Earl of Somerset as a wedding present from King James. So much for James's rigid Calvinist upbringing.

Encouraged by the positive phalanx of Howards now surrounding the throne in senior positions, Robert Dudley, knowing well in what bad shape was the English Navy, wrote to Chaloner with news of his latest design for a warship. It was, he said: "of so wonderful a consequence of force and swiftness as I dare boldly say the like was never known to the world, and wonderfully far beyond those I mentioned in my discourse to the Prince, my master, of famous memory". This new "Counter-galleass" was designed for use by the Venetian Republic and the Duchy of Tuscany against the Turks; both of them were pressing him to build it for them. However, Robert now offered King James, as bait, first refusal of this brilliant design: "out of my affection to my country and duty to His Majesty." Furthermore: "No three of the King's greatest ships royal is able to endure the force of one counter-galleass......to have but ten of them would make a Prince absolute patron of the seas." Robert was a good and brazen salesman, unhindered by false modesty. Exploiting his relationship with the wanton Frances, now Countess of Somerset, he also wrote to her new husband extolling the virtues of his ship. Despite his lack of grey matter, Somerset actually replied expressing interest. So, also did King James, when Chaloner had passed Robert's offer on to him. An agent was sent to Pisa to interview both the Earl of Warwick and his ship.

Either because he did not really want the King to benefit from his design, or could not resist another opportunity to tease him, Robert then completely overplayed his hand by suggesting that the only person fit to take the galleass to sea was himself. In a "winner takes all" approach, he wrote that: "I must pretend to desire to be general (with a title), of such a squadron of these vessels, and to be a command and government by itself, not to be under the Admiral of England, but as the galleys is in France, a different command at sea, nor hazard the reputation of my own works under the discretion or skill of another." To demand that he should be given the command of a fleet of galleasses, quite apart from the authority of his uncle, the Lord Admiral, was not likely to meet with approval. It would also involve the granting of some form of pardon together with the King's permission for Robert to work in England. This proposal was greeted by a deafening silence and the matter of the galleass dropped.

Also overplaying her hand was his cousin, Frances, now Countess of Somerset. Her husband's rise to power had been greatly assisted by his more intelligent friend, Sir Thomas Overbury, but Overbury had been violently opposed to the Somerset marriage, even writing the widely-read poem, "A Wife", which advised great caution in choosing a life's partner. This was plainly aimed at Frances who enlisted the help of her father, Suffolk, and the King, both of whom were jealous of Overbury's influence and hold over Somerset. All three of them were anxious to be rid of him. An attempt was then made to send Overbury to Russia on a mission, but he refused to go. His fate was sealed. He was sent to the Tower, on a pretext, in April 1613, and died, horribly, in September, of a variety of poisons deliberately administered in his food. His sufferings were such that he was praying for death by the time they had finished with him. Four accomplices of Frances and Rochester had been hired for the purpose and installed in the Tower. The happy couple were married almost immediately after Overbury's death.

However, two years later, in September 1615, the Governor of the Tower of London informed King James that the wardens in charge of Overbury had deliberately murdered him. By then, the King was pre-occupied with replacing his estranged favourite, Somerset, with the equally beautiful George Villiers. With his hold over James weakened, Somerset was unable to prevent the murder investigation that followed. In October 1615, the Earl and Countess of Somerset were arrested, together with their four named accomplices, and sent to the Tower. The trial which followed was tortuous and scandalous and far eclipsed Robert Dudley's case in Star Chamber. One of the jurors was actually the young Earl of Essex, Frances's former husband. It was not an edifying spectacle. All six of the defendants were convicted and sentenced to death in May 1616. The sentence was promptly carried out upon the wretched accomplices, but the Somersets remained in the Tower, though generally believed to be guilty. It was also believed that the King had connived in the murder of Overbury and that leniency was shewn to the Somersets because they had threatened him with further spectacular revelations regarding the death of Prince Henry. This seemed confirmed, on their later release, by the over-generous pension given them by the Crown. The country reverberated for months and months. Frances and her husband were not released, in fact, until 1622 and then retired, disgraced, from public life.

Robert, however, had not nearly finished with King James. Through the many members of his family now stalking the corridors of power in England, he learnt how frequently the King's wishes were being thwarted or delayed by Parliament. Over the years he had observed how much more smoothly affairs of State were conducted in Tuscany, the harmonious working of one of the richest states in Europe, and the ease of its government.

Again, he set about writing a treatise, this time: "A Proposition for His Majesty's Service to Bridle the Impertinences of Parliament." The work was an impertinence in itself and a substantial commentary which took him time to concoct. Between its lines, he was clearly suggesting that King James should take a few leaves from the Tuscan book on how to manage his country. It gave great relief to Robert's feelings for King James, far from fond, to politely point out the failings of his government and to gently rub his nose in the success of Tuscany's.

Robert's suggestions were many and varied and his enjoyment in making them satisfied both his sense of humour and an awareness of retribution. He had not forgiven nor forgotten King James's part in robbing him of his inheritance and his titles.

The work began with a recommendation to garrison every large town in England, with curfews imposed and control exercised over all main highways. These garrisons, when needed, could be quickly united into an army at times of emergency. The huge cost of this would be met by heavy taxation; a "Decimation", as it was known in Italy, consisting of an annual payment of one tenth of every citizen's estate to the Crown. There was some sense in this, since James had no standing army at all save for the Yeomen of the Guard. Robert could remember the threatened invasion by Spain and the hasty levies added to a large permanent force, both naval and military. The well-manned camp at Tilbury was not forgotten.

A 5% tax should be levied on the incomes of all notaries and attorneys (this was a direct hit at the bribery-prone lawyers Robert recalled so well, whose "fees and gettings are expensive in England".) A 7% tax should also be levied on dowries and marriage portions. Landlords of inns and taverns should be obliged to buy licences to trade and there were a great many more ideas of this kind.

A possible two million pounds could be pocketed by the King by these means, after which, he blandly suggested, a further £60,000 could be saved by the King's "reducing the Royal Household to board wages as most Princes do." The most lucrative part of the scheme then followed: "earls and grandees should pay for their privileges, as in Italy and Spain. For example, barons to be made earls at £19,000 apiece." He then suggested a tariff, starting with dukes at £30,000 down to viscounts at £5,000. Robert knew very well that King James, having scattered peerages far and wide on his accession, now understood that money could be made from social ambition and, having revived the rank of baronet, had been happily selling it for £1,080 apiece since 1611.

The "Proposition" was, therefore, divided into the two parts. The first to establish powerful and autocratic control by the King; the second to produce a hefty income from that control. His tongue firmly in his cheek and a broad grin on his face, Robert wrote that he was driven to recommend these measures to His Majesty out of love and duty and not because he wished to leave Italy for England. Let James make of that what he would.

The whole treatise was sent to King James via Somerset, prior to his fall and imprisonment, with the recommendation: "If Your Majesty resolve to proceed on the former courses, counsel, if I may without presumption so call it" should be examined "by someone most trusted by his Majesty, which I conceive of, or rather wish it may be, my Lord of Somerset". As expected, neither Robert's "Proposition" nor his presentation of it was appreciated by His Majesty. There was no response at all and James had, thereby, deprived himself of a chance to rebuild his depleted and useless navy with the aid of a brilliant man who had more than proved his expertise in nautical and many other fields. Robert had never expected a pardon from King James. The most he had hoped for was to be able to visit his own country with impunity. The difficulties of installing his Italian family in England would have been quite insurmountable and it was no longer the wish of either Robert or Elizabeth to live anywhere but Florence. There was no great disappointment, therefore, over the outcome of the "Proposition"; it had served, as expected, only to relieve Robert's feelings. The building of his own house in Florence showed that he had no longer any thought of removal to England.

By now, both Robert and Elizabeth regarded Tuscany as their home and, from the reports and stories of their many English visitors, realised that the England of their childhood and youth no longer existed. It was a very different country to the one they had left in 1605 and, in comparison, somewhat mediocre. The spirit of the old Queen's reign and the achievements of the dashing and enterprising leaders it had encouraged were no more. Adventurous young gentlemen could no longer dash off to the Indies in search of gold, glory and gallantry, as Robert had done, but were more likely to be packed off on what was to become the "Grand Tour" with tutors and keepers. This always included Florence.

Raleigh, the epitome of the Elizabethan era, brilliant and ahead of his time, had written along similar lines as Robert's "Proposition", in his "Prerogative of Parliament". The King had ordered his execution and he was beheaded in October, this year of 1618, supposedly as propitiation to, and at the request of, Spain, neither of them valid reasons.

Just before this, in August 1618, King James hit out hard at Robert Dudley by creating Sidney, who had managed to retain his favour, Earl of Leicester. At the same time, Lord Rich, by name and by nature, was created

Earl of Warwick. Lord Rich was the eldest son of that famous Elizabethan beauty, Penelope Devereux, sister of the ill-fated Earl of Essex.

Although he had expected this for some time, Robert's hurt and fury were intense. It was a blow even Elizabeth could not ease or touch. She knew the demons that drove him and she saw him off, soon after, on the long ride to Pisa with a heavy heart. The wound of bastardy had been re-opened, just as it was healing, and little could ease the pain. A hard ride, gruelling work and concentration were the only remedies.

In the courtyard of their house, where orange and grapefruit trees from Pisa now grew, she kissed him good-bye before he mounted, and handed him the stirrup-cup, her eyes full of unshed tears. She was apprehensive that he would ride too hard, to ease his anger, and she quietly asked William Bradshaw to keep close to him. He always rode like Jehu and she eyed the big chestnut horse beneath him with misgiving, knowing its speed and erratic behaviour. It was already stamping, sidling and tossing its head.

The elder children, Maria, Cosimo, Anna and Maddalena, who were gathered on the steps to see him off, caught his mood and were unusually subdued. Even Anna, at the sight of whom his eyes usually lit up, today got no more than a paternal wave before he rode off. Her small mouth drooped and she slipped her hand into her mother's. As they clattered off down the Via della Spada past the Church of San Pancrazio, Elizabeth turned, kissed Anna, promising a visit to the Medici Palace later that day, and went to her own room to write a letter to the Duchess Maria Maddalena. An idea had come, unbidden, into her head, and she needed time to think carefully. This idea was to grow in consequence far beyond her expectations. Elizabeth was intelligent, but no schemer, and her love for Robert now urged her to ask a favour for him which she would have much preferred not to do. It was her nature to give rather than to receive, even if it was on behalf of her husband.

That afternoon, she piled the elder children into her carriage and was driven to the Medici Palace where the Ducal family was ensconced. Maria Maddalena was anxious to see her and had replied at once to her missive. For all her stateliness, the Duchess was devoted to her and received her in a warm embrace. Having sent the children off to play with a model toy army recently bestowed on the Medici, she drew her into her own chamber and firmly shut the door on the rest of her entourage. Elizabeth was seldom troubled and was more likely to be found attending to the misfortunes of others; to see her so distressed was unusual.

Elizabeth laid the matter straightly before the Duchess, omitting nothing, and asked for her help. Something must be done to give Robert back some part of what he had lost. Maria Maddalena, despite the fact that she was several years younger than Elizabeth, had been obliged to mature early. She had become Grand Duchess of Tuscany at the age of eighteen, she was now twenty-six years old and had borne eight children in nine years. The health of her husband, Cosimo, was causing her concern and it was often necessary for her to take matters into her own hands.

She moved to the long windows looking over the immaculate gardens below her and stood for some time in thought, listening as she did so to Elizabeth's concerns. She understood well the rage this final loss of his rightful English titles would cause Robert and the blow to his pride. Some palliative measure must be contrived.

One thing could be done immediately, and there was one other, in time, that she might be able to accomplish. She turned, with a swish of the silken train which fell from her shoulders and sat down beside Elizabeth.

Would Robert accept the position of Great Chamberlain to the Court of the Medici? It was an office of authority, but it would mean less time for his many other projects and being obliged to delegate more. Temporarily, it might ease the pain of seeing his own English titles bestowed on others. An additional, and more significant action, would be to approach her own brother, the Hapsburg Emperor, and ask him, through the Pope, to reinstate Robert as Duke of Northumberland, as his grandfather had been, besides confirming his earldom of Warwick. This would take time and patience, particularly as the old Duke had died, a fervent Protestant, with his head on a block for treason; hardly a recommendation to His Holiness. If Elizabeth agreed that this might be acceptable to Robert, she would begin correspondence at once. It would mean, of course, that his titles, though recognised in Europe, could not be accepted in England, where the Earldoms of Leicester and Warwick had now been given to others. Northumberland, however, was in abeyance and might, under a future monarch, be accepted in England.

This was more than Elizabeth had hoped for. She thought Robert would be delighted and eager to do his part in recovering his grandfather's dukedom. Two great ladies then looked at each other and burst into laughter at the thought of what the beautiful Italian tongue would make of the title "Northumberland". The variations on "Warwick" had been bad enough – no two were alike.

Maria Maddalena was as good as her word and in a very short time Robert was invited to become her Great Chamberlain. This honour was doubled when the Duchess Maria Christina, the Dowager, insisted that he should perform the same office for her as well. The Earl and Countess of Warwick had, almost overnight, become two of the most important and influential people at the Tuscan Court. Robert's opposite number at the Court of King James was now the Earl of Pembroke, his old friend, with whom he had caroused so often in his youth.

Maria Maddalena had done more. She had immediately set in motion the necessary contact with her brother, Ferdinand, recently elected to succeed as Emperor of Germany and of the Holy Roman Empire, asking him to right the wrongs done to the Earl of Warwick. Ferdinand was not a tolerant man and prone to lapses in humour. He could not abide Protestants and their doings in any shape or form. He was, at this time, at loggerheads with King James over the rights of the Palatinate whose Protestant ruler was married to James's daughter. It was a good moment for such a move. Maria Maddalena gave Robert all due praise, referring to "his singular integrity of life and morals, his prudence, knowledge of affairs and rare ingenious inventions." She emphasised what he had achieved for her father-in-law, Ferdinand, and her husband, Cosimo. He had been misused as a Catholic, his English estates escheated to the Crown of England and his titles given to others. Robert had certainly been at her elbow as she wrote this eulogy. It was a good thing the Duchess had not known him in his hell-bent youth.

A few months after all this, Elizabeth gave birth to a fifth son in the comfort of her house in Florence. He was the eighth child she had given Robert in eleven years. Looking down at her with love, Robert determined there should be no more for a while. She made light of childbirth and only Cosimo had been difficult, but she was over thirty years old and seemed a little fragile; the delicate eyelids, closed as she slept, looked faintly blue and the beautiful curve of throat and chin too slender. She must be allowed to regain her strength and enjoy the young lives they had created. They would name the cross-looking bundle in the cradle, Antonio.

Robert had mentally sketched out the paths his sons might follow. Besides ducal, court, church, and military service, there should be one destined for the sea. Looking into the already bright blue eyes in the cradle, he decided it must be this one.

CHAPTER THIRTEEN

"Great Chamberlain"- 1620-1629

Robert Dudley's position as Great Chamberlain was to put him in charge of the many splendid entertainments demanded by Duke Cosimo II. He was now obliged to pursue some of the passions and pleasures of his life. Indeed, his appointment made it imperative that he did, and few were better able to organise the jousts, mock-battles and naval and military spectacles that Cosimo demanded. Like his godfather, old Sir Henry Lee the Queen's Champion, and his own father, Leicester, Robert had the heart of a showman and had been helping to organise such events since early youth. They were a part of his life from Tilbury on; he had seen the pageantry that Leicester produced and taken part in it; it was in the blood, though he had been too young to see the great production at Kenilworth of 1575. Being both likeable and persuasive, he was good at bending others to his will, and his natural authority made him a born impresario. His works at Pisa and Livorno were coming to an end and were at a stage where he could safely delegate. The frantic travelling was, at last, slowing down.

It might have been expected that his appointment would cause resentment among the oldest and semi-royal families in Tuscany and it certainly did raise some hackles at the outset. But Robert Dudley had an instinctive gift with any who crossed his path and from any walk of life. From the days of his first voyage, when the hoary sailors serving under him would have cheerfully sailed over the edge of the known world with him, to the be-jewelled courtiers of Florence, he could, if he wished, charm any bird out of any tree. It was a part of his nature and not a ploy.

The Duke, now physically in a near invalid state and denied the pleasures of a full and active life, concentrated his remaining energies on the arts, sciences, architecture and a great deal of building and re-building within and beyond Florence. He had extended the forecourt of the Pitti Palace by lengthening the front and adding wings to the rear so that spectacles of every kind could take place there. It was now large enough for tournaments, races, jousting and theatre of every kind. This new level of entertainment, much appreciated by the people of Florence, reached fever pitch when the Duke's sister Catarina, formerly the intended bride of England's heir, the lost Prince Henry, married the Duke of Mantua. The festivities lasted for days. Caterina, who looked remarkably like her brother Cosimo and unmistakably Hapsburg, was to return, a widow and childless, to Tuscany six years later, when she was appointed Governor of Siena.

Quite apart from this great wedding, Duke Cosimo delighted in spectacle and lavish parties of all kinds, not only for the elite, but for the population as a whole. Financially he still had the wherewithal to fund any of his enterprises. His one enormous error which would, in time, precipitate the decline of the Medici, was to curtail the banking houses his father and grandfather had set up across Europe. It was the beginning of the slow erosion of the family wealth. Brought up in the strictest of religious practices, he considered banking too venal and not worthy of such a noble family. His mother may well have influenced him, so closely was she tied to the apron strings of Rome. Not only her husband but one of her sons and two of her grandsons had been, or would become, Cardinals of Rome. Since the death of Duke Ferdinand she had become somewhat obsessed by the Church and the family connections with the Vatican, though this contact was shortly to stand Robert Dudley in very good stead.

For the time being, Robert, and increasingly his family, were drawn into and began to assume a lead in the running of the Tuscan Court. There was little in Europe to equal the opulence and elegance of everyday life in Florence. The magnificence of the Medici palaces – Vecchio, Uffizi and Pitti, evolved over nearly two centuries, were breathtaking and the home of priceless works of art collected or judiciously acquired from all over Europe. Jewels the size of eggs, beautifully crafted into necklaces, pendants and waist chains, adorned the persons of the courtiers. Any portrait dripped with them and as much detail was given them as to the sitter. The fatuous exaggerations of the late 1590s, the puffed pantaloons of the men and the enormous, throttling ruffs, had subsided into something much neater and more flattering. Lace rufflettes and collars now adorned necks and the lavish slashing and pulling of fabrics quietened to reveal the ravishing beauty of silk and brocade, draped over hooped skirts or hanging from shoulders to form trains. The hideously elongated waistlines of late Elizabethan fashion had not affected the Italian scene so acutely, and clothes, though sumptuous, did not distort the wearer.

Both Robert and Elizabeth employed full-time tailors and seamstresses, not to mention dressers, and each had a large robing room to house their ever-changing wardrobes. Their clothes matched their many duties and must always be immaculate and innovative. They were constantly on parade with, sometimes, two changes of costume in a day, followed by one in the evening. It was a demanding existence and a most expensive one.

William Bradshaw, in tandem with Philip, the steward, was now their official major-domo and master of their households and stables. Unofficially, William remained one of Robert's closest friends. He had absorbed Tuscan life like a sponge and had married Seraphina, one of the gentle, black-eyed girls from Pisa, who became Elizabeth's closest attendant, her companion and her support through every contingency, including childbirth. Their roles had been reversed when Elizabeth had proudly delivered, with her own hands, Seraphina's two sons now aged eight and six. There was little the two women did not know about each other, spoken or unspoken.

The house in Via della Vigna Nuova was now their home and into it had gone all Robert's expertise and Elizabeth's love of beauty. The ground floor consisted of kitchens, servants' quarters and store rooms. Steps rose directly from the courtyard entrance to the first floor and led to the entrance hall, reception rooms, dining hall, Robert's library and a large music room. The second floor held the family and guest rooms and a small chapel. The third floor was Robert and Elizabeth's own fortress; their bedrooms, wardrobes and dressing rooms. The fourth floor was the children's domain: bedrooms, nurseries, and schoolrooms. The courtyard, opening on to the Via della Spada, was fragrant with the scent of the fruit trees from Pisa, planted in huge tubs around it. The stables were further down the Via di Belle Donne, well away from the house and the church of San Pancrazio.

Immediately next door was the Palazzo Rucellai, an ancient family of great standing from whom Robert had originally bought the houses and land on which to build. They were an enormous tribe, as steeped in Florentine history as the Medici and it was a mark of esteem that they had consented to sell any part of their land to a foreigner, let alone one with such a history. A nudge from Duke Cosimo may well have helped.

The Warwick household was bustling and exuberant; full of children's laughter and never still. It was also full of song and music; the music room being the centre of activity with some excruciating sounds sometimes issuing from it. The children were allowed to choose which instrument they wished to study and, at this stage, practice seldom made perfect. They all sang from an early age, led by their mother, and some had been blessed with her voice. The household was always moving in one direction or another. The energy of its owners generated action of every kind, from the meticulous planning of grand occasions to wholesale upheaval out to the Villa Rinieri or to Pisa.

This was one of the happiest periods of Robert's life. He had started a new existence at the age of thirty-one, embraced a new culture and worked, as few of his contemporaries would have dreamed of doing, on several major enterprises, all of which he had brought to successful conclusions. There had been few failures and he had found time to pursue, like a ferret down various rabbit holes, several interesting sidelines such as the manufacture of silk, the invention of a curative which now had a large following, the design of various machines and much writing on a wide variety of subjects of which those on naval matters had acquired especial renown. He was married to a woman of legendary beauty whose sweetness of nature made her loved by all, and he had fathered eight healthy children. He had built a large house in Florence and been given an even larger one in the country. He was beloved by the Ducal family and was now in charge of their households and many aspects of their lives; all this by the year 1620, in fifteen years.

Set against this, he had abandoned a family of five in England and lost an historic castle and estate and the majority of his wealth and position in his own country. He had earned the unremitting antagonism of his King and many of his countrymen, among them some of his relations, and he had never again seen his mother nor set foot in England.

Robert would never cease to appreciate a beautiful woman or enjoy her company, but he was no longer tempted to stray. There was, simply, no equal to Elizabeth. He adored her, and, for such an egoist, fully appreciated not only her loveliness but her generosity of spirit and the courage that matched his own. She allowed nothing to wear her down and she rode or drove long distances when pregnant, which was a frequent state of affairs. They were two of a kind and he needed no other.

Of the children she had borne him, Maria, Cosimo, Anna, Maddalena, Carlo, Ambrogio, Giovanni, Antonio and Teresa, eight remained. Giovanni had died as a baby. Of this ever-increasing brood, only one was beginning to cause concern. If ever there was strife among them, which naturally there was, the root of the trouble nearly always lay with Carlo. He was as robust and good-looking as the other boys, but with the narrow eyes and defiant stance of his grandfather, Leicester, and he was every bit as selfish. He loved his mother but was jealous and demanding of her attention. This inevitably led to dislike of his father and antagonism in every aspect of their relationship. There was already strife in their dealings with one another and Robert was often obliged to walk away before he beat Carlo senseless. It did not bode well for the future and Robert was thankful that his heir, Cosimo, had inherited his mother's nature and at ten years old was already an outstanding personality. He was tolerant of his brother, Carlo, but never allowed him to bully the others.

The year 1620 was to be a momentous and far-reaching one for Robert and his family. On March 9th, Maria Maddalena's brother, the Holy Roman Emperor, issued letters patent confirming Robert Dudley's right to the Dukedom of Northumberland and the Earldom of Warwick "throughout the Holy Roman Empire and all the provinces and dominions of the same." His wording of the patent made it clear that he was recognizing Robert as his grandfather's wholly legitimate heir and that he was not conferring the title on him, nor creating it for him. It was also stated that he had suffered the deprivation of his title unfairly and because of his religion. King James would find it difficult to challenge the Emperor by bestowing the dukedom on yet another favourite, or by promoting the present Earl of Northumberland, Henry Percy, to the same dukedom. He was at this time, in any event, having to plead with Ferdinand over the Palatinate. The letters patent had been endorsed by Pope Paul V himself and, for this, Robert suspected that he had Duchess Maria Christina to thank. They understood each other well and he knew she had great fondness for him and had long been an ally.

The news came from the palace through Duke Cosimo and Maria Maddalena that bright March morning and they insisted that a public ceremony of celebration be held to establish Robert as a Duke once all the relevant documents had arrived. There was to be no failure in spreading the news and making sure of its acceptance throughout Tuscany; they were delighted by the success of their mission.

Robert stood very still in the centre of his hall that morning, holding the roll of parchment in his hand with the moment anchored in his mind to savour for the rest of his life. This was confirmation from the very highest authorities of what he had always believed. His father and mother had been lawfully married, he was their legitimate son, the witnesses to the marriage had been right and his mother, as she admitted, had been frightened into a denial. He had been entered as an earl's son at Oxford, he had inherited Kenilworth as Leicester's heir, perhaps to atone for what had been done to him, and he knew in his bones that the evidence he had gathered for the wretched case in Star Chamber had been true. He began to laugh as he thought of the last Duke of Northumberland, his grandfather, and what a ruthless old reprobate he had been. His own father had not been much better, and he must make sure that whatever came later, he himself would leave the title unsullied.

But then the laughter died. There was a dark side to this triumph for it was already slurred. Had he not done precisely what his father had done? Abandoned a wife and children, not one but five, to whom, he knew full well, he had considered himself husband and father? If he had never encountered Elizabeth, he would still be that husband and father. His daughters in England now had to battle, as he had battled, for their legitimacy and their rights. He had condemned them to a childhood such as his own and he had done nothing to help them except to leave them sufficient money for their upbringing and their dowries in the hope that they would make good marriages. This was, in fact, imminent; the girls were now of age, but matrimony might prove difficult with such a background and an exiled father. The dukedom would certainly help but there were many who would cavil at their origins and Alice would have to work hard to find husbands for them. There was a black cloud of misdeed over the rejoicing and Robert was honest enough to recognize it and pause in his triumph.

For the moment it lifted as Elizabeth came running down the curved stairs, her face alight and her hands stretched out to him. Behind her, laughing and jostling, surged his children. Maria, now twelve, led them carrying the baby Teresa and was followed by the younger ones, with

Cosimo, soon to be Earl of Warwick, bringing up the rear brandishing a small pennant painted with the bear and ragged staff. They flocked around him, happy and eager, and the cloud receded. He opened his arms to them and gathered them up. These, at least, should lack for nothing that he could give them. Small Antonio grabbed Robert's leg to steady himself and Anna, lifting her flower-like face to him, was hoisted up and kissed.

In London, his old friend and ally Ottaviano Lotti had been recalled to Florence after many years and was replaced by Amerigo Salvetti. Robert now asked Salvetti to act on his behalf, in conjunction with Mr. Yates, his former contact, over the matter of the final payments for Kenilworth due from the Crown. It would not be long before he would have to think of dowries for his girls in Italy too, a monumental expense if they were to marry into the great families of Italy as he wished. Duchess Maria Christina was willing to take Maria into her household as a lady-in-waiting and to find a husband for her in due course; the other girls would follow.

Here, in Florence, Robert was now plunged into another Medici wedding. This time not quite so lavish and, of necessity, arranged at speed. The Duke was sinking fast; there was grave concern over his health and he was not long for this world. His youngest sister, Claudia, now sixteen, was hurriedly betrothed to the even younger Duke of Urbino. This was a political and dynastic marriage arising from the expected acquisition of Urbino by Duchess Maria Christina as part of her dowry from her grandmother, Catherine de Medici. It would give rise to a great deal of trouble in the future.

A few months later, in February 1621, Duke Cosimo II died of consumption. He was only thirty years old and, though a pale shadow of his father, he had ruled justly and as well as he was able. He had been popular with his subjects and had maintained Tuscany's supremacy at sea, thanks to the expansion of his navy and merchant fleet under Robert's auspices. Cosimo's greatest achievement was the completion of the harbour mole or pier at Livorno, a massive undertaking, recently finished under Robert's supervision and of which they were both extremely proud. Robert wrote that he had: "completed the mole at no great cost and over a period of twelve years, when similar works undertaken elsewhere cost millions of scudi and took twice as long to finish." He had never been noted for modesty but his record in Tuscany was remarkable. He could now add this, and his other engineering achievements, to the credit he had achieved with the Tuscan Court.

On the Duke's sad death, the Great Chamberlain went into immediate action and arranged a funeral as magnificent as that of any previous Medici. "Il Duca Di Nortombria" oversaw every detail of the ceremonial and Elizabeth helped the grieving Maria Maddalena to set the music. Duke Cosimo was interred in the New Sacristy; the Medici Chapel being, as yet, unfinished.

His namesake and godson, Cosimo Dudley, dressed in black satin with a white ostrich feather in his hat, slow-marched immediately behind the heir, now Duke Ferdinando II, carrying the dead Duke's coronet on a black cushion. The two boys were both eleven years old, had known each other all their lives, and were well used to public appearances. Their round faces solemn and controlled, they moved with assurance and in full view up the aisle, but as the singing began the strength and beauty of young Cosimo's voice, of which he was unaware, rang out over those around him so that heads began to turn. He had inherited his mother's unfettered gift for song and Elizabeth, standing behind him, raised her voice to join him in farewell to a patient man and a generous friend. Cosimo heard it, turned his head to smile at her and together they sang the "Nunc Dimitis", their voices rising with the choir and the other young Dudleys in spontaneous tribute. It was a canticle they all knew well and it created a moment that would be long-remembered but it marked the end of childhood for the two boys in the aisle.

The young Duke Ferdinando was easy-going, biddable and good-natured. He was on the large side, with the fleshy Hapsburg mouth, a big nose and dark, sleepy eyes. He was not particularly bright or academic and his tutors were not optimistic; neither was he particularly athletic and would become stout. At the beginning of his reign he was, inevitably, very much under the thumb of both his grandmother and his mother; he had been appointed their ward. Now lacking a father, whose memory, for him, was mainly that of an invalid, he turned, just as that father had before him, to a man of awesome stature who seemed able to provide help on any matter; his friend Cosimo Dudley's father and his mother's Great Chamberlain. Robert found himself caught between Maria Christina and Maria Maddalena. They did not always agree, particularly on the subject of the Grand Duke and he was there to serve them both. He was also obliged to take orders from the boy Duke himself and these could run counter to his mother or grandmother's wishes. Friendly advice usually resolved any disagreements, occasionally backed by his son Cosimo, who, like a brother to Ferdinando, could be extremely blunt with him in private. The only time the two boys came to blows was when Ferdinando refused to accept that he had not won in any game or contest. He was a bad loser and prone to temper tantrums.

In 1621, Robert also had news of the death of his eldest child in England. This was particularly sad because Alice had done well and their daughter, Alicia, already betrothed and awaiting her marriage, died at the age of twenty. She was able to bequeath £3,000, a surprisingly large sum, to her mother for charitable use. Both Robert and Lady Douglas had been generous to all his English daughters and they were to marry well.

Meanwhile Salvetti, Lotti's successor in London, was making heavy weather of extracting the balance owed Robert on Kenilworth. This debt had been outstanding for years and Salvetti was heartily sick of it, as was the Duke of Northumberland. The correspondence dragged on intermittently. When Robert Sidney died, his son did his best to grab two of the manors but, after King James's death in 1625, his son, Charles I, gave the whole estate to Robert Carey, Earl of Monmouth, but still without paying Robert any part of the debt owed him. This matter was like a festering sore to Robert and was eventually to erupt in high-handed action.

In 1624, when Duke Ferdinando's aunt Claudia lost her young husband, Frederico Ubaldo della Rovere, the heir to Urbino, she returned to Florence with her infant daughter, Vittoria della Rovere. She had managed, at least, to produce an heiress to the State and young Duke Ferdinando was promptly betrothed to Vittoria at the age of thirteen, despite the fact that they were first cousins. This would, it was hoped, ensure the future of Urbino; it was to become part of Tuscany when the present Duke was gathered to his fathers, Vittoria and Ferdinando both having valid claims. These seemingly watertight schemes were not approved by the Pope, now Urban VIII. He and his family, the voracious Barberini, prepared for battle and claimed Urbino for the Church on the grounds that it would be a vacant state when the old Duke died, thus ignoring the claims of Duchess Maria Christina, part of whose dowry the State had been. Quite unable to see the wood for the trees, the Vatican always her guiding light, the Duchess assented when the Pope sent troops into Urbino ahead of the old Duke's death in order to prove, no doubt, that possession was ninth tenths of the law. Papal authority must not be challenged. Well did Urban VIII know it.

Maria Christina's subservience to Rome was absolute and, in private, she had taken to arraying herself in the penitential garb of black with a widow's cap and absence of jewellery save an enormous cross. Furthermore, the two duchesses had unwisely allowed into Tuscany a positive flood of priests and churchmen, giving them positions of authority throughout the state administration system. The power this engendered was soon felt, to the dismay of Florentine officials and the population generally; the priesthood was gradually taking control of Tuscan government. They were not above corruption and over the coming years their interventions would begin to erode the strong Tuscan economy. Immense sums were spent on these gentlemen in maintenance and pensions.

Both Duchesses realised that, with the Grand Duke still a mere boy and not often in the public eye, their position as rulers of the State needed bolstering. They pursued a course of even more public show and extravagance. Their Regency needed to be seen in all its glory and they and their rich retinues proceeded to parade themselves with increasing magnificence, which was no help to the economy. Everywhere, they were accompanied by their increasingly powerful Chamberlain.

Regrettably, though it was well concealed among his ducal associates, the Chamberlain was not particularly religious. He had skipped from the Church of England to Catholicism with nimble grace and from necessity. The Howards had always leaned towards Rome and it had not been difficult for him, nor for Elizabeth. She, however, was deeply sincere in her adopted religion and believed, beyond doubt, that Robert's former marriages had not been lawful in the eyes of the Church and that she was his only true wife. She had a strong affinity with the Mother of God and their children were, naturally, being brought up as good Catholics. Teresa, a particularly devout child, swallowed a small gold statue of Our Lady at the age of three and no amount of purging or bread and butter ever caused it to reappear. This became a family joke and Teresa's religious devotion was always attributed to it. In due course, and in expectation that she would take the veil, she would be sent to the Convent at Boldrone, close to the Villa Rinieri.

When not in the throes of such domestic emergencies, her father was well aware of the huge influx of priests and the consequences of their establishment in Tuscany but found himself in a difficult situation. According to both Papal and Imperial opinion, his dukedom had been restored partly on the grounds that he was a wronged and persecuted Catholic, not exactly a martyr, but heading in that direction. He could not, therefore, decry the flood of priests and their influence, nor advise the two Duchesses to do so without offending Pope Urban VIII whose predecessor had so obligingly supported his claims. He could only go with the tide and acquiesce in their unquestioning obedience though it went against the grain to do so. The new Church hierarchy in Tuscany received him unreservedly and Elizabeth even more so. Was she not a relation of that remarkable English Catholic martyr, Robert Southwell, whose excruciating death had been so well documented?

In England, the reign of James I lurched along its rocky path, with George Villiers, his present favourite, installed as Duke of Buckingham, no less, and now risen to heights of undeserved power and wealth. Through various and devious means, he had managed to oust certain members of the Howard family from their positions and, without being in any way qualified, he had taken the place of the hero of the Armada, Lord Howard of Effingham, as Lord Admiral. How much, if anything, he knew about ships or the Navy remained to be seen. His influence was rampant and Prince Charles, too, was under his thumb. It was felt that the less said about his relationship with the King the better. James's health was failing; his power gradually being sapped by his son and his favourite. He died in March 1625, leaving a successor in whom the concept of the Divine Right of Kings was firmly entrenched and with the greedy and profligate Buckingham holding the reins of power. It was not a happy combination and there were widespread rumours that James had been assisted heavenwards by one or both of them. He had become redundant to either.

Robert was certainly disenchanted with them, particularly over the failure to reach any settlement on Kenilworth. Much against the wishes of Elizabeth, who very seldom opposed him over anything, Robert now embarked on a course of retribution which was to do him little good. This was prompted, to some extent, by his highly expensive way of life and a genuine need of money.

He maintained that the English Crown was in his debt to the tune of £200,000 for the price of Kenilworth and including the interest owed over the years it had remained unpaid. He now proposed to extract this amount from non-Catholic English ships trading in Livorno and the English mercantile houses installed there, regardless of the pains he had taken over the years to build and enlarge the port, thus promoting trade. It was no empty threat. He had managed to secure an edict to this effect from the Curia Ecclesiastica of Florence whose Vicar General he had cultivated and become friendly with. When this move did not appear to be getting him anywhere, and he had received no confirmation that the edict would be implemented, he wrote in January 1627 directly to the Grand Ducal Secretary that: "Seeing no hope from England of my affairs being settled, even though so often through your kindness recommended to King Charles by His Serene Highness, we must now come to the last remedy to obtain justice, which as High Highness denies it to none, he may the more readily concede to me." This missive was accompanied by the promise of a barefaced bribe of 400 ducats and a "handsome present" to the Secretary's wife from Elizabeth should the outcome be successful. The letter was followed by another, from Pisa, to the same effect and demanding authority to carry out his threats.

Elizabeth was horrified, told him, in tears, that she would never consent to such a scheme, nor be a party to it, and shut herself in her room for the first time since their marriage. She would have nothing to do with bribes, now or ever. Robert was amazed and taken aback, but it gave him pause for thought. Bribes were common enough practice and he had never known such a reaction from her over any of his enterprises.

Meanwhile, the young Grand Duke, aged seventeen, had set out on a tour, first to Rome, then to Vienna and afterwards, to France, accompanied by Cosimo Dudley, now the Earl of Warwick, as a gentleman in waiting. He was not, therefore, in a position to support Robert's demands and his Grand Ducal Secretary could certainly not authorise any such action on his behalf in his absence.

Encouraged by the Vicar General, Robert then directly approached the Camera Apostolica in Rome, the appropriate authority, who were only too delighted to endorse his demands. A decree was published enforcing the Florentine edict which stated: "This letter of Gregorius Navo, Auditor-General of the Camera Apostolica, commands by the same the Grand Duke Ferdinand and all the Ministers under him, under pain of 1,000 gold ducats, that they shall confiscate and sell all or any of the goods of English Parliamentarians and English people conjointly, excepting only professed Catholics: to the end that they may give and repay to Robert Dudley, Duke of Northumberland, to Cosimo Dudley, Earl of Warwick, his son, and to Elizabeth Southwell wife of the above-mentioned Robert, and to all other children which are or shall be born to the above consorts, 8,000,000 ducats with other 200,000 ducats as interest for the same: by reason of the unjust occupation and confiscation made of the above-named Dukedom: and this according to the decree promulgated by Pietro Niccolini, Vicar General of the Archbishop of Florence, and confirmed by the afore-mentioned Gregorius Navo." All very definite.

This imperious and dictatorial injunction was posted on the main door of the Duomo in Florence and provoked a storm of anger amongst the many Florentines who read it, from members of the Court and, in due course, from young Duke Ferdinando on his return. Particularly furious was Elizabeth, publicly named and, to her mind, shamed, by such an edict. She immediately packed and set off, with the younger children, to Rinieri, leaving Robert to manage the situation that he had created and to supervise the elder ones. He had never before witnessed her anger nor had it directed against himself.

The Duke of Northumberland had gone too far and trespassed on the goodwill of his host nation. It was an act of high-handed arrogance, a result of pent-up fury and resentment, and it could have cost him his position as Chamberlain, his work in Pisa and Livorno, his house in Florence and all the influence he had in Tuscany. Everything, in fact, that he had worked so hard to build, including the goodwill of the Florentine people and their Court. His future and that of his family looked very doubtful indeed and, had it not been for the affection of the two Grand Duchesses, in whose eyes he could do no wrong, and the instant support they gave him, he might well have found himself out in the cold and looking for asylum elsewhere.

One effect this episode had was to rouse Duke Ferdinando to resist such a peremptory order from the Apostolic Chamber to a Head of State, particularly under the threat of a fine. He terminated the Regency and himself took over the Government of Tuscany. However, his duty to his Mother and his Grandmother was so ingrained that they were still to retain much of their authority.

Eventually, the agitation and gossip died down and the Northumberlands retained their position. Robert's aggressive measure came to nothing, the edict was ignored by the Florentine Council, and no action was taken against English ships or merchants. Gradually the whole episode was forgotten. Robert climbed back on his pedestal and Elizabeth forgave him although she did, from that time on, keep herself much better informed of his future plans and intentions.

Soon after this regrettable episode, and once Duke Ferdinando assumed rule, there was, happily, a distraction which served to wipe it from memories where it might have rankled. Yet another Medici wedding was looming. The Duke Ferdinando's young sister, Margharita, was married amid the greatest splendour, to Edouardo Farnese, Duke of Parma. The Great Chamberlain excelled himself and the nuptial celebrations, all agreed, were faultless. Elizabeth, again, assisted with the music, particularly the singing, and employed Count Bardi to arrange a spirited version of Peri's "Eurydice" which was performed one evening in the spacious Pitti Palace. This was the best example of the "Recitativo" yet seen in Florence; opera was moving on. Maria Dudley, a particular friend of Margharita, was in close attendance on the bride both before and during the wedding ceremonies.

Both Maria and Anna, now aged sixteen and eighteen and ladies-in-waiting to Duchess Maria Christina, attracted a good deal of attention on this occasion, as their mother had before them. They were much alike and unusually beautiful, but Anna's was a rare perfection which made people halt, look and find they could not look away. She was used to this; it had happened all her life and she was quite unconscious of it. She had Elizabeth's startling ice-blue eyes, long-lashed and large, creamy skin and a sweetness in her smile that was irresistible. Maria was slightly darker, but with the same beautiful skin and the grey eyes of her father. Elizabeth had held them back from Court life for as long as she could. She did not want them thrust into the marriage market at too young an age, as she had been, and forced to fend off unwanted suitors from the age of thirteen. They had grown up in tandem with the ducal children and with the children of many other courtiers and although their manners were perfect, they were no shrinking violets.

Cosimo Dudley, now the Earl of Warwick, was also very much a part of the wedding ceremonial. He was, like his father, an excellent horseman and always rode behind Duke Ferdinando on festive occasions. Ferdinando, less athletic and already putting on weight, did not appear to the same advantage. Nor did he often take part in the jousts or equestrian displays performed in the enlarged forecourt of the Pitti Palace. Cosimo, to whom these things were meat and drink, had inherited his father's height and, in general, stood inches taller than any Italian boy his age. For his part in this occasion, he was appointed Commander of the Grand Duke's Squadron, to Robert's pride and joy.

During the recent visit to his uncle, the Holy Roman Emperor, Ferdinando had been taken to see the performances at the Spanish Riding School in Vienna and these had made a lasting impression on young Cosimo who accompanied him. He wheedled his way into the good graces of the Head Riding Master and persuaded him to take him in hand. The thrill of being mounted on one of the superb Spanish stallions and given instruction on the intricate and, sometimes, arcane means of training them, was one of the most exciting events of his young life. Some of the aids given were unfamiliar but he was an apt pupil and resolved that, one day, he would breed horses like these and pave the way for a similar riding school in Tuscany. Greatly daring, he went so far as to ask the Master to let him know if one of the foals bred in the mountain pastures ever came up for sale. How he would induce his father to shoulder the cost was another matter, but he knew that Robert would be equally enthusiastic. He would not be the first Englishman to acquire one of the famous stallions. Philip Sidney, a renowned horseman in his day, had done so, and bred a line of merit. Both Cosimo and his father found it hard to find horses up to their weight in Italy. The grey stallions from the Imperial Karst Stud, founded in 1580 near Lipizza, were large and had the perfect conformation for ceremonial or military work. The Master, amused by the boy's passionate enthusiasm and impressed by his ability, said that he would consider the matter and consult the Emperor.

In June 1628, Elizabeth gave birth to a fifth daughter and proof of the unshaken friendship and affection of the Medici was made apparent when the Duke's elder sister, the tiny, misformed Maria Christina, stood as godmother at the christening held in the Baptistry of San Giovanni. This was where all Florentine children were baptised. The baby was named after her Godmother and the infant Maria Christina was immersed, squalling and furious, by no less a personage than Cardinal Francesco Barberini, a nephew of the feuding Pope Urban VIII. This marked the beginning of a significant friendship which was, in due course, to introduce Robert to his Holiness himself. His support of the Grand Duchesses in their unquestioning loyalty to Rome was paying off, in combination with the general, if mistaken, view that he had been a persecuted Catholic. There was to be an interesting sequel to this family event.

It was just after the baptism that Robert wrote a lengthy epistle to the Grand Duke and the senior officials of the Court on behalf of Ambrogio, his third son, then around twelve years old. He was big for his age and exceptionally well built and he was shortly to join his sisters at Court as a page to the Duchess Maria Christina. He had obligingly and precociously developed a passion for a daughter of Oratzio Rucellai, easily done since they were near neighbours and the children ran constantly from one house to the other. Robert would be delighted to arrange a future marriage but this was aiming high and it was necessary to display his own family credentials well in advance of any proposal.

He began the letter by stating that, at this time, June 1628, he had five sons and five daughters living, that eighteen year old Cosimo was already Commander of the Grand Duke's Squadron "being much esteemed and favoured by his patron" and that his other sons "are well brought up in every sort of virtue. They are taught the arts of delineation, dancing, riding and other knightly exercises." There was a much also on the subject of family history, proving his own somewhat hazy connections with the English throne. Of his daughters, he wrote: "The condition of the eldest girl is known to everyone, as also her deportment at Court, where she is invited by their Highnesses to all their fêtes, and is much respected by them. She is a great favourite with the Princesses, especially the Duchess of Parma, now married." Regarding Maria's dowry, obviously worth a mention, he wrote that it: "will be in accordance with the person with whom we treat, and will not be less than that of the highest persons in Florence, or that which the Prince of Massa gave his daughter. She is under the protection of "Madame Serenissima" who is seeking a good match for her and favours her very much."

Indeed, "Madam Serenissima" had been busy and plans were already under way for Maria's marriage, though temporarily halted by Robert's untoward behaviour over the seizure of English assets at Livorno. Duchess Maria Christina had suggested Oratzio Appiano, Prince of Piombino, as a bridegroom.

Piombino was a small coastal state opposite the Isle of Elba on which it held a certain amount of land. It was a very ancient principality, having survived since the twelfth century and its main citadel, Valle Castle, overlooked the sea. Oratzio Appiano was in his twenties, a personable man with lively brown eyes and great charm, often at the Tuscan Court since the *de facto* ruler of Piombino at this time was the redoubtable Princess Isabella, his aunt. He had been instantly taken with Maria, her beauty and her liveliness, and he had not been allowed to set eyes on her younger sister until matters were arranged; Anna, at this time, had not yet appeared at Court. Robert and Elizabeth approved the match, liked Oratzio Appiano and set about finding the large sum required for Maria's dowry. Maria knew her duty as the eldest daughter in an increasing family, however tight-knit, and instantly acquiesced over their choice of bridegroom. From the first, Appiano treated her with admiration and kindness, she felt that she could grow to love him, and she was delighted at the thought of becoming a Princess. She was a sweet-natured girl, but, like all the Dudley children, had a decided mind of her own.

The wedding took place at Piombino, in the old citadel of Valle Castle, to the sound of sea birds crying in the wind, the crash of waves on the rocks below and salt air blowing up from the spray. Always at ease near the sea, this pleased Robert enormously; he felt his eldest child would be happy here and appreciated the Prince's knowledge of tide, ocean and the ships in which he frequently sailed across to Elba. The Princess Isabella, a formidable lady with several marriages behind her, had much in common with Robert. She had fought her corner at Piombino for many years and knew her way around the courts of Italy well. She welcomed Maria into the family with delight, approving both her beauty and the polish acquired in the Tuscan Court. The entire Northumberland family were present, and the boys, Cosimo, Carlo, Ambrogio, Antonio and Ferdinando were let loose on the rocks and sand of the large cove below the citadel to fish, swim or sail. Reciprocal visits were arranged for the Appiano family to stay at the Villa Rinieri, particularly over the summer months when Piombino was considered unhealthy and fever-ridden.

From the moment that Anna appeared in the train of the Duchess Maria Christina, Robert was besieged by requests for permission to address her, some from the oldest and most revered families in Italy. Anna was obliged to realise, at last, what a profound effect she had upon the men who set eyes on her and she looked to Robert for shelter, begging him not to commit her, just as Elizabeth had done with Admiral Southwell. There was a good reason for this. Anna had fallen in love with a man she could not marry; Giancarlo de Medici, the younger brother of the Grand Duke with whom she had played, fought and laughed ever since she was a small child. He had been just one of many brothers to her; until now.

Giancarlo was the best looking of Maria Maddalena's brood and had been a wicked little boy. He was entered for the Church at an early age, according to family tradition, though in this case the choice of candidate was decidedly mistaken. He had previously joined the Sovereign Military Order of Malta with a view to a military career before entering the Church. He had also been appointed "Grand Prior" to Pisa for political reasons. Even at this age, he was a great collector of works of art and had a good eye for beauty, be it clothed in flesh or marble. He gave full rein to these talents and his exploits were to become notorious. Duke Ferdinando, his elder brother, was wary of him and seldom crossed him; he was by far the stronger character and some of his doings were to become quite bizarre.

He had returned from Pisa at the height of his sister's wedding celebrations and at the start of the jousting, to find that all his contemporaries were jostling for Anna's favours. Poetry was being written, ballads sung and competition for her attention ran high. He had not seen her for some time and found the little sister had grown up, and most beautifully; his first encounter with her, in his Grandmother's train, left him breathless.

He immediately applied to Robert, who was organising proceedings, for permission to take part in the joust, got himself armed and horsed in a hurry, and rode into the sun-baked Pitti Court with his fellows, carrying a pennant bearing the Dudley arms, having coaxed it out of Cosimo for the occasion. The formal parade over, he broke ranks, rode over to where Anna sat with the Duchess Maria Christina, raised his visor, revealing a flushed face and a mass of dark curls, and told her he would love her till he died; all this in the patois of their childhood, a mixture of English, German and infantile Italian, perfectly understandable to her and to most other people listening. He then tossed, not a single rose, but a whole bouquet, to her and rode back to his friends. He proceeded to acquit himself with great distinction, though not quite in the league of Cosimo Dudley. So far as Anna was concerned, the damage was done. She sat, her lovely face glowing and her eyes rivetted to the departing rider. She had always loved him but realised, in that moment, that it would no longer be as a brother.

Robert's feelings about this display, and the hectic courtship that followed, were mixed. He had not appreciated the Dudley pennant being carried by a Medici as a display of devotion to a Dudley daughter; nor had Giancarlo asked his permission to address Anna. Above all, he wanted Anna's happiness; she was his favourite child of all the many, but he could not allow this to go further. It was clearly a case of calf love, painfully real to Anna, but part of an endless stream for Giancarlo, mounting soon to a positive flood. He was incapable of saying "No" to himself, or to any woman. The affair was doomed even if Giancarlo abandoned his future in the church altogether, as his Grandfather had done, and married Anna. The chances of him abandoning his pursuit of women were slim whatever he chose to do. Robert recognised a dedicated libertine and sent Anna on a long visit to Piombino, hoping her sister and the sea air would calm the terrifying throes of first love. The Giancarlos of this world were seldom prepared to wait.

CHAPTER FOURTEEN

Gathering Storms – 1630-1631

In the late summer of 1630, a troop of horsemen rode down the road at Boldrone to the Villa Rinieri. Though travel-stained, they were immaculately clad in Hapsburg insignia and colours, and their horses were superb. Two immediately caught the eye. They were led by the riders, one stallion and one mare of outstanding physique; big, grey and well-muscled, their long manes and tails rippled as they passed. Folk flew out of their houses to catch a glimpse.

Turning through the gates of Rinieri, the horsemen formed an orderly squad and rode up the drive at a smart pace.

The Duke of Northumberland and his family were at dinner and, hearing the pounding hooves, he and his sons came out to meet them. The family were all informally clad, the men brown from the scorching summer sun and the hunting, hawking and sailing at Piombino earlier in the summer. It could be seen that Cosimo, Earl of Warwick, almost twenty-one, was now the same height as his father. Through narrowed eyes, he focused on the led horses with a look of dawning wonder in their grey depth. Could this be reality or a far-fetched dream?

It was no dream. The Austrian Emperor remembered well the case of the Duke of Northumberland and had been charmed by his son during the visit of his nephew, the Grand Duke of Tuscany. He had not been so greatly charmed by his nephew who, he thought, looked depressingly like the rest of the Hapsburgs though a darker, more florid version, and who had behaved with undue arrogance during the visit. The Master of the Spanish Riding School, however, during an interview with the Emperor, had dwelt on Cosimo's rapt interest in the horses and every facet of their breeding and well-being, and had passed on the boy's request to buy one from the stud.

Having been instrumental in the father's elevation to a Dukedom, the Emperor's interest now focused on the son. He decided that he would continue in the role of arch-benefactor which would also serve as a put-down for his pompous nephew. Ferdinando had not treated him with the respect his choleric nature demanded.

So it was that eighteen months later two superb specimens of the Spanish line, a mare and a young stallion, arrived in Tuscany, as a present from the Emperor for the Duke of Northumberland and his estimable son and in time for that son's birthday.

Having left the dinner table wondering idly who these visitors might be, Cosimo was now too overcome to speak; no dream could have been fulfilled so unexpectedly or magnificently. Robert was equally bowled over by such a gift and one that appeared over-generous. Cosimo and the other boys immediately became wholly absorbed with the horses and the entertainment of their escort. They had all to be welcomed, fed and housed and this they immediately set about.

Later, with Elizabeth in their own private chambers, however, Robert raised his eyebrows questioningly over this munificence. What could their son have done to deserve such largesse? The Emperor was known, famously, as a womaniser; one fear could obviously be forgotten, so what then had taken place in Austria? The answer was, in fact, quite straightforward, as was the Emperor himself. He had liked Cosimo for his enthusiasm and honesty, he had been intrigued by the history of his father and pleased with his own role in furthering Northumberland's claims and he was delighted to give generously where it might teach his conceited nephew a lesson. He could not stand any form of Protestant and was under the impression that Robert and his wife were persecuted Catholics who had fled England for religious reasons. He was also gleefully delighted to favour anyone hated by James I of England, with whom he had been doing battle over the Palatinate, and he was a single-minded man who was not to be turned from any opinion he had once formed. He loathed King James and roared with laughter when he heard him described as: "The wisest fool in Christendom."

Once the Imperial escort was on its way home, duly thanked and entertained, and carrying reciprocal gifts, the serious business of assessing the two horses began. Among the gifts for the Emperor had gone several phials of Robert's "Pulvis Warvicensis" to alleviate the gout he suffered from, and a bolt of heavy gold-embroidered silk satin from one of Robert's factories. The miraculous cure-all was a suggestion of the Princess Isabella, who was staying with them from Piombino. She was well acquainted with the Emperor and his ailments.

Of the two horses, the stallion was enormous, standing over sixteen hands and more than adequate for Robert's slightly increased weight. The mare was a little smaller and perfect for Cosimo and they were both blessed with the calm temperament of their breed. They had been backed and broken, but it would take time and patience to accustom them to the cheering crowds among whom they were destined to move. Having rested them after their long journey, Robert and his sons spent many happy hours working with them, both in and out of the schooling rings at the ducal Villa della Petraia next door. It was a golden end to a golden summer. Most of the Court were still at their country residences and there were no official functions to attend in Florence. Peace reigned among the family; even Carlo, who left few stones unturned to provoke his father, joined in with enthusiasm. He was becoming an excellent horseman himself and would soon rival Cosimo.

The gilded childhood enjoyed by Robert's offspring was coming to a close. Never again were they to be so close and so united. Storm clouds were gathering as the autumn leaves began to blow into the fountains at Rinieri and the pines to sough in the wind.

A dark shadow was creeping up behind this lovely summer; rumours were coming from the south. Plague was on the move once more and Rome was beginning to feel its foul fingers searching out, at first, the weak, the poor and the vulnerable then spreading gradually among the affluent, the nobility and, not least, the priesthood. Huddled together in their monasteries, convents and churches, these had less chance of escape than the farmers working the land. There were already cases in Florence.

Plague, like the poor, was always with them. It was endemic in Europe, breaking out every now and then, as in 1603, in vicious epidemics lasting months and wiping out entire communities. Sometimes, it came as a few cases spread thinly over a period of time; sometimes the terrifying purges continued and decimated the population. The wise pontificated on the nature and causes of the disease, its origins, preventions and possible treatment. Sadly, there was, as yet, no proof for theories, no tried or tested cure. The only belief held was that any survivor of the plague was then immune and would never succumb again. This did appear to carry some truth.

225

Florence was beginning to feel its black breath and, by mid-September, the Medici brothers showed both spirit and enterprise in an effort to check it. They forbade large gatherings of any kind, including Church festivals, encouraged citizens to remain outdoors as much as possible and set up a Council of Health to enforce sanitary regulations particularly in the overcrowded monasteries which had been ordered to receive and tend the sick. They also set up special hospitals and lazarettos, paid for from their own pockets, and centres to deal with the hungry and homeless. There were soon many children roaming the streets like starving little dogs. Robert's own patent remedy was not, unfortunately, either a preventative or a cure for plague.

On a baser but practical scale, the young Dukes financed and organised the digging of huge sulphur-laden "plague pits" into which the bodies of the dead were thrown and burnt. The pungent, reeking, yellow smoke cast a pall over the city and depressed its already fearful people. Works of art were muffled against possible damage and stained glass became a little dingy.

Robert forbade any of his family to return to Florence, though Cosimo was to escort the Princess Isabella back, by a circuitous route, to Piombino where he could spend some time with the now pregnant Maria.

Robert, himself, went promptly to Florence at the request of the Ducal family, not to organise entertainment, but to discourage it and to advise on their projects to alleviate the already suffering capital. The plague was now ripping through Florence, bringing the city almost to a standstill. He at once took charge of the supplies of food. Those usually bringing produce in from the surrounding countryside were now most unwilling to do so, markets were closing and stocks were running short as a result. Robert organised Royal Guard squadrons from the various palaces and sent them to the outlying farms to buy and bring back food for distribution at various centres besides the markets themselves; all this being financed by the Medici family. It crossed his mind that it would have delighted his departed friend, Duke Ferdinand I, to see his family so employed. They were all frequently about in the city, directing operations and even the hedonistic Giancarlo was pulling his weight.

The priesthood, however, grown fat and lazy under the protection of the Dowager Duchess Maria Christina, strongly complained to the Vatican of their enforced involvement and the curtailing of the Church's activities during this time of crisis. The result was Papal interference, compliantly backed by the Duchess, and an attempt to restrain the good work being done by the Medici family. As a result, Duke Ferdinando was forced to disband his Council of Health and his commands to the priesthood with the inevitable consequence that hygiene standards slipped and the plague raged on for many unnecessary months in and around the city, resulting in the death of over twelve thousand.

Robert, returning one evening in September to the Via della Vigna Nuova, after several days foraging among the outlying farms, found Anna awaiting him by the fire in his library. He strode forward incredulously, folding her in his arms and gently scolding her for her rashness and disobedience. Never could he be angry with this treasured child, but what could have brought her to Florence without her mother's permission? The answer was plain and did not please him. Her fears for Giancarlo had grown so great that she had, somehow, to see him. Her love for him had never faded, as Robert had hoped, but had grown tenfold. He was too much a part of her young life ever to be put aside and the months at Piombino had served only to increase her longing for him. It was a strange but ardent relationship, part lover, part brother, and the enforced stay at Rinieri had fed her anxiety for his safety. She must see him and she begged Robert to arrange a meeting. There were no tears, Anna seldom wept, but Robert was not proof against the intensity of longing in the perfect little face turned up to him. He promised he would send Giancarlo to her.

For Anna, the timing of this meeting was good. Giancarlo, usually leaping from one lover's bed to another, had, necessarily, to curtail his normal activities because of danger from plague and was, therefore, more than willing to meet Anna. He loved her dearly, not only as a part of his extremely active love life, but also of his childhood. The sight of her beautiful face at once evoked the best in him. He knew well that he would have Robert to deal with if he put so much as a toe over the line with Anna and how savage retribution might be despite his rank. Like all his generation of the Medici, Giancarlo stood in considerable awe of the Great Chamberlain. He had seen him in rare moments of anger and run for cover, recognising thinly disguised violence when he saw it and knowing Robert's reputation as a swordsman. He was allowed two hours only with Anna.

Swearing undying love, he soothed her fears, kissed her tenderly and repeatedly, his dark eyes kindling with the lust never far from such encounters, and made her promise to return to Rinieri and remain there until the city was safe. He would visit her as soon as it was possible and he promised also that he would speak to her father about matrimonials as soon as his obligations to the Church were resolved. He was, in due course, destined to be a Cardinal of Rome. He left her in a glow of great happiness and misplaced faith in him.

The following evening Robert returned to find his house in a state of uproar which subsided into a deafening silence as he strode through the entrance hall. Philip, his ageing steward, alone stood his ground and came forward to meet him. Would His Grace please come at once to the chamber of the Lady Anna who was gravely ill. Messengers had been sent to find him and a doctor summoned. Taking them three at a time, Robert raced up the stairs and flung open Anna's door. His heart lurched at what he saw. Anna, whom he had left that morning smiling and joyful, lay like a perfect image of herself, pale and unmoving, her eyes closed and her linen shift scarcely moving on her breast. With the greatest effort, her eyelids slowly opened and through the long silky lashes, the brilliant blue of her eyes smiled at him for one moment before they closed for ever. One fluttering sigh, and she was gone, as a small bird through an open window.

They laid her in the Church of San Pancrazio, close by the house, to await burial. Robert would not allow the rest of the family to come to Florence for fear of infection. When eventually they did, it was to find only a marble plaque within the church. Written on it were the words:

"Beauty, grace, virtue where are they now
A Northumbrian Princess, Anna has concealed them with
Herself Beneath this stone"

A light had gone out of their lives, particularly Robert's, to whom, of all his children, Anna had been the dearest. She had died of the pulmonary manifestation of the plague which spared the victim the worst symptoms of the disease but, attacking the lungs, killed with horrible speed. But for her devotion to Giancarlo, Anna would not have come to Florence but, instead, would have been married long since to one of the army of suitors besieging Robert for her hand. Knowing this, he could not tolerate the sight of the boy for many months despite his fervent protestations of grief.

On Elizabeth the tragedy fell particularly hard. She was pregnant with their thirteenth child; two now dead and one stillborn. The blow was intense and, though gallant even in the face of such a loss, the enforced separation from Robert made it particularly difficult to bear. Now aged forty-four, she was not as physically strong as she had been. With Cosimo gone to Piombino, she held the rest of her family together at Rinieri until Robert considered it safe to return to Florence. Maddalena, now almost eighteen, had been due to join Anna as a Lady in Waiting to the Duchess Maria Christina. Ambrogio had already been serving as a page and would return when the Court was re-established in the city. He was pining precociously for his love, the young daughter of Orazio Rucellai, and could not wait to get back to Florence. Robert's overtures had been welcomed and an understanding reached on Ambrogio's future betrothal to a child of this great Florentine family. The horses from Austria were a distraction, however, and together with his friend and contemporary, Leopoldo de Medici, he spent many hours long-reining and riding them. Leopoldo, also destined for the Church, was quartered in the Ducal Villa Petraia close to them and spent much time at Rinieri.

Wholeheartedly forgiving Robert his high-handed rashness over the proposed fleecing of English Protestants and their shipping, Elizabeth had taken up the cudgels on his behalf, through Salvetti in London, and herself continued their efforts to extract some part of what was due to Robert from Kenilworth. With their enormous family, money was badly needed. She had charmed Salvetti into continued effort, although he wrote wearily that he would not abandon the pursuit though he: "had but the faintest chance of winning out with honour". He depressingly reminded her that Robert's last true friend and supporter at the Stuart Court, the Earl of Pembroke, had recently died. However, Elizabeth had no intention of giving up and continued to prod the Royal Exchequer for settlement. She knew that on this subject Robert would never rest easily.

Having endured a grim winter, Florence gradually returned to a comparatively normal state. Families, which had been holed up in their summer residences because of plague, began to reappear. Supplies were beginning to flow again into the markets, the stinks of the plague pits were drifting away on the wind as they were gradually filled in and, although there were still small outbreaks of the disease in the poorer districts, the Ducal brothers continued their good work and began to have the city cleansed.

The Duke of Northumberland, who, despite heartbreak, had worked untiringly with them, now considered it safe for his family to return to the Via della Vigna Nuova. Although still deeply mourning Anna, he arranged a great feast with friends, neighbours and members of the Court already returned, to welcome them back to Florence. Elizabeth, though heavily pregnant, was delighted. It was a mark of the regard in which the family was held and their acceptance by the Tuscan nobility, that their house was packed that evening with the greatest in the State, among them some of the oldest families in Italy. Medici, Rucellai, Appiano, Orsini, Rospigliosi, Pamphili and Farnese were represented among the guests, and Galileo, himself put in an appearance. Torches flared in the already lighter twilight glow of a March evening. Silk, satin, velvet, lace and jewels flowed into the house in a dazzling wave of colour and brilliance. The Duke of Northumberland and his family knew how to give a party.

Seated at one end of the enormous table and separated from her by tall candlesticks, exquisite china and glass and a board groaning with delicacies, Robert raised his glass to the enduringly lovely woman at the far end who had given up so much for him, smoothed his path with her tact and charm and won the love of all who knew her. He was well aware of what he owed her and, in a rare moment of humility, acknowledged it. She had dazzled and won over many of his enemies with her laughter and her beauty. It was a private gesture as their eyes met down the length of the table, but it was caught by his children and some of their guests who promptly followed him, all standing to drink her health. The compliments, for once, were deeply sincere.

Among the guests were dotted the elder children, Maria, Cosimo, Carlo, Maddalena, Ambrogio, and young Antonio, manfully making conversation with a bishop. Teresa, Ferdinando and Maria Christina, with the promise of sweetmeats being sent up later, had been hanging over the stairs to watch the guests arrive in all their splendour. Later there would be music, dancing and card playing. The city was beginning to sparkle again.

Soon after this, Robert's family, many now out of the nest, went their ways. Maria, nearing the birth of her first child, was escorted back to

Piombino by her husband. Cosimo, Maddalena and Ambrogio would be taking up their duties with Duke Ferdinando and his family in the Pitti Palace, and Elizabeth would resume her place beside Robert and with the Duchess Maria Maddalena until the arrival of their next child in April.

Late in 1630 Robert had been commended for his work in Florence directly to Pope Urban VIII by the Duchess Maria Christina and the entire Medici family. At the Pope's invitation and despite the plague, he had travelled to Rome to meet him. This honour was arranged by Cardinal Francesco Barberini, Pope Urban's nephew, who had baptised the infant Maria Christina Dudley in Florence in 1628. The two men had taken an instant liking to each other despite the differences in their backgrounds, ages and circumstances. The Cardinal had clearly recognised the influence held by Robert over the Medici. He had become a powerful father-figure in a house ruled by two women and a twenty year old boy. They did more than seek his advice, they took it. Such a force behind the throne could be extremely useful to the Barberini.

Having reviewed Robert's history and in no way blinded to the ruthless ambition and intrigue behind it, not to mention his marital arrangements, His Holiness agreed that whatever his personal shortcomings might be, the Duke of Northumberland was well worth both cultivating and rewarding. Dudley had never questioned the subservience of the two Grand Duchesses to Rome, the flood of the priesthood into Florence and their subsequent influence, nor Papal interference during the recent efforts to relieve the spread of plague. In fact, he never trod on Papal toes. Pope Urban, who was himself a Florentine, suspected that Robert was too astute to try. Quite apart from anything else, he wished to meet a man who had achieved so much in an astonishingly varied career. Not forgotten was that his own predecessor, Pope Paul V, had given support for the recovery of the Northumberland Dukedom. There were other considerations as well, not least the future of the Duchy of Urbino. Pope Urban wanted a smooth transition to its annexation by Rome with no unforeseen resistance from the Medici. The Duke of Northumberland might well be persuaded to use his influence in that direction.

When the two met, amid the splendour of a reception at the Vatican and introduced by Cardinal Francesco, it was an encounter similar to that between Dudley and Duke Ferdinand in Tuscany all those years before. Robert's inborn assurance was apparent and it was quite plain to

Pope Urban that he was being inspected by an equal, not flattered by a supplicant. They were all too alike. Large men in every sense; arrogant, knowledgeable and capable, they were unused to being questioned and they enjoyed the good things of life. They also discovered that they shared a dry sense of humour, veiled to begin with, but recognized. In their widely differing fields, they were both bold, ambitious entrepreneurs who seldom refused a challenge or accepted a defeat. There was instant rapport. Cardinal Francesco, satisfied, smiled quietly to himself.

The result of all this Papal bonhomie was that Robert was, in effect, admitted to the Roman nobility. In a Bull of late 1630, Pope Urban created the Duke of Northumberland a *"Patrizio Romano"*, a Roman Patrician, and accorded him the authority to form an Order of Knighthood. This was, perhaps, a veiled inducement to ensure Robert's future co-operation with the Papacy. Robert was delighted, as Pope Urban knew he would be. The setting up of an Order, with himself at its head, appealed to his sense of grandeur and love of ceremonial. Few knew better than he did how to go about it and he was given a free rein. He decided that there should be seventy-two members, the Grand Master being none other than the Holy Roman Emperor, so that it was named "The Imperial Military Order". This was a graceful nod to the Austrian Emperor for his kind offices, not to mention his beautiful horses. Robert himself would be "The Master of the Order". It was all very grand. The members of the Order must be men of high military standing and courage. His son, Cosimo, had certainly earned a place. This unexpected honour gave Robert some distraction from the desolation of Anna's death. It was a diversion to design the rich robes, ermine cloaks, coronets and weapons to be worn by his Order and to plan its membership and structure. He devised the insignia, a double headed eagle, and planned methods of recruitment if the Order was ever asked to fight. He was unsure whether all this would actually come to pass; it would certainly be costly and nothing further had come as yet from the seizure of Kenilworth.

Keeping Maddalena and Ambrogio at Court was costly also and the devout Teresa was shortly due to go to the Convent of Crocetta at Boldrone, another large expense. Elizabeth was beginning to express doubts as to the wisdom of this move. Teresa was developing a distinct personality somewhat at odds with her piety; she had a lively and wicked sense of fun. Also being educated with the nuns at Boldrone was the young Vittoria della Rovere, already betrothed to Duke Ferdinando and the future Grand Duchess of Tuscany. She was now nine years old and would remain there until of an age for marriage.

In April 1631 a seventh son was born to the Duke and Duchess of Northumberland and he was immediately baptised Enrico after the late Henry Stuart, Prince of Wales. Elizabeth's recovery, this time, was slow and William Bradshaw's Seraphina watched over her like a cat with kittens. She, more than any other, could see through Elizabeth's gaiety and knew that she would never show exhaustion to her husband or her children. There was the usual celebration and they all tumbled in and out of her room, chattering and laughing. After almost annual arrivals, there was little they did not know about babies. Those babies were handed from one to another, cradled and sung to from birth; small parts of a large whole. Birth was a very family affair in Tuscany and, after the loss of Anna, a new baby was especially welcome.

Maria would have liked a similar event, in the heart of her family and with her mother beside her, but Oratzio was determined his heir should be born at Piombino. There were fears for the future of the principality and he and the Princess Isabella would have to fight to prevent its partition. Cosimo, however, had promised a visit in June if his Court duties permitted; the two families were on the best of terms and the young Dudleys were as welcome there as the Appiani were at Rinieri.

The united efforts of Robert and his sons had enabled the two horses from Austria to now participate in ceremonial occasions. At their first appearance, there were gasps of admiration. They were magnificent and much larger than the Italian horses. It was this occasion that prompted an onlooker to describe Robert as: "A handsome, personable man, tall of stature and of admirable comport; and above all noted for riding the great horse, for tilting and for being the first of all that taught a dog to sit in order to catch partridges". His methods of training his dogs, originating at Kenilworth, had been noted and copied in Tuscany. The same source added that he was "a compleat gentleman, an exact seaman, a good navigator, an excellent architect, mathematician, physician, chymist and what not....", an impressive description.

The Austrian horses greatly enhanced the public appearances of the Great Chamberlain and the Captain of the Royal Bodyguard. There were a few sour looks from Duke Ferdinando, as his uncle the Austrian

Emperor had intended, and a suggestion that Cosimo should hand over his mount. This was refused point blank, as friend to friend, and the Duke was too indolent to make an issue of it. Cosimo, for all his charm and good-nature, could show steel when he chose. His twenty-first birthday was approaching and he was very much his own man.

His younger brother, Carlo, was a different story. He had no wish to take a position at Court, he resented authority of any kind and his manners were often far from engaging. At seventeen, Robert gave him a position of some responsibility in the shipyards at Livorno, hoping he might develop a taste for the sea and the handling of ships; also to give him the independence he seemed to need. However, he behaved with such pride and insolence that Robert was obliged to withdraw him. Only to his mother did Carlo show any affection or grace. He was a changeling child with the arrogance and cold eyes of his Grandfather, Leicester, and none of his charm. He had few friends outside his family and tended to consort with those from lower orders who looked up to and admired him as their leader. It was in Robert's mind to forcibly send him aboard one of the Tuscan warships and see if the strict discipline practised at sea would bring about a change in him. For Carlo, it would undoubtedly be sink or swim.

All concerns about Carlo were shortly to be dismissed as the year 1631 gathered grim momentum. It was one that would never be forgotten by Robert Dudley and marked an irreversible turning point in his life from which there could be no return.

In June, Cosimo took leave to visit Maria and her baby son at Piombino, as he had promised. Maria was pining for her family and he always enjoyed the sailing around Elba. He would return in time for his twenty-first birthday celebrations at home.

Late in the evening of 25th June, a terrified rider clattered to a halt in the courtyard of Robert's huge house. Dismounting, the messenger from Piombino flung the reins to a servant and staggered up the steps, grey with fatigue and sweating with fear.

He met the Duke coming out of his library and sank to his knees before him. The Earl of Warwick had been struck down by a virulent fever, believed to be a form of mala-aria and, despite every effort to save him, he had died two days later. The Princess Maria was in a terrible state of grief and held herself responsible for his death. She begged His Grace to come at once. There was a long, long silence. Stealing a glance at the Duke's face, the man looked quickly away. A purse was thrown to him and the Duke stalked slowly back into his library.

The following day, Robert set out for Piombino with Elizabeth beside him. She refused to let him go alone and Maria had need of her mother. Two days later, having ridden hard, they stood looking their last on their gallant, handsome son, his face already blurred by death into unfamiliar lines. He was all Robert had ever hoped for and he was gone, given no time to fulfil a future so full of promise. Father and son had been close and likeminded. For his mother, nothing could ever replace her first-born son.

Running through Robert's numb mind was the question: where, in this, was the God whom he had worshipped, after his fashion, all his life?

Cosimo was buried at Piombino, as a high wind sent waves crashing against the fortress wall and a grey mist blew in from the sea.

Back, once more, in Florence, the Grand Duke and the two Grand Duchesses held a Mass in their Chapel, their grief almost as great as that of Cosimo's own family. Everyone had loved him and his twenty-first birthday was awash, not with laughter, but with tears. Duke Ferdinando, quite overcome, was unable to control his grief and wept without restraint. Death was an ever-present reality in seventeenth century Europe, never entirely unexpected, but it was not easy to reconcile it with so young and vibrant a life.

As the family struggled back to normality, the aching voids left by Anna and Cosimo, though never forgotten, gradually became blurred as the everyday demands of life and the Court took over and helped to subdue the pain. Robert began to delegate more to younger courtiers, many now anticipating his retirement, and turned his attention, again, to writing. There was so much seething in his mind that must be recorded before his own life ended. How much time would he be given? He was fifty-one years old, as hale and handsome as ever though, perhaps, his shadow was growing no less. Nevertheless, he remained an awesome figure, tall and stately, a patriarch in every sense. Ever present, however, was the unpalatable thought that his heir was now the only child of his whom he actively disliked; Carlo, the changeling, was already claiming the title, Earl of Warwick.

It was not long before he also claimed ownership of Cosimo's Austrian mare, but this Robert firmly vetoed. She had been trained for ceremony

Cosimo Dudley

and would be ridden only by a member of the ducal household until she was put in foal. If Carlo had no wish to serve the Medici, then Ambrogio, now fifteen and riding in Duke Ferdinando's train, would take charge of her. This led to a bitter confrontation between father and son after which Carlo stormed out of the house in impotent rage, spitting defiance at Robert who knew that, sooner or later, it would come to blows. Elizabeth had always managed to mediate until now, but, with Cosimo's death still a raw wound, even she would not be able to keep the peace.

The rest of the summer was spent, as usual, at Rinieri, with family and friends coming and going in large numbers, and with the two Grand Duchesses installed nearby in the Villa Petraia, the young from both households intermingling as they always had.

It was noticeable that Elizabeth needed a great deal more rest than she usually did; she did not ride out so often and spent the heat of the afternoons under an ancient maritime pine tree quietly absorbing the sounds, scents and sights of summer. Her face, in repose, was as beautiful as ever, but the piercing blue of her eyes was muted, the glow had gone from her skin and her movements, though still graceful, were slower and more deliberate.

Robert was, unconsciously, avoiding travel to either Pisa or Florence, while Maddalena, a competent little person, was taking a large part in the direction of the household, particularly of the nursery and with the baby, Enrico. She had matured very quickly after Cosimo's death. Philip, their ancient steward, had remained in Florence with a reduced staff, while William, Seraphina, and their children were the mainstays at Rinieri.

Carlo put in few appearances but, when he did, the atmosphere immediately became strained. Maddalena dealt with him very briskly and he seemed to accept her authority. She would not allow the casual, if not slovenly, state in which he sometimes appeared and she was good at forestalling any impending rages or signs of aggravation. Robert, laughing appreciatively, told her she would make an excellent ambassadress and that he would find her a husband who would not waste her talents. She opened her lovely grey eyes at him and told him that there were limits to her obedience and that she intended to be very particular about her choice of husband; she was in no hurry although almost nineteen. She bore a marked resemblance to her elder sister, Maria, and she had a flair for organisation undreamt of by most generals. Robert recognised this talent with deep appreciation, seeing both himself and his father in this capable child. Several offers had already been made for her hand.

The Summer was drawing to a close, the visitors were leaving and preparations began for the household's return to Florence. The shutters of the Villa Rinieri were put up against the winter winds and a small, chill, breeze blew from the distant mountains. It had been an apocalyptic year for the Duke of Northumberland and it was not yet over.

Elizabeth chose to ride the short distance back to the city. Robert lifted her on to the Lippizaner mare, now a docile and reliable mount, and swung himself into the saddle of the stallion beside her. Maddalena, Ambrogio, Antonio, and Teresa fell in behind them, with Ambrogio leading Ferdinando on a small pony. Carlo, still sulking, had gone on ahead and the two youngest rumbled along behind in a coach with their nurses.

They halted at the Convent of Crocetta in Boldrone to leave Teresa with the nuns where she was to prepare for her novitiate. Elizabeth's doubts had been brushed aside by Teresa herself who assured them that she was not at all interested in men, or ever would be, but would become an excellent nun. Looking at her, a budding beauty, Robert also had doubts. As she was only eleven, they had not committed her, knowing well how adolescent attitudes may change, and they would allow her to make a final choice in a few years.

Waiting to receive Teresa with the nuns, was the young Vittoria della Rovere, heiress to Urbino. Her mother had re-married and she was a very lonely little girl, plump and plain but with beautiful dark eyes. It would not take Teresa, one of a large, extrovert family, much time to gather her up and assume the role of elder sister.

Premonition in his soul, Robert watched Elizabeth in the days to come as she tried to resume her duties in Florence. The long hours of standing at Court functions, the constant changes of dress, the lengthy ceremonies and Court procedures, so much a part of her life from a young age, were tiring her. Like a child at the end of a party, she sought to be with everything familiar and dear to her. Robert and the Duchess Maria Maddalena, aware that the blows sustained during the year had sapped her strength, agreed that she should curtail her Court appearances and that Robert should delegate some of his.

In company with his old friend, Andrew Tracy, Robert eventually agreed to pay a much-needed visit to Livorno at the beginning of September.

Leaving Maddalena, also exempt from Court duties, in capable charge of the household, they set off one beautiful morning in early autumn under a clear sky with the Appenines snowy and remote on the far horizon to their right. Business in the port was thriving and expanding. More grand houses and warehouses were constantly being added to the waterfront and Robert's own description was fully justified. "Livorno has been rendered not only the key of Tuscany for commerce, but also of Italy, to the extent of eight millions of scudi of merchandise now annually brought there." This was no exaggeration. Livorno had become the gateway for Tuscan, and through it, Italian, trade.

Nearing Florence on their return a few days later, they were met by William, tearing towards them at full gallop. His news was bad. Elizabeth had been taken ill the night before and they must make haste. It was September 8th. They raced back to the city without another word.

Brushing his household aside and shouting for a doctor, Robert hurtled up the stairs. Elizabeth turned her head as he burst in and smiled at him. As with Anna, he had feared the worst; that he had come too late. After that, he never left her.

Her breathing was difficult, some infection had struck her weakened form, tested by constant childbirth and by the shocks sustained during this terrible year. Robert immediately gave her his own medicinal draught and waited anxiously for a result. The doctors summoned gave it as their opinion that the illness was connected with the plague, and her children were barred from the room. They left small gifts of flowers, fruit or missives outside her chamber, whispering together or praying in the chapel. Carlo rode like the wind to fetch Teresa from Boldrone.

As the sky began to lighten on the morning of September 10th, pale streaks of aquamarine cutting into a rosy dawn, Robert, who had watched the night through, sensed a change in Elizabeth. Her breathing had become quiet and intermittent.

An hour later, within the arms into which she had walked so unhesitatingly and against the heart to which, in a moment and for a lifetime, she had given her own, she quietly drew her last breath. Her presence, her scent, her love and her laughter lingered for a while but, as the sun rose on a new day, she was no longer there.

CHAPTER FIFTEEN

Feuds and Fatalities -1631-1638

Towards the end of this fateful year 1631, circumstances brought to a head the vexed question of Urbino. The ageing Duke, Francesco Maria, appeared to be tottering to the grave in some haste. Pope Urban VIII had made his designs on the future of the state quite plain and it was the urgency of this situation which roused Duchess Maria Maddalena to act on behalf of her son, Duke Ferdinando, and her future daughter-in-law Vittoria Della Rovere. There was a limit to her submission to Rome and she determined to seek help from her brother, Emperor Ferdinand, and to take a stand against the annexation of Urbino by the Pontiff. Papal troops were already stationed there.

The little Princess Vittoria was only nine years old at this time, but the knot between her niece and her son must clearly be tied as soon as possible and their joint claim to Urbino recognised. Vittoria was her grandfather's sole heir while Ferdinando's claim came through his grandmother, Duchess Maria Christina. Urbino was a legacy from her grandmother, Catherine de Medici; marriage between Ferdinando and Vittoria should prove their right to the state.

In November 1631, with her two sons, Matthias and Francesco as escort, Duchess Maria Maddalena set out for Austria. In the hope of seeing military action, both these young men were only too delighted to accompany her. The Emperor was engaged in a promising war against King Gustavus Adolphus of Sweden over the defence of the Protestant communities in his territory, which Archduke Ferdinand was determined to eradicate. He had no fondness for Protestants.

Maria Maddalena got no further than Bavaria. She was taken ill at Passau and died there within a few days. Her horrified sons brought her body back to Florence where she was buried in San Lorenzo. Shock and grief brought thousands out to mourn her. The Duchess had been universally popular, loved for her generosity, her magnificence and her flair for great occasions. Her red hair and her presence, both in the palazzos and on the hunting field, would be sadly missed. She was only forty-two years old.

Immediately behind her coffin paced the tall, black-clad figure of her Great Chamberlain, his face a mask but his mind facing the further disintegration of his world. It was a mere two months since he had lost the great love of his life and, with her, most of its joy; the pain was deeper than anything he could have imagined.

The close and personal relationship that had evolved over twenty-six years between himself and the rulers of Tuscany seemed to be coming to an end; Elizabeth had been a vital part of it, beloved and admired by all who knew her. Of his era, there remained only the Duchess Maria Christina. The younger generation of the Medici had different values and, although Duke Ferdinando had begged him to remain as Chamberlain after Elizabeth's death, he was beginning to feel his age.

A contributor to this was his present heir, Carlo, Earl of Warwick, whose provocations infuriated him. Without his mother's feelings to consider, he became increasingly insolent and intractable. He broke every unwritten rule in the household, shouting at the servants, ordering things when and as he wished and generally behaving, not as the heir, but as a joint owner of the establishment. When Robert was present, constant confrontation ensued. Carlo was not stupid, but he was arrogant enough to refuse any form of advice and he positively hated his father. Holding Carlo in check to some degree was his elder sister, Maddalena. She had become the buffer between father and son and she was a strong character. She had also assumed motherhood of the baby, Enrico, and the very young Maria Christina. Her own marriage was under consideration at the time and she would make sure her voice was heard.

Elizabeth's children, particularly Carlo, had been devastated by her death. She had orchestrated their lives while allowing them a freedom of choice not usually given in a family of her era and she had been the advocate when dealing with their father.

Carlo had scorned the formalities of Court life and after a particularly explosive interview with Robert had flung out of the house and gone into hiding with his unsavoury friends in Florence, creating riot and rumpus in their company which included violent robbery. The hold-up of a nobleman's coach in the dark hours had led, inevitably, to prison. The man, well known to Robert, was returning, full of the joys of life, from a nocturnal visit to his mistress and the situation was embarrassing for both of them. Between them, an understanding was reached averting a looming scandal on both sides and Carlo was released. Robert, refusing to have him in the house, sent him to Rinieri to cool his heels for an indefinite time.

Robert had already begun negotiations for Maddalena's marriage to a man he knew well. Spinetta Malaspina, Marchese d'Olivola, came from another old Italian family. There was common ground between them in that Malaspina was a friend of the late Earl of Pembroke and also of his son, Charles Herbert, who had stayed both with him at his estate near Sarzana and with the Dudley family in Florence.

Malaspina was considerably older than Maddalena and a nobleman of the ancient order; his family, like the Appiani, traced their origins to the tenth century. Their lands included a large part of Lunigiana, of which they were feudal lords under the Hapsburg Emperor, and their main castle of Olivola stood on the beautiful slopes near Carrara, close to both the mountains and the sea and within easy reach of Pisa. In April of 1630, Malaspina had been appointed High Steward to Christina, heiress to the throne of Sweden.

Maddalena insisted that, as a condition to the marriage, she would take the two younger Dudley children, Maria Christina and Enrico, with her to be brought up as members of her family. Not surprisingly, this was something of a challenge for Malaspina who was expecting a young bride who would conform in every way to the pattern of his life and immediately provide him with heirs. However, on acquaintance, he was so captivated by Maddalena that he was prepared to welcome a whole nursery full of children to win her. Robert, watching the progress of this very correct courtship, could not help appreciative laughter. His daughter was a power in the land who, with diplomatic skill, not to mention much feminine charm, was going to get exactly what she wanted from any marriage. Malaspina threw caution to the winds and agreed to all her requests. He was not proof against a pair of glorious grey eyes, neither did he realise that in marrying Maddalena, he would be embracing her entire family, including Carlo.

Robert had also acquiesced in these arrangements. Much as he loved his two youngest children, he recognised their need for a mother and an upbringing in the country, rather than a life spent partly in the city with nurses and tutors as their main companions. Olivola was a particularly lovely part of Italy between Sarzana and Fivizzano. He and Maddalena were wonderfully well entertained there by Malaspina, together with Carlo, Ambrogio and Antonio and it was plain that it would be an excellent home for the youngest of the Dudleys.

During this year of 1632, Robert had, at last, given some thought to his four remaining daughters in England. He transferred his rights to the Countess of Leicester's jointure lands to his English girls, in the hope that something would emerge that might benefit them.

The following year, 1633, was one for marriages and the ceremonies would keep Robert from the writing which now absorbed all his spare time. His library was sacrosanct and a hive of industry; the carefully ordered manuscripts and rolls of words and drawings mounting at a furious rate. No other person was, at this time, allowed to touch them and there was inward order in the outward chaos. He was planning a monumental work, long since begun, which would be years in the making and was to become recognised as one of the greatest compilations on naval and maritime matters ever written. His memory remained as sharp as ever and he found the task an escape from the bleak emptiness into which he had been plunged after Elizabeth's death. His grief and longing for her were sometimes unbearable and his feelings were better imagined than described. The desolation was only now beginning to be filled by this enormous undertaking; it would encompass his life and experience from the age of eighteen to the present time and he would do it justice.

In August this year, Robert received news from London that came betimes. Salvetti wrote jubilantly that 8,000 scudi was to be paid to the Duke of Northumberland as recompense for the Kenilworth estates. Robert waved a silent salute to his faithful friend Chaloner who, up until his death, had done so much to instil into the King the need to answer the Dudley case, and that Robert was unlikely to give him any peace until he did. That Duke Ferdinando then wrote personally to congratulate Robert suggested that he may have already lent him money for the dowries of his daughters and was hoping for re-payment. This was made plain in a letter from the Duke to Salvetti in which he expressed the hope that the money would arrive soon so that he, himself, could be reimbursed. The payment was a pathetic tithe of the value of Kenilworth but, with so many daughters to marry, it would be welcome to the Dudley coffers.

The first great wedding of 1633 was that between the Grand Duke Ferdinando II himself and the Princess Vittoria Della Rovere. The bride was now eleven years old and the Duke twenty-three; the marriage was not to be consummated until she was older. The pomp and feudal magnificence of the wedding was as great as any preceding it; trumpets sounded, horses cavorted, guards marched past. The spectacles and entertainments that followed went on for days and kept the Great Chamberlain fully employed. He had, by now, perfected his role, which dealt with the organisation and display on these occasions, and he was supported by a vast, well-trained staff. There were, of course, always variations; no two ceremonies were alike and it was often up to him to provide the innovation.

The bride, a plump child, was deeply devout as a result of her upbringing and education. She would return to Boldrone until she took up her position as Grand Duchess in 1639. It could be seen how marked was the resemblance between the cousins; both were dark versions of the distinctive Hapsburg mould. Vittoria's chief attendant at her marriage was Lady Teresa Dudley who had befriended her since her own arrival at Boldrone two years before and brought a little light and laughter into an austere life.

Teresa looked speculatively upon a Court which had, and still did, absorb so many of her family's lives and wondered what it might possibly hold for her. She was well accustomed to the pomp and protocol involved; even after two years shelter in a convent it held no terrors for her and she filled her role as attendant to the bride with grace and assurance. Teresa would never be as tall as her sisters but she made up for it with a sparkling personality and an air of suppressed energy so like her father. Though very much an individual, she was to become a fascinating combination of both parents and she had inherited, in abundance, Elizabeth's voice and musicality. The nuns of Boldrone, though raising their eyes to Heaven and wondering what kind of a cuckoo had landed in their nest, appreciated the voice, such an asset to their choirs, and took pains over its training.

The second wedding, that of Maddalena Dudley to Spinetta Malaspina, Marchese d'Olivola, was almost as grand. The bride, taking her father firmly in hand, had laid before him the complete plan of proceedings as she wished them to be. Unostentatious organisation was her forte and few details had been forgotten. Grand Duchess Maria Christina, who was very fond of all the Dudley girls – particularly the ever-resourceful Maddalena – had contributed, importantly, to the cost, which would be astronomical. This was all the more appreciated, since Robert was to find himself entertaining no less a personage than Queen Christina of Sweden, then in Tuscany, who had expressed a wish to attend the marriage of Malaspina, her High Steward. Robert, always the moving spirit in these events, felt suddenly redundant and confined himself to the equestrian side of the day and to the giving of his daughter's hand in marriage.

The wedding went without one hitch. The bride, serene and lovely, was attended by her younger brothers and sisters, her father and her elder brothers riding in a phalanx behind her carriage. The sun shone, and Robert's heart lifted as he observed his family, with Royalty in their midst, presenting a perfect occasion. More importantly, the couple themselves appeared already devoted. The loss of his two youngest to Olivola would be a wrench but in their best interests. On her departure to her new home, Maddalena had left him with as few problems as she could and promised frequent visits, particularly when he was in Pisa, an easy ride from Olivola. He had one moment's anguish as the small Maria Christina clung, howling, to his leg at the moment of farewell yelling "Papa, Papa" at the top of her voice.

Robert went often to the church of San Pancrazio, a short distance behind his house. There lay the two he had loved, or would ever love, more than any others. Mother and daughter, as beautiful as each other; one life richly fulfilled and the other barely begun. Elizabeth's tombstone lay in the church above the crypt where she was buried. Here, the years rolled back and memories in waves flooded in and over him; like a rock in a rising tide they battered and assaulted him, until the surge subsided leaving him drained and stranded. He clung to the belief that life is never over and that love is never done. Throughout his own life he had struggled to the surface after every set-back but never had he gone down so deep or had so far to return. His salvation lay in the mounting piles of manuscripts in his library.

It did not lie in his heir. Robert had offered Carlo a place as an officer in the ship of his choice in the Tuscan navy until he had gained experience enough to command his own. Carlo had refused on the grounds that his father was trying to be rid of him and in this there were some grains of truth; at his age Robert had been building his own ships in order to sail to South America. Carlo's choice of companions was always dubious and, when in trouble, he tended to disappear with them, usually causing further unpleasantness.

By 1634, of his remaining children besides Carlo, Robert still had charge of Ambrogio, Antonio, Ferdinando and Teresa. The only one not yet out of the nest was Ferdinando, now thirteen, and the quietest and most contemplative of them. He was still with his tutors and appeared to have more erudition and application than the others. Robert could not see him as a courtier. He had a grave, sweet smile and, like Teresa, had inherited his mother's voice. In due course, it seemed likely that the Church might call him also. Meanwhile, with two of the elder boys employed at Court, Teresa at Boldrone, and the younger two with Maddalena, only Ferdinando remained at home with Robert and the huge house seemed very quiet.

Ferdinando took a keen interest in his father's work and was graciously allowed to help with the compilation and research. He was genuinely interested and became adept at keeping all Robert's reference material in order, inventing an efficient and space-saving method of storage – a vital task with such a mass and variety of subject matter. Even so, Ferdinando was obliged to requisition one end of the music room as the volume grew. This enormous undertaking was to cover the building and manning of ships, minute sailing instructions under every weather condition, the use of a wide range of navigational instruments – some of Robert's own invention; theses (his own and other people's) on the conduct of a navy and cartography covering most of the known maritime world. It was a Herculean task, encompassing a lot of Robert's previous work and it meant that he was spending less time at Court. This was a natural progression of affairs; Robert was now almost sixty years old. He still spent hours in the saddle, could run a course as a feared opponent in the jousting field, and never tired of hunting. These things were as natural to him as breathing and as much a part of his life. He was respected by the whole Tuscan Court and genuinely beloved by the Medici. He should have been heading for a well-earned and respected retirement but this was unlikely to happen. He had a monumental project to complete and a further seven children to establish in life. Events in England, also, had a habit of evolving in unexpected ways, causing him grief, amusement and fury in turn.

The young Earl of Pembroke, Charles Herbert, came to visit Italy the following year, staying first with Maddalena and her husband at Olivola, then, in January 1636, going on to Robert and his sons in Florence. He was, for his father's sake as well as his own, always a welcome guest and Robert had more than wondered whether he and Teresa might not make a good match if she could be persuaded to abandon the veil. She was not yet committed and, apart from anything else, it would save him the huge cost of her consecration. Her dowry would be almost as much, however, and Teresa herself, now almost fifteen, was showing distinct signs of worldliness.

The boys, all at home at this juncture, had been fencing, challenging each other to mock duels with a great deal of jostling and laughter and not a little rivalry. As they sat down to dinner, Robert noticed that young Charles Herbert was very flushed. He put it down to a strenuous bout with the foils, but, by the time the fruit and wine were set on the table Charles had become unusually silent. Concerned, Robert leaned forward quietly and asked if he were feeling ill. Speechless, he nodded and Ambrogio, sitting next to him, took his elbow and helped him upstairs.

Robert immediately summoned the best doctors known to him, requesting Duke Ferdinando at the same time to send his own physician. They hustled the boy into bed, sponging him with cold water from the ice-houses. His temperature rose steadily and, by the following day, his mind was wandering. Robert had immediately given him a dose of his own powder, but this did not appear to be having any effect; it had failed with the plague victims and, worse, with Elizabeth herself. Duke Ferdinando's physician was in favour of copious bleeding and, in the face of such a virulent fever, Robert reluctantly agreed. They even packed solid ice around him as the fever mounted. Robert, banishing his own family for fear of infection, sat with the boy throughout the nights, talking gently to him as his mind swung in dizzy circles around his short career, his home, his dogs and his horses. For five days he lay in this state and, despite every effort made to save him, he died. The illness was adjudged to have been small-pox but no disfiguring rash had broken out. Deeply saddened by this tragedy, Robert sent the body back to Olivola for burial escorted by Carlo and an armed party. It was a place Charles had visited often and loved and here he lay for many years until he was returned to England.

This death was one other in the decimation of those close to Robert. First Anna, followed by Cosimo, then, within months, Elizabeth herself, the Duchess Maria Maddalena, and now the young Earl, the son of one of his greatest friends.

In December 1636, these were followed by the death of Duchess Maria Christina. She died as she had lived, with the utmost composure and dignity. She was the last of her generation, outliving her husband, her son and her daughter-in-law, Maria Maddalena. She had brought both grace and probity to Tuscany: a very Grand Duchess indeed. She had, however, allowed her piety to overshadow her judgement and her zealous obedience to Rome had, indirectly, set Tuscany on a downward path. The uncontrolled influx of priests, many corrupt and parasitical, had changed the structure and character of the State. There were now more than four thousand nuns in Florence alone. Almost every office was under religious control and the Grand Duke's officials were treated with insolence. The priesthood refused to pay taxes unless authorised by the Pope, or to obey Tuscan law and, more sinister, the Inquisition had been installed in the cloisters of Santa Croce which became the most feared place in Florence. Here the Holy Office doled out fines and punishment at will. At the Duchess's death Tuscany was firmly under the thumb of Rome and its citizens were forced to watch such horrors as the "*autos da fe*" held in the Piazza Santa Croce. Robert himself had seen the smoke rising, and, following it to the source, heard the shrieks of the victims and witnessed their unspeakable agonies. His blood might boil but he was too old and too English to try to prevent it nor did his own spiritual past bear close scrutiny. Under Duke Ferdinand I, such things would never have been allowed.

Robert and his whole family mourned the Duchess. She had been more than a friend; she had genuinely loved them, looked after the girls in her train as a grandmother, and promoted their marriages. Financially, she had been very generous in times of need. Her influence had held at bay any decline of manners and morals in the Tuscan Court and her relationship with Robert and Elizabeth, while retaining its formality, had been extremely close. Since the deaths of her husband and her son, she had relied on Robert almost as a family member, depending upon him a great deal more than on her own male relatives. In daily contact with her for almost a quarter of a century, he had even spoken his mind on her religious views; but to no avail. She had begged him to remain as Chamberlain after her death in order to guide and guard the young Duchess Vittoria.

Meanwhile, Pope Urban VIII lost no time in the annexation of Urbino. Upon the death of Duke Francesco Maria, the grandfather of Vittoria, he swiftly moved further Papal troops into the state. Vittoria was granted the small Duchies of Rovere and Montefeltro together with an astounding collection of artwork from Urbino. This was transferred to the Pitti and Uffizi Palaces and that was that; no further effort was made to regain Urbino.

By the summer of 1638 Robert's relationship with his heir had reached a crucial depth and had become unpleasantly public knowledge. This was due to Carlo's habit of ranting against his father to anyone who would listen to him and it made Robert's position in the Tuscan Court increasingly awkward. Matters came to a head while Isabella, Princess of Piombino, was staying at Rinieri, as she usually did, during the months of July and August. Maria and her children were also there when Carlo put in an unexpected appearance. Since the death of Cosimo, none of the Appiani remained by the coast at this time of year; the mosquitoes spread the virulent form of malaria that had killed him.

Princess Isabella, now a dear and trusted friend, wrote to Robert in Florence concerning Carlo and his behaviour at Rinieri. She feared that he was drinking excessively and, when in his cups one night, had informed those interested that he "would be obliged, eventually, to kill his father." Naturally, this utterance had stunned his audience and the Princess felt obliged to warn Robert what might be in the wind. She wrote that: "Carlo, since his return from prison shows extreme ill-will towards you, saying he will not rest until he kills you." She added that Carlo had produced a pistol and told her he was never without it. She begged Robert to have a care and to watch his back. Carlo, for all his bravado, had not been joking. Maria, also, had been much distressed by her brother's wild talk and added her voice to that of the Princess.

Robert decided not to await any further oblique threats and rode the few miles to Rinieri to confront his heir, accompanied by William Bradshaw only. Arriving as the late evening sun was sending long shadows across the garden and making splashes of gold of the fountains, he left William and the horses at the stables and walked alone up to the house in the fading light. William's protests were forceful but unheeded.

With a pricking in his thumbs undimmed by age, Robert knew he was not alone. A few moments later he saw a figure moving between the ilex trees and sensed that it was far from friendly. He made straight for it, sliding the small dagger at his waist from its sheath. It was his only weapon.

Rapidly rounding a yew hedge, he almost collided with Carlo, moving much more cautiously and with a pistol in his hand. They stared at each other with no surprise, Carlo's eyes narrowed to slits. Robert dropped his hand over his son's wrist and savagely wrenched it; the gun was loaded but not primed.

In a few unmistakeable words Robert made it clear to Carlo that Tuscany was not large enough for both of them. He would send him into exile to serve the German King, Mathias, and Carlo was not to darken the family doors for a full year. He could collect his effects from Via Della Vigna Nuova and Robert had no wish to see hair or hide of him for a long time to come. He was now to return immediately to Florence. He had no way of telling how Carlo had known that he was coming to Rinieri that evening and preferred not to think about it.

Carlo's answer to this, on his return to Florence, was to go roistering around the city with the unsavoury hangers-on who always followed him, with the result that they all ended the night locked up, yet again, in the Bargello. Here, he behaved with amazing arrogance, insisting on a servant to wait on him and that the servant should have freedom of access to the city. Of Robert he demanded, as a condition of his departure, new and expensive clothes for his sojourn in Germany.

After this incident, though longing to be rid of him, Robert cancelled any plans to banish Carlo and sent him, under armed escort, to Malaspina and Maddalena at Olivola. He hoped that his sister would be able to deal with him, as she had done in the past, and better than he could. Perhaps the company there, including his young sister and brother, might improve his frame of mind. Robert also hoped that he would not be obliged to look upon Carlo's handsome, hawkish countenance, so like his grandfather's, for some time. He wondered how it was that he could dislike so intensely anything that he and Elizabeth had created. Carlo appeared to have few redeeming features.

Unfortunately, this was not to be the end of the saga.

In January the following year, Carlo broke bounds, headed for Florence with his reprobate friends and, fuelled by pent-up hatred of Robert, attacked his own home in Via Della Vigna Nuova in company with nine of the party, all wielding firearms. Robert was in the church of San Pancrazio at the time which was lucky for them. They threatened the servants and stole whatever silver and valuables they could find. Poor Philip, their ancient and retired steward who had known Carlo from babyhood, implored them, in tears, to leave. William Bradshaw was at Rinieri at the time; had he been there, there would certainly have been bloodshed.

Mortified and furious, Robert wrote to Grand Duke Ferdinando; "Don Carlo, with nine men armed with arquebus, entered my house while I was at Mass, and carried away all the silver that was not locked up, to the value of 300 ducats. I hope some serious mark of displeasure from the Court will be shown for so great a crime against his father and defiance to the laws of the Prince."

Duke Ferdinando, who had little liking for Carlo, ordered him to report to the Bargello, yet again, for punishment. Carlo immediately fled into hiding with his gang.

Swallowing his pride, not easy for him, Robert wrote again to the Duke explaining that he could neither control his son, nor understand such base behaviour in any child of his.

When his fugitive existence became too uncomfortable, Carlo sought protection in the church of Santissima Annunziata, claiming sanctuary at the altar. He was soon scooped up from there by the Duke's men who hustled him off, this time to secure quarters within the monastery of San Dominico at Fiesole, where Ferdinando was now a novice monk. Carlo immediately took advantage of his young brother, playing on his feelings and trying to bribe him into letting him out. When Ferdinando resolutely refused, he created such mayhem that he was removed forcibly back to the Bargello, a lot less comfortable, and there left to cool his heels for several months.

There followed a difficult and tragic period in Robert's life. Carlo was such a constant source of anger and anxiety to him and seemed capable of any kind of outrage that he began to wonder whether his heir was, perhaps, not a model of sanity. Should he be incarcerated permanently before further damage to himself, or anyone else, was done? This was a terrible thought and would be a worse decision. Robert had often visited prisons in Florence and memories of a cell in the Tower of London lingered. Dark deeds of many kinds could, and did, happen in such places.

He went, one quiet evening, to San Pancrazio as twilight filtered gently through the city and the myriad candles began lighting up around him. He felt the need to consult Elizabeth. He had formed the habit of coming here in moments of distress and found comfort in being in the place where, more than all others, he felt nearest to her. Sitting mute beside her stone and straining his senses for a reply, he asked what she would have him do. Before his closed eyes came the image of her standing, as he had first seen her, with her hands resting on the spinet and her smiling eyes piercing the huge gulf now between them, and the answer came. How could he shut away any child of theirs from the light of day for the rest of his life? The image faded but the message remained. He would have to struggle with Carlo as best he could.

Robert was so disgusted by his heir's outrages, which were totally beyond his comprehension, that he refused to visit him in the Bargello or communicate with him other than to provide for his immediate needs. He turned, instead, to the daunting task in his library and to the future of his other children.

But Nemesis had not done with Robert. Much later, looking back on these troubled years, he gave thanks that it was not yet within man's ken to know the future; with foreknowledge, he would have been hard pressed to live through them.

Ambrogio, now twenty-one, had been appointed to the household of Cardinal Carlo de Medici, uncle to the present Grand Duke and had accompanied him to Rome in 1637. This was a big step in his career and well-earned. He had been at Court for several years, taken part in much ceremonial and always played a part of any equestrian activity. Like Cosimo, he was a very tall, well-built young man with a wicked twinkle and a quick wit. He had the diplomat's ability to transform a confrontation from threat to laughter and, like his mother, to spread good-will in any company. His unwavering childhood love for Annabella Rucellai was now recognised by a formal betrothal and Robert was in the process of arranging the date for their marriage. Annabella had been equally constant and, being a few years younger, was content to wait. She was a gentle little creature whose horizons and huge brown eyes were entirely filled by this magnificent man. An alliance with the Rucellai was akin to one with the Medici and Annabella's dowry would be a large one. Robert, with the benefit of hindsight, had been reluctant to allow any of his children to marry as young as he had himself and, where his sons were concerned, before having a chance to prove themselves or to enlarge their careers.

Robert was feeling the financial pinch as his family spread their wings. Equipping and dressing them for Court, in itself, was a crippling expense and the tutors, servants, horses and allowances were steadily mounting in cost. Ferdinando, to his relief, was still in his novitiate and spending very little in the Monastery of San Dominico, as was Teresa at Boldrone.

Having dealt with Ambrogio's requirements for Rome and sent him on his way, he turned his attention to the career of Antonio. This fourth son was less boisterous than his elder brothers and refreshingly biddable. His intense blue eyes missed little, however, though he was charming and courteous. He had readily followed his five brothers and sisters to Court and into the service of the Medici, but, as his father had done, he was now looking for an escape to a much wider world. Robert's flash of insight when first viewing him in the cradle had been right. A naval life would suit Antonio very well. He had taken part in many of the palace pageants, enjoyed them all and was as much an extrovert performer as any of the Dudleys. However, he wanted to spread his wings and Robert, who was particularly fond of him, wished to give him all the help he could.

With the future in mind Robert had, as early as 1628, written a fulsome description of his own and Elizabeth's descent and family connections. Even if called upon to prove that his family was descended from royal blood on both sides, he would be prepared. Stretching consanguinity somewhat, he had, unabashed, claimed kinship with King Henry III and, for Elizabeth, with King Edward II. The chronicle had included the honours granted to himself and his children by the Medici and the high regard in which they held him. This catalogue of self-aggrandisement, accompanied by an illuminated genealogical tree, might well be needed for the future, he believed. It had been produced ahead of the marriages of Maria and Maddalena. It was now required to assist Antonio to gain Duke Ferdinando's recommendation for membership of the Order of St. Stephen, a long and convoluted business. This was an old and revered Tuscan institution reserved for the highest in the land.

Following the recent death of a Cavaliero Piccolomoni, there was now a vacancy within the Order and Robert was not slow to put forward Antonio's name. Sponsored by the Grand Duke, he was accepted and duly invested, at the age of eighteen, as a Cavalier of the Order and wore the white robe, spurs and medallion given to its members at the lengthy ceremonies of induction.

Antonio was immensely proud of the honour and thanked the Grand Duke with becoming modesty. To enter the Tuscan Navy as a Knight of St.Stephen was a dream's fulfilment; his future and his enjoyment of it, seemed assured and he was now bound for Pisa to begin training.

Teresa's future was another matter. This year, having finally made the decision that a religious life was not for her, she had positively bounced out of the Convent in Boldrone in the train of the Duchess Vittoria who was now to take up her position beside her husband as his wedded wife. As her close friend and attendant, Teresa had taken to Court existence with the vivacious energy she brought to most things in life and the Court had been quite unprepared for the small whirlwind that now descended on it. Teresa sparkled like a jewel and her endearing personality dissolved jealousy or dislike. She was strikingly lovely though not strictly a beauty as her sisters were, and no one could take their eyes off her. Her sea-blue gaze was direct, and those caught in its beam were truly caught. She had her Mother's precious gift of laughter and a needle-sharp wit. Very soon she was an almost greater favourite than her sisters had been.

Teresa had kept the close friendship of the young Grand Duchess whose arrival at Court and start to married life had not been happy. There were rocks ahead on many fronts. Her husband, during the years of their betrothal and marriage, had been able to indulge in all the worldly pleasures of life while she was stitching samplers in the convent and, although not as profligate as his brother GianCarlo, there was little he had not experienced. She was both unaware of the realities of life as a Grand Duchess and unprepared for marriage after her cloistered upbringing. She was, also, deeply and intolerantly devout as a result of it. Conjugally, she and Ferdinando were not suited in any way and it was a penance for her to do her duty as a wife. To her, he was an older, overweight relation, and to him she was nothing but a tiresome child.

It was at this point that Robert and his daughter began to work together. On her arrival at Court, Teresa was the one real confidante to whom the young Grand Duchess could turn. Robert had promised his old friend, Duchess Maria Christina, that he would advise and protect Vittoria when she came to Court if she wished him to remain as her Great Chamberlain. Because he was the father of her friend, Teresa, she at once confirmed his appointment. To win the child's confidence was important and Teresa, without betraying Vittoria's trust in any way, simply opened the door for him. The Duke of Northumberland was her father, he could be relied upon in every matter and, furthermore, Vittoria would do well to listen to any direction he gave her. A lifetime's love and understanding of women, however young, made the rest easy for Robert. Father and daughter worked well together and, with tactful skill, they managed to smooth or avert the many crises which inevitably arose between the ducal pair. History was repeating itself. Had not both Duke Cosimo II and the young Ferdinando II turned to the Great Chamberlain in much the same way?

Robert was now serving his third successive Grand Duchess of Tuscany. He would, in fact, have much preferred to retire with grace at this time and devote his time to his literary work, but he had given a promise and the huge salary he was paid was still much needed; he was certainly going to earn it.

Having come to some kind of terms with the married state, Vittoria began to make up for the joyless years spent at Boldrone. Besides her devotion to the Church, she was to prove pleasure-loving and extravagant. Determined to impress in her own right, she demanded an unending series of balls, fêtes, theatre and other extravagant entertainments. Before long, her Great Chamberlain was to find himself at full stretch when what he wanted most was to shut the doors of his library on the world.

Later in the year, like a ripple over still water, news came to Tuscany that a particularly virulent fever, not plague, was stalking the streets of Rome. It was not much heeded; Rome was a long way south. Robert knew that Cardinal Carlo de Medici was shortly returning to Florence, accompanied by Ambrogio, and was not immediately worried. He would, nonetheless, be glad to see his son back. The ripple spread and, with it, the rumours. People were dying like flies some travellers said: the disease struck quickly – a grown man could eat his breakfast heartily and be dead by the evening. Those travellers were told they were not welcome in Florence and advised to circumvent the city.

As the days went by and there was no sign of the Cardinal's train, Robert became anxious and, with William Bradshaw, rode out towards Siena to see what information could be had on the road. Not far from Poggibonsi, having seen few people and gathered little news, they decided to head for home. They had just turned the horses when William looked back over his shoulder and gripped Robert's arm hard. Coming up over the rise now behind them was dust from a large company of horsemen and the tips of the colours carried by outriders. They immediately retraced their way and cantered up the slope to meet the oncoming cavalcade. Then it was that they could see the colours were furled, but behind them flew four black pinnaces from the corners of a gun carriage carrying a long ebony box.

His eyes searching the riders in the column as he went, Robert spurred up to what was clearly the Cardinal's coach. The door was already open and the Cardinal stepped down, his hands outstretched to Robert. The ebony box contained no body, but the armour, clothes and colours of his son and a silk-wrapped lock of his hair.

CHAPTER SIXTEEN

Magnum Opus – 1638-1649

The Duke of Northumberland sat before a roaring fire in one of the smaller rooms at Rinieri, a glass of hot spiced wine in his hand, his greyhounds draped over his feet and his son, Enrico, now aged seven, curled, exhausted, on his knee. They were both nodding in the warm firelight having been hunting most of the day.

It was the first time Enrico had been out with Robert and he was determined to keep up and prove himself. It had been a wonderful bright, crisp day and they had brought down two beasts after some hard riding. Following the long jog home, he and his pony were drooping but he had insisted on rubbing down and tending the little animal himself before crawling, fed and bathed, on to his father's knee. He had done well and his eyes were swivelling in his head and beginning to close.

Maddalena and Malaspina had insisted on joining Robert for Christmas at the end of this bleak and bitter year. With them had come Maria Christina and Enrico together with their own two small children. So too had come Maria and Oratzio Appiano from Piombino with their family and the Princess Isabella. Ferdinando, given leave by his Abbot at Fiesole, had arrived the previous night. Invited with reserve, Carlo was also due, bringing Teresa with him. She too, had been given leave by the Duchess Vittoria.

Between them they had decked the great house for Christmas, organised the household and done all they could to raise their father's spirits and bring a little joy to the end of a joyless year. It was a gallant effort. Compared with past Christmases they were not a large gathering but Andrew and Mary Tracy and several of their family would be joining them tomorrow. Robert could hear, through the open door, the sounds of excited children tearing up and down the stairs singing the old Christmas songs and playing the games that generations had played before them. At their age it was easy to put grief behind them. He could see some small person on a hobby-horse staggering past the open door.

257

The family, shattered and still reeling from the brutal course of events towards the end of the year, had felt the need of each other's company for what could have been a very sad Christmas.

Ambrogio had been buried by the Cardinal, with all honour, in Rome. A wall plaque was put up in the church of San Pancratzio and a memorial service held there, the singing led by Ferdinando and Teresa, tenor and mezzo-soprano joining in a harmony of sound not easily forgotten. They had sung together all their lives and the music was hauntingly beautiful. Annabella Rucellai was too overcome to attend, her life in pieces at eighteen; she never married and, later, took the veil at Boldrone.

But the year was not yet finished, nor its malice. In November, they had gathered once more, in Pisa, to bury Antonio, then poised to sail with the Tuscan navy and follow his star, as Robert had done at his age. He was scythed down by the same infection decimating Rome and now intermittently on the rampage throughout Italy; lightning had struck twice and with its proverbial speed. The young Knight of St.Stephen had barely set foot on board his ship nor had the blue eyes ever searched far horizons. Robert had lost two irreplaceable sons within months. Of Antonio, interred in the Duomo in Pisa, he wrote: "he was my great comfort, being so obedient."

Grief-stricken, Robert had then begged leave of absence from the Duchess Vittoria and immersed himself in his books.

Amid this chain of bereavement, it seemed a cruel irony that the most promising and beloved of his children had been lost, sparing the one who was both vicious and wayward to succeed him as Duke of Northumberland and to inherit all that he had achieved. Carlo had already done much to bring the family name into disrepute. The fact that he had not succeeded was due to the abiding affection and respect in which his father was held by the whole Medici family including, now, the young Duchess. He was an integral part of their lives, known to many of them since childhood, respected, consulted and revered.

Looking down at the tousled head on his shoulder, Robert could see traces of Elizabeth and gave thanks for it; the arched brows and the small, straight nose were hers, her eyes looked out from the faces of Maria and Maddalena, her voice sounded through Ferdinando and Teresa and her volatile high spirits could be seen in Maria Christina. She was not far away.

At this point in his reverie, the level of sound from the stairs rose sharply and Maria Christina herself erupted into Robert's room, curtsied briefly to her father, and at once tried to displace the sleepy Enrico. This youngest daughter was dark and mercurial, her life a series of wails of woe or gales of giggles; there were few half measures. At ten years old, she was wilful and demanding and wore her heart on her sleeve; there was no subterfuge in her nature and her restless energy produced both tantrums and loving generosity in equal abundance. She could remember her mother and the disruption and distress of leaving her father and family for Olivola at the age of three. Maddalena, who loved her dearly, dealt well with her moods, gave her the affection she craved, but insisted on courtesy and respect. Robert shifted Enrico's weight and made room for her beside him. The dark curls settled against his shoulder and the bright hazel eyes laughed into his. This giddy little daughter would not stay for long; her attention shifted swiftly and would soon send her flying off in some other direction. Robert could not, as yet, see her gracing the Tuscan Court with any degree of dignity.

Reflecting on the imminent arrival of his heir, he recalled a letter, written by Carlo to Ambrogio, in which he blamed Robert for bringing his sons up as Englishmen, whereas they were, in fact, Italians. That, maintained Carlo, was the cause of all his anger and resentment. This pronouncement, written at the height of his trouble-making, had made little impression on Robert who was not given to introspection and took people at face value, nor did it excuse, in any way, Carlo's appalling behaviour.

He had done his duty by Carlo for the last time and persuaded him to accept, though grudgingly, a post as gentleman of the chamber to the now Cardinal GianCarlo de Medici. Always destined for the Church, GianCarlo had eventually found his way there via an appointment as High Admiral of the Tuscan navy though it was doubtful whether he had ever been to sea or knew one end of a ship from the other. GianCarlo's interests lay elsewhere. It spoke volumes for Robert's standing with the family that they were prepared to give his heir a chance; his transgressions were well known to them all. So far, there had been no serious ructions and, possibly, at the age of twenty four, he might have gained some notion of responsibility. Robert sighed; he would make no further move on Carlo's behalf. His future efforts would be concentrated on his other, more worthy children. Carlo had, at least, shown some sign of sense in proposing a marriage for himself to Countess Marie Madeleine, the daughter of a Provencal French nobleman, Charles Antoine Gouffier, Marquis de Boisy and Seigneur de Crevecoeur. She was a widow, rich and, reputedly, very beautiful. As the heir to a dukedom, however English, he would no doubt be accepted.

Teresa's arrival with Carlo immediately enlivened the party. She had only to enter a room and her buoyant nature changed the atmosphere for the better. Her sparkle lit the dark places of her family's grief and she had the gift, perhaps a legacy of her days in the convent, of giving to those in trouble the comfort of her presence without probing their thoughts. Robert, rejoicing in her companionship and her lovely face, again caught glimpses of Elizabeth.

He was determined that Teresa should marry a man worthy of her and had already done some groundwork in this direction. She had received countless offers for her hand but appeared in no hurry to change her way of life. Robert was, at present, opening negotiations with a senior member of the Italian nobility, the Duke of Cornia, of the great Perugian family, a widower with children and, like Malaspina, considerably older than his prospective bride. Before he went further he wanted her opinion on the matter. The Duke was a good-looking man and Teresa's twinkling eyes had flickered at the sight of him. Sitting on a footstool at Robert's feet in the firelight of a late evening, she slipped her hand into his and told him that she would not be averse to the marriage. "Man is born unto trouble, even as the sparks fly upwards" she remarked biblically as she eyed the glowing fire. Let him bring on another wedding if he so wished. She would be perfectly content with the Duca di Cornia; she preferred older men, they were less silly than her contemporaries.

Christmas came and went. There were no unpleasant scenes; Maria and Maddalena kept a firm eye on their wayward brother, the younger generation's exuberance put paid to any hard feelings among their elders and the Duke of Northumberland, after some excellent hunting, returned to his library in Florence still with a heart of lead but with a determination to complete the great task he had set himself.

His plan now was gradually to disengage himself from Court duties altogether and to concentrate his literary operation at Rinieri. His engineering and shipbuilding projects were almost finished and, with them, much of his travelling. The house in Via della Vigna Nuova seemed to him more haunted by memory than he could bear and he felt freer and more at ease in the country. Besides this, there was the need for space. Rinieri had more and larger rooms where he would be able to spread his many maps and manuscripts.

His work would be divided into six books and included much of his former writing including the "Direttorio Marittimo", the detailed directions written for the Tuscan navy in 1620 which he had expanded over the years as his own practical experience increased. His early writings had contained, not surprisingly, some very faulty Italian, and this had to be corrected. The fact that the book was published in Italian and not in English proved, with hindsight, to have been a mistake. In later years, when it became well-known, it would have been more widely read in English.

The many maps and drawings, which would ultimately outnumber the pages of text, required hours of painstaking and detailed work. Some were already engraved, but many remained to be done. His engraver, Jacopo Lucini, whom he had installed at Rinieri, wrote later of this great work that: "for twelve years sequestered from all the world in a little Tuscan village, I have consumed no less than 5,000lbs of copper in engravings to illustrate this book". Lucini was to publish a second edition after Robert's death, in much larger volumes and in order to avoid the folding of the maps they contained. Over many years, Robert had collected a substantial number of maps and charts, extending far beyond the places he had actually visited and recorded himself, and the final volume would be mainly composed of these. They ranged as far afield as the Solomon Islands and covered most of the known maritime world. Much of the material had come through his early friendship and family ties with Hakluyt, but he had also been close to many other pioneers in this field. Robert had always an eye on the main chance, for the present or for the future.

The subjects covered were diverse though within an overall maritime orbit. They included, within the six books, naval and military architecture, marine strategy, naval power and sea commerce together with the necessary maps and cartography. Over a wider field, they covered meteorology, astronomy (much learned from Galileo), and hydrography. Deeply practical were the sections on the further development of shipbuilding, navigation, engineering, naval tactics together with ship management, and harbour fortifications as at Livorno. These six books, when finished, would give testimony to the surging power of Robert's brain, the depth of his knowledge and the breadth of his far-ranging vision. To be able not only to present, but also to illustrate, the many and diverse subjects contained in the books, showed great skill as a draughtsman, an artist and a writer. In the many maps in Book Six was one covering the Orinoco Delta. Among its myriad islands, Robert had named "Dudleiana", claimed by himself for Queen Elizabeth I.

How he had managed to amass this vast horde of information and material, or keep it within his reach, was a secret he was to take to the grave. The maps were not mere guesswork. Later exploration and knowledge were to prove he was wrong on few points; one or two errors around the South Pacific, perhaps, but how many had actually sailed there by 1640? Also, the array of nautical and scientific instruments illustrated in the volumes were a marvel. He had brought some of his own inventions from England, but it was Andrew Tracy, with his mercantile friends and contacts, who managed to supply Robert with many of those he needed and used for his illustrations.

Meanwhile, back in England, one thorn, in particular, remained in Robert's flesh. At Kenilworth, the two properties of Balsall and Long Itchingham had long been claimed, up until his death, by the acquisitive Robert Sidney. At the death, in 1634, of Lettice, Countess of Essex, at a great age, the rights to both properties should have reverted from her to Robert who at once renewed his suit in Chancery to recover them. Robert Sidney's son and heir, now the young Earl of Leicester, had no intention of giving up his interests and the litigation was dragging on with maddening lack of resolution and would continue for many a year. The case was later to be taken up, pursued, and eventually won by two of Robert's daughters, Anne and Katherine.

In August 1642, after eleven years of arbitrary and absolute rule, King Charles I and his followers drove his bemused country into civil war and resolved to raise his standard at Nottingham. Planning to spend a night on the way at Coventry, he was forced to turn aside from a hostile crowd and barred city gates. With evening approaching, his company looked about for shelter and found Stoneleigh Abbey not far away. There the King was given a fervent welcome by Sir Thomas Leigh, the nephew of Alice Dudley. This act of loyalty would not be forgotten by Charles who then moved on to Nottingham.

The family was to render the King yet further service in the following grim years. Robert Holburne, married to Robert and Alice's daughter, Anne, was knighted and made Solicitor General in 1643. Richard Leveson, husband of her sister, Katherine, was also close to the King and entrusted by him with missions of importance. Also, among his Counsellors was Sir Gilbert Kniveton, husband of Frances who sadly died before 1644, which was to prove a vital year for all the Dudleys.

With the Civil War now in full swing, Charles I had the grace to remember services from loyal subjects and created Sir Thomas Leigh a baron for his hospitality at Stoneleigh. This led Robert's three sons in law, doubtless prodded by Alice Dudley and their wives, to remind the King of the unjust and despicable judgement of Star Chamber in 1605, and of the arbitrary closing of Robert's case, the smothering of evidence and the locking away of documentary records that had followed. The King was told the full story, the documents were recovered and this resulted, in May 1644, with the issuing of Letters Patent, under the Great Seal of England, which stated unequivocally that wrong had been done to Robert Dudley in 1605. It was a long document, giving chapter and verse on the case. It stated the circumstances of the Earl of Leicester's marriage to Lady Douglas Sheffield and gave the opinion that Robert was, indeed, Leicester's legitimate son. It detailed the amounts due to Robert on Kenilworth and to Alice as a "femme sole", resulting from the seizure of the estate. This debt had not been honoured and the document also acknowledged that Kenilworth had been grossly undervalued. Charles had been briefed as to the amounts involved, and on his brother Prince Henry's intentions, before his premature death in 1612, to make good, in some measure, the wrongs done to the Dudleys. A tally of the total amounts owed them followed, together with His Majesty's regrets that he was quite unable, due to the Civil War, to pay them. Nor could Kenilworth and Robert's other English properties now be wrested from their present owners and given back to him. It was too late. As partial recompense, the King proposed to create Alice a Duchess. She would be known as "Duchess Dudley" with all the accompanying honours and privileges. He would give her two remaining daughters, Katherine and Anne, the titles and the precedencies of a Duke's daughters. To Robert he gave his Royal recognition of the Dukedom of Northumberland, conferred on him by the Austrian Emperor, and confirmation that his title was valid, not only throughout the Holy Roman Empire but throughout England as well. This document, kept by Robert's daughter Lady Katherine Leveson, was later to be confirmed by Charles II.

It had taken forty four years and the loss of Kenilworth for Robert to win his case. For Alice, it was the reward and recompense she had not dreamed of. She would die at the age of ninety, having had ample time to enjoy the enormous rise in her social standing, and the recognition of her many charitable works.

Sitting in his Captain's chair in the shifting light at Rinieri, Robert Dudley had few regrets about his own life and the course he had steered through it. He could never have accepted the loss of his title and his honour in his own country, even had he kept Kenilworth. Above all, he could never have accepted Elizabeth as a mistress or anything other than his wife. The means, in his opinion, had justified the end. That others had suffered through it, he acknowledged but did not dwell upon.

Robert now turned the full force of his remaining energy to the completion of his books and their many illustrations. Memories had come surging in, of people, lands and adventures. They must be recorded for the future, for the young who would surely embark, as he had done, on missions that would open up the world to coming generations. There was a great inheritance to be passed on and it must move down the ages.

His "Magnum Opus", was now almost completed, and in the process of being printed, in three volumes initially. The charts, based on the map projections used by Mercator in the last century, were in the baroque style and the engravings were of exceptional quality. Robert was obliged to spend much time in Florence supervising the printing work. He was as meticulous as he had been when building his ships all those years before and he gave the printers no chance to produce anything that was not perfect in his view. It was very detailed work and his eyes, though good for his age, were beginning to tire easily. The whole work amounted to a maritime encyclopaedia way ahead of its time. He had reason to be proud of it.

Now, he must arrange Teresa's marriage contract and somehow find the enormous sum for her dowry. She was the third daughter to marry into one of the oldest and most respected families in Italy and there was still the volatile Maria Christina to consider. He must secure the future of his two youngest children, and soon. He was too old a father for them, he reflected, but their elder brothers and sisters, Maddalena in particular, would treat them as their own.

Enrico had embarked upon a Court career, under Teresa's watchful eye, in the spring of 1644 as a page to Cardinal Giancarlo de Medici. Knowing the flamboyant past of this cleric all too well and that few such leopards change their spots, Robert was not easy about the appointment and would try to alter it. Enrico was as good-looking as all the Dudleys and he was only thirteen. The moral standards within the Tuscan Court were not what they had been in the days of the Duchess Maria Christina. Robert himself now seldom appeared at Court nor took part in the organisation of events there but he was well aware of the changes taking place and the degeneration.

There had been the shocking scandal three years before, soon after the birth of the ducal heir, yet another Cosimo, when the Duchess Vittoria dscovered the Duke in bed with a page, Count Bruto della Molere. Her shock was so deep and her religious scruples so outraged that she promptly declined to have any further relations with him. She had lost her first two sons in early infancy and the rejoicing over this latest arrival was sadly curtailed. The couple were to be briefly reconciled in 1659 and a further son, Francesco Maria, was born.

Teresa's marriage on September 24th 1645, to the Duca della Cornia was the most splendid of all the Dudley weddings. The Grand Duke and Duchess, forgetting their differences, took matters into their own hands and insisted that it be celebrated in the Pitti Palace, at their expense, and that Grand Duke Ferdinando should stand as a witness. He was as devoted to Teresa as his wife, Vittoria, and Robert had long been a father figure to him. From the start Teresa had been obliged to make it clear to Ferdinando that any form of amatory advance was not welcome and, to his credit, they had ended as good friends. Teresa's charm and lack of inches concealed a powerful personality. She would have been wasted in a convent even had she become an abbess.

Looking at her now, on her wedding day, dressed in ivory satin embroidered all over with flowers made of seed pearls, a coronet on her shining head and her small figure moving towards her bridegroom with queenly grace, Robert realised how far his family had come since he first set foot in Tuscany.

If the marriage was not generous enough, the Duchess Vittoria gave a *"festa"* that evening in Teresa's honour, also in the Pitti Palace. The bride danced the night away with sprightly verve and only sank into her bridegroom's impatient arms as the birds began to sing. She had thoroughly enjoyed her wedding.

Very soon after this, in his library at Rinieri, Robert held in his hands the first copies of his book and with the same sense of fulfilment that he had felt in 1620, over twenty years ago, when the news arrived that he was now the Duke of Northumberland. The books were dedicated to the Grand Duke of Tuscany. Between late September 1645 and early January 1646, further copies were printed and, subsequently, highly acclaimed. "Dell' Arcano del Mare" was a unique work and through it ran the challenging thread of authenticity. What Robert also held in his hands that September morning was a statement of himself and his life's work. For many years it would be the ultimate text book on all maritime matters; that such a complex and detailed work was re-printed so soon was testimony to its renown.

Carlo's alliance with his French widow, Countess Marie Madeleine Gouffier, was not, it seemed, happy. They had produced two sons and two daughters, but cracks in the marriage were appearing and by April 1648 Carlo wrote: "My wife, the Duchess, wishes to go away" and "The Duchess is about to leave for Lombardy." He appeared to be already anticipating his father's demise by giving his wife the title of "Duchess". This was followed by a cryptic note: "The Countess wanted to go to the house of Giuliano Gondi with all her belongings." Robert, who had no wish to be involved in Carlo's marital or monetary problems, was not surprised and merely supposed that the couple had separated. The identity of Giuliano Gondi remained a mystery and Carlo had apparently taken up residence in Bologna where Robert hoped he would remain.

Teresa's marriage was tragically short. Within a year, her husband suffered a riding accident; his horse came down on top of him and he was killed instantly. Already pregnant, she was a widow before she became a mother. Her son, Fulvio, then died when only a few months old, leaving Teresa to face a long and painful law suit against Rome which could only have one ending. The Church pounced once more upon what it considered a vacant fief. In 1647, The Apostolic Chamber in Rome ruled that, with the child Fulvio's death, the family of Cornia had become extinct and that all its properties reverted to the Church. It was a case of "Urbino" repeated. Teresa was forced to embark on a long legal tussle which she pursued with characteristic vigour and courage until her death. The eventual outcome was never in doubt, but Teresa was a fighter.

Her own story had a happier ending, however. Soon after the death of her baby son, Count Mario of Carpegna in Montefeltro came to Florence and was appointed High Steward to Cardinal Giancarlo de Medici. Here he met "the beautiful and interesting young widow, Teresa Dudley, Duchess of Cornia" and instantly fell in love with her. Carpegna's family was closely connected with Urbino.

Teresa, who had been with her father at Rinieri, had only just returned to Court. Descending the same staircase down which her parents had made their first appearance at the Tuscan Court, she found an unknown man waiting on the last step looking up at her with blatant admiration. He had laughing eyes and a wickedly attractive countenance. Teresa did not hesitate. She put her small hand in his and never looked back. It was the start of a formidable and lasting love affair. They were married only months after the death of the baby, Fulvio, and Teresa found in Carpegna both compassion and a wit as quick as her own. He was, like Cornia, older than she was and he fought the Apostolic Chamber by her side as a matter of principle though there was little hope of winning. Over the years he had been given ample opportunity to observe the ruthless annexation of Urbino, closely bound to his State of Montefeltro. When, much later, he came to make his own will in 1661, he applied the law of primogeniture in favour of his eldest son, leaving his wife the guardianship of their three children, Vittoria, Ulderico and Anna Maria.

Almost immediately after their marriage in 1648 Count Mario was sent to Avignon as Vice Legate. Teresa went with him and Robert was obliged to part with another daughter. She had, again, married into a most distinguished Italian family; Count Mario had long been a Knight of St.Stephen and Gonfaloniere of Rimini. Montefeltro was one of the small states which had remained the property of Duchess Vittoria after the seizure of Urbino by Urban VIII. Teresa's ties with the Duchess were now even closer. She remained, very much, the elder sister of the two and was one of the few who could raise Vittoria's spirits and moderate her ardour for the Church. The sands, however, were running out for the Medici; Vittoria's son, Cosimo III, though he reigned for many years, was to be the last Grand Duke of Tuscany.

Sands were running out too for Robert Dudley, now aged seventy five and living almost entirely at Rinieri. Teresa and her husband would soon return from Avignon to resume their duties at the Tuscan Court. Their family would need a house in Florence on their return and Robert, in lieu of another vast dowry for Teresa's second marriage, arranged a deed giving her the use of the house in Via della Vigna Nuova for five years. He also bequeathed them something he had cherished for many years and used a great deal. It was an ebony cabinet, with silver drawers, in which he had kept small and valuable treasures. He called it his *"cherusicheria"* and it would be Teresa's on his death.

In fairness, he also arranged that after the five years, the tenancy of the house was to be divided equally between Carlo, Teresa and Enrico. Maria Christina, who always leapt before she looked, had married, very young, a landowner at Olivola, the Marquese di Clivola and, after a brief but ebullient life, died soon afterwards in childbirth. Ferdinando had duly taken orders at Fiesole and remained there. Enrico was, therefore, due to succeed Carlo as Earl of Warwick.

They all, excepting Carlo, came and went in and out of Rinieri as they had always done bringing with them a host of children, dogs and horses. The house was large enough for all of them. Robert had grown to be the patriarch he wished to be and they were always welcome. His Captain's chair became the central point of the household but was treated with the greatest respect, particularly if he were outside with his telescopes. As a treat, the older children were allowed to look through them, awestruck and laughing at all that so miraculously swam into view; another world which, by magic, was opened up to them.

Robert's thoughts as he sat, instruments to hand, amongst the scented breezes at Rinieri, listening to the splashing water of the fountains and looking across to the blue mountains in the far distance, were mainly contented and fulfilled. He had outlived six of his twelve children in Italy and several in England; he had achieved more than any of them ever would, but it was sad that the gifts he possessed had been used to such effect, not in his own country, but in Tuscany. The miscarriage of justice that June day in 1605 had deprived England of one of its most brilliant sons, leaving power to such sycophants as Somerset and Buckingham, who between them, had helped plunge the country into civil war. Robert wondered momentarily whether his treatise "The Bridling of Parliaments" had influenced those events. He had justified it by the perceived need to show the powers in England that there was a better way, as in Tuscany, to govern a country. The fact that, in so doing, he had tweaked King James's tail had been all to the good.

He had arrived in Italy, a wanderer, almost an outcast, without much wealth or influence and by his own efforts and hard work had won repute throughout Tuscany and, particularly, with its rulers. True, he was a known quantity, his birth and name had gone before him and it had been no unknown stranger who confronted Duke Ferdinand l. The immense load of work he had undertaken would not have been contemplated by any of his contemporaries in England; even Raleigh would have thought it beneath him. Luckily for Tuscany, "came the hour, came the man". It was work he enjoyed and by which he was fascinated, but the element of pride in achievement and the power and fame it brought him had certainly played to his own ambitions.

Robert was no self-analyst, but a contemporary observer would have attributed his success to complete belief in himself, bordering on arrogance, and unquestioned confidence in his own ability to achieve anything he set out to do. He had built and enlarged two vital sea ports and seen them grow into thriving cities; he had finished draining a huge area of stinking marsh, assisted in the final stages of constructing a great aqueduct and a canal, and designed and re-built the Tuscan navy into a major sea power. He had served as Great Chamberlain to three successive rulers of Tuscany and he had produced a definitive work on all maritime matters. He had been heaped with honours and privileges by the Grand Dukes and by Pope Urban VIII and had managed to build a grand palazzo for his family in Florence, all in forty four years. More than any of this, he had been eventually acknowledged by the Austrian Emperor, the Pope and now the King of England as the rightful Duke of Northumberland.

Religiously, he had steered a circuitous course, accepted as within the bounds by most of his contemporaries, and he had wisely kept his head below the parapet in this direction, though sometimes against his better nature.

The handsome old man in the Captain's chair sipped his wine with deep satisfaction. There was more to rejoice in. Against many odds, he had married one of the most beautiful women of his time and fathered twelve children in Italy. His abandoned wife, now a Duchess in her own right, and four surviving daughters in England had, eventually, thrived. These four had married well, to men close to the seat of power and they had brought his case before King Charles. His cruel abandonment of them could never be truthfully justified but he could not regret it. He had provided generously for them. His Italian girls had married into some of the best families and his own blood would flow in its aristocracy for generations to come. His one bitter regret was that of all his many children, he could not love or forgive the one who would succeed him.

The sun was dipping down below the blue mountains as he sat in his Captain's chair on the terrace below the house. He loved Rinieri; the soft wind sighed in the pines, the sound of water was all around him and his chair faced a mosaic of small fields and vineyards retreating hazily towards the mountains. It was time to rest and enjoy the harmony and peace surrounding him.

The wine in the beautiful glass was going gently down, its rich crimson winking against the intricate Venetian cutting. The weight of it in his hand was an added pleasure to the contents. It was a large glass and the wine was good. The soft air and a glow in the western sky signalled the end of a perfect day and the distant mountains were beginning to show darkly on the skyline. The Duke of Northumberland's memories drifted on from the day he had set sail in the "Beare", to his first glimpse of the New World in Trinidad, to ships and town ablaze at Cadiz, to the warm red stone of Kenilworth and to his first sight of a girl singing her heart out in Hampton Court. Then faces began to glide past his closed eyes; so many, some loved, some loathed and, above all, the one he longed for in all its beauty. He was alone, so much had been achieved and he wished to go with the end of this lovely day, and in peace. It was 6th September 1649.

EPILOGUE

During the research for this book, discoveries came so thick and fast that some facts and people were necessarily left unexplored. Robert Dudley appears to have been a rare and outstanding character and his life, though a long one for his era, was so full of action until his very last years that it has been hard to keep up with him.

He was an unrecognized genius in an adventurous age who has seldom been acknowledged for what he was other than a "Noble Bastard". He was a diverse genius too: exploration, shipbuilding, construction, seamanship, cartography, engineering, were all grist to the mill and he had a flair for organisation which produced the grandest of state occasions for the Medici rulers of Florence. These pursuits were all carried on while bringing up twelve children and writing six volumes of what was, at the time, a definitive work on all aspects of the maritime world.

His origins are still shrouded in doubt despite the fact that Charles I acknowledged his legitimate birth and his title of Duke of Northumberland. Because this recognition took over forty years to establish, it was impossible to turn the clock back, restore his titles and his land, and recompense him properly. History has continued, unfairly, to label him a bastard. The lengths to which Leicester went to prove that his marriage to Lady Douglas Sheffield never existed suggest very much that it did. Robert, himself, never believed anything else. Both he and his mother were certain enough to bring the case to a hearing, and she to testify despite her questionable past.

Robert's so-called "contract", at the age of seventeen, to a marriage with the flighty Frances Vavasour, witnessed by his relative Thomas Jobson, was an almost repeat performance of Leicester's. Again, as with his parents, there existed the fine line between betrothal and marriage; they could be conveniently interchanged. Despite the fact that Frances Vavasour jilted him and married another, the "contract" was kept and used by him later as proof that his marriages to Margaret Cavendish and Alice Leigh had been unlawful; this in order to gain Papal consent to his marriage

271

with Elizabeth Southwell. That he managed to do so and to convince the Vatican of its validity beggars belief. It is not difficult to suppose that large sums changed hands somewhere. This was shady dealing and all too akin to his father's matrimonial activities. Robert Dudley, whatever his virtues, was no saint and he had seen it all before.

He was a buccaneer in more ways than one, though he had an ingrained sense of honour and responsibility, demonstrated in his dealings with those he sailed and worked with, including the Arawak people of Trinidad. This did not prevent his imposing discipline strict enough to ensure the smooth running of any enterprise he embarked upon. Reading the accounts of those who served under him gives an insight into the admiration and loyalty he inspired; he appears an instinctive leader from an early age.

His lasting and passionate love for Elizabeth Southwell is well documented and shines through all aspects of their story. She was beautiful and high-spirited and he adored her. The only portrait that remains and purports to be of her is, almost certainly, of her mother, also Elizabeth Southwell, the wife of the blue-eyed Admiral and the daughter of Howard of Effingham. It does not do justice to a great beauty. There was yet one other Elizabeth Southwell, a cousin from Norfolk and also a Lady in Waiting to the Queen, who became entangled with the Earl of Essex and bore him a son.

The events and quotations in the book are as historically accurate as possible. Most of the characters, their actions and their impact on the life of Robert Dudley, are also researched and factual. Some have been added and some, who had no real bearing on events, have been left out.

The Armada story has been told by many, but Robert Dudley's presence in the camp at Tilbury is certain, as is his promotion to Colonel on the eve of the sea battle and the Queen's visit to the troops gathered there.

All those who appear in Robert's voyage to the West Indies are described in his own account, also in that of the old soldier, Wyatt, and of the master mariner, Abraham Kendal. I have added the red-haired Captain Peter Michell, an ancestor of my own, because he did indeed sail with Drake in his circumnavigation and, coming from Cornwall, could very well have sailed also with Robert. It is a fact that the wounded officer was sent, as promised, to the Dudley-owned hospice in Warwick for medical care on the ship's return to England.

Robert's first two marriages, both achieved at the gallop, were perhaps prompted by the need for an heir to Kenilworth and his knowledge that Robert Sidney was waiting impatiently in the wings should he fall by the wayside without one. His way of life and quest for adventure made anything possible.

The bond he had with Essex survived to the end and was remarkable in that there was little related blood between them and Robert's hatred of Lettice Knollys was well known. Some records suggest he was very much a part of the uprising from Essex House and duly imprisoned for it, but others state that though he was there at the time, he had no part in it. Had he been deeply involved it would have been in character for him to be at the forefront of any action but he does not appear to have taken a leading role and is not mentioned in most accounts. He was certainly released speedily from the Tower by some authority, royal or otherwise, and with no trial. Others, such as Rutland and Southampton, under sentence of death, spent many months in prison.

His role in the Cadiz raid and his command of the "Nonpareil" confirm the high opinion of his abilities held by the joint leaders of the expedition, his uncle Howard of Effingham and the Earl of Essex. He was only twenty-one years old, a Vice Admiral, second in command of one of the four squadrons, and in charge of one of the fighting ships of the line. To successfully command and take such a ship into battle and to get his seamen back from the drunken sack of the city was no mean feat. Although there was a proliferation of knighthoods after the capture of Cadiz, his appears well-earned.

After Cadiz, he could so easily have rested on his laurels, secure in the ownership of Kenilworth, the vast wealth that went with it and a promising second marriage. Instead he was already planning another expedition, to the Far East this time, and proposing to sail in command of it. Had he done so, he would probably never have returned. There was only one known survivor.

The pre-determined charade in Star Chamber in 1605 must have hit Robert Dudley harder than anything else in his career. After months of preparation, to find he had been out-manoeuvred, the hearing virtually turned into a trial with King James blatantly backing his adversaries, left him raging. He had fought bastardy all his life and it was his Achilles' heel. To have lost, with the status of his birth almost unmentioned, and his hard-sought legal documents locked away by Royal command, put him in a state of such fury that he turned his back on all authority and marched out, taking with him the one thing he really wanted, Elizabeth Southwell. He must have known that he was also turning his back on Kenilworth and facing a long, if not permanent, exile.

His callous abandonment of his wife, Alice, and their five daughters was not the act of the noble Earl he thought himself to be. He left them in the lurch in all ways except financially. As Kenilworth melted away into the possession of the Crown and its subsequent caretakers, they might not have existed for him at all. It was left to three of his daughters and their influential husbands to put pressure enough on the Monarchy to have their father, their mother and themselves elevated to the aristocracy. There is no record of Robert ever seeing his English daughters again. Surprisingly, they did not appear to bear him any grudge for his desertion and it was their efforts that gained him recognition of his dukedom in England. Alice, also, was able to claim some of her own interests in the Kenilworth estate. She lived to a great age and had plenty of time to enjoy life as a duchess.

The arrival of Robert and his bride in Tuscany must have caused waves of different kinds. What seems certain is that he and the shrewd Duke Ferdinand enjoyed a rapport which resulted in his being given responsibility for the re-building of the Tuscan navy and the development of its sea ports. There was much besides. That rapport developed into a close friendship and set the scene for the Dudleys' future in Italy and their position among the Medici family. Elizabeth's charm and beauty undoubtedly smoothed their path and, as a pair, they must have managed any opposition well. Their marriage and the legitimacy of their children was never questioned. Robert served three successive Grand Duchesses as Great Chamberlain, gave guidance to the two young Grand Dukes, Cosimo II and Ferdinando II, and became a figure of great authority at the Tuscan Court. There must have been some opposition or jealousy from existing members of the nobility, but no incidents are mentioned; no duels fought. Robert was by then over thirty years old with a reputation for ruthlessness and a personality that did not invite opposition.

There is no record of Robert's association with Galileo, but they were living in Pisa at the same time and, being like-minded, must surely have known each other and shared their interests.

There is no record either of Robert ever meeting Pope Urban VIII. It is another likelihood however. He had become well known to the various Medici Cardinals of two generations and it seems probable that he made the journey to Rome, either with them or for them. His infant daughter, Maria Christina, was baptised by Pope Urban VIII's nephew, Barberini, a friend of Robert's, and it is a possibility that the Vatican saw in Dudley a means of persuasion when dealing with the Medici if it were needed.

It was through Robert's Florentine daughters that his line mainly continued in Italy. Maria, Maddalena, Teresa and Maria Christina all married into old, aristocratic Italian families; Maddalena and Teresa both chose equally distinguished second husbands. Nothing is recorded of Maria Christina's offspring.

Maddalena married again, in 1660, Giambattista, Count of Lavagna. The English line of Heneage was connected with this family and the Lavagna name of Fieschi often appears among the Heneage family trees. A letter from Maddalena later appears in Tuscan Court records signed "Maria Maddalena Dudlea-Fiesca".

The children of Teresa's second marriage to Carpegna all followed their parents to high positions at Court. Ulderico, the heir, became a great favourite of the Grand Duke who made him a Knight of the Order of St.Stephen at the tender age of fourteen. His two sisters were maids of honour to the Grand Duchess, distinguished for their intellectual quality and as much admired as their mother had been. Both married into the aristocracy.

Of Robert's surviving sons, Carlo, Duke of Northumberland, continued his erratic path through life and some of his children inherited his wildness. After several signs of strife, he appears to have separated from his wife and decamped permanently to Bologna. They had two sons and two daughters; Roberto, Antonio, Carlotta and Christina. In December 1650, a year after Robert's death, Carlo, now Duke of Northumberland, wrote a painstaking letter to the Grand Duke Ferdinando and Duchess Vittoria asking them to stand as sponsors at the baptism of the newly arrived Carlotta in the Monastery of San Nicolo. Hatchets must have been buried, possibly for Robert's sake, because they duly appeared and took part in the ceremony.

Carlo's elder son Roberto retained his father's house in Bologna until his death in 1706, despite the fact that he became Chamberlain to Queen

Christina of Sweden. The second son, Antonio, although he had been made a Knight of St. Stephen, chose the Church and became a Canon of the Cathedral of the Vatican. The Canon appears to have had an acquisitive nature. He eventually inherited, through his mother, Maria Maddalena Gouffier, several farms near Fiesole and at Maiano and, in due course, all the Dudley property in Florence. Through a series of circumstances and with his brother Roberto's consent, this included the house in Via della Vigna Nuova.

There was a cry for help from Carlo to Duke Ferdinando in May 1676 on the subject of a proposed marriage between his daughter Carlotta and the Prince of Stromboli. He was clearly aiming high and could not raise the dowry. Carlo implored the Grand Duke to remember his father's many services to the Medici family but nothing came of that. Unwelcome by the Medici in Tuscany, he lived in Rome for many years and later, in 1686, having created a terrible and embarrassing scene at Court, Duke Carlo found himself once more within the familiar walls of the Bargello where he died intestate and unmourned on 25th October 1686.

Carlo's other daughter, Christina, a lady in waiting at the Court of Savoy from an early age, was one of the most celebrated beauties of her time. She was married, at fifteen, to the Marchese Andrea Paleotti. The chronicler, Tioli, records that: "for beauty, spirit, and *"bizaria"* few or none could equal her, and that neither Prince nor Cavalier could pass without admiration and wishing to know her...... none were so daring and adventurous". Christina's daughter, Diana, married into the great Colonna family and yet another, Adelaide, married the English Duke of Shrewsbury, became lady in waiting to the Princess of Wales and a leader of London society. Adelaide's brother, Ferdinand, a thoroughly bad lot and constantly in trouble, followed her to England and was finally hanged at Tyburn for murdering an Italian servant. Not, however, before he demanded of the executioner that he should be strung up apart from the other condemned so that he was not defiled by their death struggles. With one exception, therefore, no member of Robert Dudley's Italian family set foot in England for two generations. This was Duke Carlo who, in 1677, visited the land of his fathers in order to present his ducal claims and rights, probably monetary, in the House of Lords. They roared with laughter at what they considered an eccentric. His grandchildren, Adelaide and the appalling Ferdinand, in whom Carlo's bad blood had re-appeared, were the next to do so.

Of Robert Dudley's sons only Duke Carlo and Enrico remained by

1652 when Enrico became Earl of Warwick, presumably at the death of his brother Ferdinando. At the time Enrico was a joint owner, with Carlo, of their father's house in Florence, Teresa's matrimonial lease having expired. The brothers, with seventeen years between them, did not get on, and there are records of a suit for debt brought by Enrico against Carlo. Four generations later the title "Duke of Northumberland" and the male line of the Dudleys in Italy had died out. The female line, through Maria, Madalena and Teresa continued and flourished: Robert and Elizabeth lived on in their beloved Tuscany.

Elizabeth's monument in San Pancrazio was destroyed by Napoleon's invading soldiers in 1798. The only Southwell portrait remaining in Florence is that of Sir Richard Southwell, by Holbein, in the Uffizi Palace. It was presented to Duke Cosimo II by the Earl of Arundel, a great collector.

Robert's body was taken to the monastery at Boldrone, possibly at the instigation of Ferdinando Dudley. It remained there, at least, until 1674. There is no record of it being taken to San Pancrazio and it is possible that Carlo may have been responsible for this.

Villa Rinieri at Castello, later owned by the Corsini family, became known as the Villa Corsini and, later still, as the Villa Castello, as it is to this day.

It is strange that the Earl of Leicester's only surviving son should have had so little recognition in England. Having removed to Italy, he may have been forgotten by his contemporaries, but the wider view of history should, perhaps, have given him the interest he deserves. The gloss and notoriety surrounding his father, Leicester, was partly the result of his association with Queen Elizabeth I, but his feats were in no way comparable to those of his son though his rapid rise to power, wealth, land ownership and high positions, was undeniable. Having made a shambles of the Netherlands campaign, the Earl redeemed himself when commanding the English forces during the Armada invasion, though he never fought. He had made contributions to English sea ventures but never sailed himself. His successes did not, in any way, equal Robert's and he only produced two children as opposed to twenty. Had he, also, been disinherited and branded a bastard from the age of five, he might have fought, worked and proved himself as his son did. Proof, however, was not enough in Robert Dudley's case. Though he himself must have died content with his many achievements this gifted and charismatic man has gone down to posterity as a "Noble Bastard".

BIBLIOGRAPHY

Camden, William: Annales in the History of the most Renowned and Victorious Princess Elizabeth (1675)

Chaney, Edward & Wilks, Timothy: The Jacobean Grand Tour

Cherbury: The Autobiography of Lord Herbert of Cherbury

Cornacchini, Dottore Marco: Medical treatise on the Warwick Powder

Cressy, David: Charles I & the People of England

Cripps-Day, F.H: History of the Tournament

Daniel, John: Egerton Papers and State Trials

Dudley, Sir Robert, Duke of Northumberland and Earl of Warwick: Dell' Arcano del Mare.

Dugdale, Sir Wlliam: Antiquities of Warwickshire, v.i 1656. Warwickshire and Baronage

Englander, Norman, O'Day and Owens: Culture and Belief in Europe 1450-1600

English Heritage: Kenilworth Castle

Froude, J.A: A History of England from the Fall of Wolsey to the Defeat of the Armada (12 volumes 1856-1870

Galluzzi: Storia del Granducato di Toscana

Gould Lee, Arthur: The Son of Leicester

Gristwood, Sarah: Arbella, England's Lost Queen

Hakluyt Society: Voyage of Robert Dudley to the West Indies 1594-1595

Hibbert, Christopher: The Rise and Fall of the House of Medici

Kamen, Henry: European Society 1500-1700

Lacy, Robert: Robert, Earl of Essex. An Elizabethan Icarus

Lovell, Mary S.: Bess of Hardwick First Lady of Chatsworth

Murphy, Caroline: Isabella de'Medici

Nicholl, Charles: The Reckoning: The Murder of Christopher Marlowe

Nichols: Pedigree of the Dudleys

Norwich, John Julius: The Popes

Oxford Dictionary of National Biography

Parks, Tim: Medici Money

Raleigh, Sir Walter: Discoverie of Guiana 1596

Robinson, J.H: Readings in European History 2 Vols 1906

Role, Raymond: Sir Robert Dudley, Duke of Northumberland

Sitwell, Edith: The Queens and the Hive

Strachey, Lytton: Elizabeth and Essex

Temple-Leader, John: Life of Sir Robert Dudley, Earl of Warwick and Duke of
    Northumberland

Thomas, the Rev Vaughan: The Italian Biography of Sir Robert Dudley

Tradescant: Tradescant's Orchard

Trevelyan, G.M: Illustrated English Social History

Waldman, Milton: Elizabeth and Leicester

Warner, Sir George: The Voyage of Sir Robert Dudley to the West Indies.

Wood, Anthony: Athenae Oxoniensis

PERSONAE

ANJOU: Duc d'Anjou. Third son of Henry II of France and Catherine de Medici. Later King Henry III of France.

APPIANO: Prince Oratzio Appiano of Piombino. Married to Maria Dudley.

APPIANO: Princess Isabella of Piombino.

BACHELER: Daniel. Musician employed by Sir Francis Walsingham, Sir Philip Sidney and Queen Anne.

BACON: Anthony. Son of Sir Nicholas Bacon, Lord Keeper. Intelligence agent to Walsingham and Essex.

BACON: Francis. Attorney General, Lord Chancellor, Baron Verulam, Viscount of St.Albans. Brother of Anthony Bacon.

BALTHASAR: Guide to Captain Jobson on exploration of Orinoco River.

BARBERINI. Cardinal Francesco. Nephew of Pope Urban VIII.

BARDI: Count. Leader of first Opera company in Florence.

BARRATT: Sir Edward. Friend of Sir Henry Wotton, English Ambassador to the Venetian Republic.

BARROW: "Ancient". Old retainer of Robert Dudley from Kenilworth. Served on expedition to Trinidad and taking of Cadiz 1596.

BLOUNT: Sir Christopher. Married to Lettice, widow of the Earl of Leicester.

BRADSHAW: Seraphina. Married to William Bradshaw

BRADSHAW: William. Nephew of "Ancient" Barrow. Servant and lifelong friend of Robert Dudley. Later in overall charge of his Tuscan establishments.

BORGHERINI: Dr.Giulio. Italian "physician" to the Earl of Leicester.

BURGHLEY: Lord William Cecil. Secretary of State to Queen Elizabeth I.

CAREW: Sir George. Master of the Ordnance

CAREY: Catherine. Wife of the Lord Admiral, Howard of Effingham.

CARPEGNA IN MONTEFELTRO: Count Mario. Second husband of Teresa Dudley. Father of Ulderico, Vittoria and Anna Maria di Carpegna.

CARPEGNA: Ulderico. Son and heir of Count Mario Carpegna and Maddalena Dudley.

CARR: Robert, later Viscount Rochester and Earl of Somerset. Favourite of King James I.

CARRICK. John Stewart, Earl of Carrick. Second husband of Elizabeth Southwell, mother of Robert Dudley's wife.

CAVENDISH: Margaret. First wife of Robert Dudley. Sister of the explorer Sir Thomas Cavendish.

CAVENDISH: Sir Thomas. Explorer, Circumnavigator and privateer. Brother of Margaret Cavendish, first wife of Robert Dudley

CECIL: Sir Robert. Later Earl of Salisbury. Secretary of State to Queen Elizabeth I. Son of Wlliam Cecil, Lord Burghley.

CHALONER: Sir Thomas. Tutor to Robert Dudley at Oxford. Diplomat. Tutor and Chamberlain to Prince Henry of England.

CHERBURY: Lord Cherbury. Visitor to Tuscany from England.

CLANRICARDE: Richard de Burgh. 4th Earl of Clanricarde. Earl of St.Albans.

CLEWER: William. Servant of Earl of Leicester.

CLIVOLA: Marchese. Husband of Maria Christina Dudley.

COKE: Sir Edward Coke. Attorney General.

CORNACHINI: Dr.Marco. Recorder and promoter of "The Warwick Powder".

CORNIA: Duke of Cornia. First husband of Teresa Dudley.

CORNIA: Fulvio. Son of Teresa and the Duke of Cornia. Died in infancy.

CUFFE: Henry. Greek scholar. Advisor and friend of Earl of Essex. Executed after the up-rising of 1601.

CUMBERLAND: George, 3rd Earl of Cumberland. Explorer and the Queen's Champion jouster.

D'OLIVOLA: Spinetta Malaspina, Marchese d'Olivola: First husband of Maddalena Dudley. High Steward to Christina, Queen of Sweden.

DACRE: Lady Dacre. Sponsor at Robert Dudley's christening.

DANVERS: Sir Charles: Fellow soldier and co-conspirator in the Essex up-rising of 1601. Beheaded.

DAVIS: John. Second-in-command to Sir Thomas Cavendish on last expedition. Discovered the Falkland Islands.

DELLA ROVERE: Grand Duchess Vittoria of Tuscany and Princess of Urbino. Married to Ferdinando II, Grand Duke of Tuscany.

DENBIGH: Robert, Baron Denbigh. Son of Robert, Earl of Leicester, and Lettice, Countess of Leicester. Died in infancy.

DERBY: Countess of Derby. Mistress of the Earl of Essex.

DEVEREUX: Lady Dorothy. Sister of the Earl of Essex. Married, first to Sir Thomas Perrot and secondly to the Earl of Northumberland.

DEVEREUX: Lady Penelope. Sister of the Earl of Essex. Married to Lord Rich.

Mistress of Lord Mountjoy.

DRAKE: Admiral Sir Francis. Explorer, Sea Captain and pirate.

DRURY: Thomas. Nephew of Sir Edward Stafford.

DUDLEY: Alicia Douglassia. Eldest English daughter of Robert Dudley and Alice Leigh. Died young.

DUDLEY: Ambrogio. Son of Robert Dudley and Elizabeth Southwell. Died young

DUDLEY: Anna. Daughter of Robert Dudley and Elizabeth Southwell. Died young.

DUDLEY: Anne. English daughter of Robert Dudley and Alice Leigh. Married to Sir Robert Holburne

DUDLEY: Antonio. Son of Carlo, Duke of Northumberland. Grandson of Robert Dudley.

DUDLEY: Antonio. Son of Robert Dudley and Elizabeth Southwell. Died young.

DUDLEY: Carlo. Later Earl of Warwick and Duke of Northumberland. Son of Robert Dudley and Elizabeth Southwell.

DUDLEY: Carlotta: Daughter of Carlo, Duke of Northumberland. Grandaughter of Robert Dudley.

DUDLEY: Christina. Daughter of Carlo, Duke of Northumberland. Grandaughter of Robert Dudley

DUDLEY: Cosimo. Later Earl of Warwick. Eldest son of Robert Dudley and Elizabeth Southwell. Died young.

DUDLEY: Enrico. Youngest son of Robert Dudley and Elizabeth Southwell. Later Earl of Warwick.

DUDLEY: Ferdinando. Son of Robert Dudley and Elizabeth Southwell.

DUDLEY: Frances. English daughter of Robert Dudley and Alice Leigh. Married to Sir Gilbert Kniveton:

DUDLEY: John. Cousin of Earl of Leicester. Given charge of Robert Dudley as a child.

DUDLEY: Katherine. English daughter of Robert Dudley and Alice Leigh. Married to Sir Richard Leveson.

DUDLEY: Lady Mary Dudley. Sister of Lady Douglas Sheffield. (Another Dudley family).

DUDLEY: Lord Dudley. Brother-in-law to Lady Douglas Sheffield. (Another Dudley family).

DUDLEY: Maddalena. Daughter of Robert Dudley and Elizabeth Southwell. Married, first, Marchese d'Olivola; second Giambattista, Count of Lavagna.

DUDLEY: Maria Christina. Youngest daughter of Robert Dudley and Elizabeth Southwell. Married the Marques di Clivola. Died young.

DUDLEY: Maria, Princess of Piombino. Eldest daughter of Robert Dudley and Elizabeth Southwell. Married Prince Oratzio Appiano of Piombino.

DUDLEY: Robert. Son and heir of Carlo, Duke of Northumberland. Grandson of Robert Dudley

DUDLEY: Sir Robert, later Earl of Warwick and Duke of Northumberland. Son of the Earl of Leicester and Lady Douglas Sheffield.

DUDLEY: Lord Robert, Earl of Leicester. Father of Robert Dudley.

DUDLEY: Teresa. Daughter of Robert Dudley and Elizabeth Southwell. Married first the Duca della Cornia. Second the Count of Carpegna in Montefeltro.

DUDLEY: John, Duke of Northumberland, Grandfather of Sir Robert Dudley, beheaded for treason.

EGERTON: Thomas, 1st Viscount Brackley. Keeper of the Great Seal and Lord Chancellor.

ELIOT: Captain Robert. Agent within the Vatican working to obtain permission from Pope Paul V for Robert Dudley's marriage to Elizabeth Southwell.

ELLESMERE: Lord Ellesmere. Solicitor-General. Present at Star Chamber.

ERISA: Mrs.Erisa, later Lady Parker. Witness for Robert Dudley at Star Chamber.

ESSEX: 1st Earl of Essex. Husband of Lettice Knollys.

ESSEX: Robert Devereux, 2nd Earl of Essex. Stepbrother of Robert Dudley, husband of Frances Walsingham. Father of Robert, 3rd Earl of Essex.

ESSEX: Robert Devereux, 3rd Earl of Essex. Son of 2nd Earl of Essex. Husband of Frances Howard. Divorced.

FAWKES: Guy. Responsible for attempting to blow up Parliament. Executed.

FROBISHER: Explorer and Navigator.

FRODSHAM: Magdalen. Later Mrs.Salisbury. Witness for Robert Dudley at Star Chamber.

GALILEO: Galiliei: Inventor, astronomer and scientist. Accused by Vatican of heresy.

GONDI: Giuliano. Unidentified friend of Countess Marie Madeleine, wife of Carlo Dudley.

GOUFFIER: Countess Marie Madeleine. Wife of Carlo Dudley, later Duchess of Northumberland

GOUFFIER: Marquis de Boisy and Seigneur de Crevecoeur. Father of Countess Marie Madeleine married to Carlo Dudley.

GREVILLE: Sir Fulke. Courtier and Soldier.

HAKLUYT: Richard. Explorer, recorder and cartographer. Friend of Robert Dudley. Married to Anne Cavendish.

HAPSBURG: Archduke Charles of Austria. Father of Maria Maddalena, Grand Duchess of Tuscany.

HAPSBURG: Ferdinand. Emperor of the Holy Roman Empire: Brother of Maria Maddalena, Grand Duchess of Tuscany.

HAPSBURG: Maria Maddalena. Grand Duchess of Tuscany. Wife of Duke Cosimo II. Sister of Ferdinand, Holy Roman Emperor.

HATTON: Sir Christopher. Courtier and favourite of Queen Elizabeth I.

HAWKINS: Sir John. English Admiral and explorer.

HAYWARDE: Sir John. Lawyer and chronicler. Present at Star Chamber 1605.

HEIGHAM: Sir Clement. Suitor of Elizabeth Southwell

HOLBURNE: Sir Robert. Solicitor General of King Charles I. Married to Anne Dudley, English daughter of Robert Dudley.

HOLLES: Gervase. Husband of Eleanor, sister of Lord Sheffield.

HORSEY: Sir Edward. Old family friend. Present at Leicester/Sheffield marriage.

HOWARD OF EFFINGHAM: Lord High Admiral of England. Brother of Lady Douglas Sheffield. Uncle to Robert Dudley. Later Earl of Nottingham.

HOWARD: Elizabeth. Mother of Elizabeth Southwell, wife of Robert Dudley. Daughter of Lord Howard of Effingham, the Lord Admiral. Married to Admiral Southwell.

HOWARD: Frances: Cousin of Robert Dudley. Married first to 3rd Earl of Essex, second to Robert Carr, Earl of Somerset.

HOWARD: Henry: Earl of Northampton. Cousin of Robert Dudley.

HOWARD: Lord Thomas Howard. Later Earl of Suffolk. Cousin of Robert Dudley

HOWARD: Lord Thomas Howard. Later the Earl of Northampton.

JOBSON: Captain Thomas. Related to Robert Dudley. "Lieutenant General" of the expedition to Trinidad of 1594.

JONES: Inigo Jones. Architect, designer and surveyor.

JONES: Owen. Servant of Earl of Leicester. Witness for Robert Dudley at Star Chamber.

KENDAL: Abraham. Master mariner, explorer and cartographer.

KING CHARLES I OF ENGLAND:

KING GUSTAVUS ADOLPHUS OF SWEDEN.

KING HENRY IV OF FRANCE: Henry of Navarre. Formerly leader of French Huguenots.

KING JAMES I of England and Scotland. King James VI of Scotland

KING MATHIAS l: – 1458-1490. King of Hungary.

KING MATHIAS OF GERMANY.

KING PHILIP II OF SPAIN: Former husband of Mary Tudor, Queen of England.

KNIVETON: Sir Gilbert Kniveton. Husband of Frances Dudley, English daughter of Robert Dudley.

KNOLLYS: Lettice. Married first Walter, lst Earl of Essex, second Robert Earl of Leicester, third Sir Christopher Blount.

LANCASTER: James. English explorer.

LAVAGNA: Giambattista, Count of Lavagna. Second husband of Maddalena Dudley.

LEE: Sir Henry. Queen's Champion. Godfather to Robert Dudley. Founder of Accession Day Jousts.

LEICESTER: Robert Dudley, Earl of Leicester. Father of Sir Robert Dudley.

LEICESTER: The Earl of Leicester. Son of Robert Sidney.

LEIGH: Alice. Second wife of Sir Robert Dudley. Later, Duchess Dudley.

LEIGH: Catherine. Elder sister of Alice Dudley.

LEIGH: Lady Catherine. Mother of Alice.

LEIGH: John. Brother of Alice Dudley.

LEIGH: Sir Thomas of Stoneleigh. Father of Alice Dudley.

LEIGH: Sir Thomas of Stoneleigh. Nephew of Alice Dudley.

LEVESON: Sir Richard Leveson. Counsellor to King Charles I. Husband of Catherine Dudley, English daughter of Robert Dudley.

LORRAINE: Grand Duchess Maria Christina of Lorraine. Wife of Ferdinand I Grand Duke of Tuscany. Mother of Cosimo I.

LOTTI: Ottaviano: Florentine Minister in London for many years.

LUCINI: Jacopo. Engraver for "Dell' Arcano del Mare".

MAR: Earl of Mar. Guardian of Prince Henry Stuart.

MARLOWE: Christopher. Poet and playwright. Murdered in Deptford in 1593.

McELVEY: Large grey ship's cat from the Isle of Luing. Served aboard the "Beare" and the "Nonpareil"

MEDICI: Admiral Antonio de Medici. Commanded the assault on Famagusta in 1607.

MEDICI: Anna de Medici. Daughter of Duke Cosimo II and Duchess Maria Maddalena.

MEDICI: Cardinal Carlo de Medici. Son of Duke Ferdinand I.

MEDICI: Caterina: Sister of Duke Cosimo II. Married to the Duke of Mantua

MEDICI: Claudia. Sister of Duke Cosimo II. Married to the Duke of Urbino. Second marriage to Archduke Leopold of the Tyrol. Mother of Duchess Vittoria.

MEDICI: Cosimo II. Grand Duke of Tuscany: Eldest son of Grand Duke Ferdinand I and Duchess Maria Christina.

MEDICI: Duke Ferdinando II. Eldest son of Duke Cosimo II and Duchess Maria Maddalena.

MEDICI: Duke Ferdinand I, Grand Duke of Tuscany. Former Cardinal of Rome. Son of Cosimo I, of Tuscany.

MEDICI: Francesco. Son of Duke Cosimo II and Maria Maddalena.

MEDICI: GianCarlo de Medici. Son of Duke Cosimo II and Duchess Maria Maddalena.

MEDICI: Leopoldo. Son of Duke Ferdinando II and Duchess Maria Maddalena.

MEDICI: Margherita de Medici. Daughter of Duke Cosimo II and Duchess Maria Maddalena. Married to the Duke of Parma.

MEDICI: Maria Christina. Eldest daughter of Cosimo II and Maria Maddalena

MEDICI: Mattias. Son of Duke Cosimo II and Duchess Maria Maddalena.

MEDICI: Prince Cosimo. Elder son of Duke Ferdinando II and Duchess Vittoria. Later Duke Cosimo III, the last Medici Duke.

MEDICI: Prince Francesco Maria. Younger son of Duke Ferdinando II and Duchess Vittoria.

MEDICI: Queen Catherine de Medici: Widow of Henry II of France.

MEDINA SIDONIA: The Duke of Medina Sidonia. Commander of the Spanish Armada of 1588. Commander of the defence of Cadiz 1596.

MEYRICK: Sir Gilly. Agent and friend of the Earl of Essex. Executed after the conspiracy and uprising of 1601.

MICHELL: Captain Peter. Gunnery Officer on expedition to Trinidad. Had previously sailed with Drake in "Golden Hind". Fought with Robert Dudley at Cadiz 1596.

MUNCKE: Captain. Commanded the "Beare's Whelpe" on expedition to Trinidad.

NAVO: Gregorius. Auditor General of the Camera Apostolica.

NICCOLINI: Pietro. Vicar General of the Archbishop of Florence.

NORRIS: Sir John. Commander in almost every Elizabethan campaign.

NORTH: Roger, Baron North of Newington. Former Ambassador to France. Had charge of Robert Dudley as a child.

NORTHUMBERLAND: Countess Dorothy. Formerly Lady Dorothy Rich.

ORLANDINI: Cavalier Annibale. Tuscan friend of Robert Dudley.

ORMONDE: The Earl of Ormonde. Son of Douglas Sheffield by her first marriage.

ORSINI: Don Paolo Giordano Orsini. Courtier of the Medici Court.

OVERBURY: Sir Thomas. Friend of Rochester. Murdered in the Tower.

PALEOTTI: Adelaide. Daughter of Christina. Married the Duke of Shrewsbury.

PALEOTTI: Christina Dudley. Daughter of Carlo, Duke of Northumberland. Married Marchese Andrea Paleotti.

PALEOTTI: Diana. Daughter of Christina. Married a Colonna.

PALEOTTI: Ferdinand. Son of Christina. Hung at Tyburn.

PALEOTTI: Marchese Andrea Paleotti. Husband of Christina Dudley.

PARMA: The Duke of Parma. Philip II of Spain's Governor of the Low Countries.

PARSONS: Father Robert. English Jesuit priest living in Rome.

PEMBROKE: Charles Herbert, young Earl of Pembroke. Son of Henry 2nd Earl of Pembroke. Died in Florence.

PEMBROKE: Henry, 2nd Earl of Pembroke.

PEMBROKE: Mary, Countess of Pembroke. Sister of Sir Philip Sidney.

PEMBROKE: Philip. Son of the Earl of Pembroke

PEMBROKE: William. Son of the Earl of Pembroke

PHILIP: "Purveyor" of the Dudley household. First in Pisa, then in Florence.

PICCOLOMONI: Cavliero. His death provided a vacancy in the Order of St.Stephen for Antonio Dudley.

POPE: Gregory XV – 1621-1623.

POPE: Paul V – 1605-1621. Endorsed Robert Dudley's Dukedom.

POPE: Urban VIII – 1623-1644. Florentine of Barberini family. Created Robert Dudley a *"Patrizio Romano"* with permission to found his own order. Annexed Urbino.

POPHAM: Captain George: Explorer and sailor.

QUEEN ANNE. Anne of Denmark. Wife of King James I.

QUEEN CHRISTINA OF SWEDEN:

QUEEN HENRIETTA MARIA. Princess of France. Married to King Charles I of England.

RALEIGH: Sir Walter. Courtier, Sea and Land Commander and Explorer.

RICH: Lady Penelope Devereux: Sister of the Earl of Essex, wife of Lord Rich. Mistress of Sir Charles Blount, later Lord Mountjoy.

RICH: Lord Rich: Son of Penelope Devereux and Lord Rich. Later Earl of Warwick.

ROBSART: Amy. First wife of Earl of Leicester.

ROBSART: Rosetta. First wife of Sir Edward Stafford. Cousin of Amy Robsart.

RUCELLAI: Annabella. Daughter of Duke Oratzio Rucellai. Betrothed to Ambrogio Dudley.

RUCELLAI: Duke Oratzio Rucellai. Neighbour and friend of Robert Dudley.

RUTLAND: Roger, 4th Earl of Rutland.

SALVETTI: Amerigo. Successor to Ottaviano Lotti. Tuscan representative in London.

SHAKESPEARE: William. Poet and playwright.

SHEFFIELD: Lady Douglas Sheffield. Mother of Robert Dudley. Sister of Lord Howard of Effingham, Lord High Admiral of England.

SHEFFIELD: Sir Edmund. Son of Lady Douglas by her first marriage. Half-brother to Robert Dudley.

SIDNEY: Sir Henry, Lord Deputy of Ireland. First husband of Lettice Knollys.

SIDNEY: Sir Robert. Brother of Sir Philip Sidney. Later Lord Chamberlain to Queen Anne, Viscount de L'Isle and Earl of Leicester.

SIDNEY: Sir Philip. Poet, Diplomat and Soldier. Died after battle of Zutphen. First husband of Frances Walsingham.

SOUTHAMPTON: Henry Wriothesley, Earl of Southampton. Poet, playwright, actor and supporter of the Earl of Essex.

SOUTHWELL: Admiral Sir Robert Southwell. Father of Elizabeth Southwell, wife of Robert Dudley.

SOUTHWELL: Elizabeth. Mistress of the Earl of Essex. Cousin of Elizabeth Southwell, the wife of Robert Dudley.

SOUTHWELL: Elizabeth. Wife of Robert Dudley – Duchess of Northmberland

SOUTHWELL: Elizabeth. Daughter of Howard of Effingham. Wife of Admiral Sr Robert Southwell. Mother of Elizabeth Southwell

SOUTHWELL: Margaret. Sister of Elizabeth Dudley. Lady-in-Waiting to Queen Anne.

SOUTHWELL: Robert. English Catholic martyr. Related to Elizabeth Southwell.

STAFFORD: Sir Edward Stafford of Grafton. Husband of Lady Douglas Sheffield. Stepfather of Robert Dudley.

STROMBOLI: Prince of Stromboli. Intended husband of Carlotta Dudley.

SUTHERLAND: Duke of Sutherland. Distant cousin of Lady Alice Dudley.

THORNTON: Captain Richard. Sailed to the New World in 1608 and discovered the port of Chiana, later Cayenne.

THROCKMORTON: Sir John. A neighbour of Robert Dudley at Kenilworth.